Engineering
Measurements

Engineering Measurements

Second edition

C V Collett
MPhil, CEng, MIMechE, MIProdE, Cert Ed

A D Hope
BSc(Hons), PhD, CEng, MInstMC

Department of Mechanical and Production Engineering
City of Birmingham Polytechnic

Longman
Scientific &
Technical

Longman Scientific & Technical
Longman Group UK Limited
Longman House, Burnt Mill, Harlow
Essex CM20 2JE, England
Associated companies throughout the world

First published in Great Britain by Pitman Publishing Limited 1974
Second edition 1983
Reprinted 1983
Reprinted by Longman Scientific & Technical 1986

British Library Cataloguing in Publication Data

Collett, C. V.
 Engineering measurements.—2nd ed.
 1. Mensuration
 I. Title   II. Hope. A. D.
 620'.0044   T50
 ISBN 0-582-98873-X

Produced by Longman Singapore Publishers (Pte) Ltd.
Printed in Singapore.

Contents

Preface

Measurement is an essential part of the development of technology and as technology becomes more complex so the techniques of measurement become more sophisticated.

This volume covers the main requirements of the Institute of Quality Assurance examinations and Technical Education Council (TEC) courses in instrumentation.

The authors consider the appeal of the subject matter to be broadly based and they suggest that it will be of use and interest to technician engineers taking the HND and as introductory reading for first year undergraduates and for practising engineers.

Although the change to SI units is now substantially completed, some British Standards are still in the course of revision and have not yet been published in the new units. Consequently standards are sometimes quoted which are still in Imperial units. Where this has been done the approximate SI equivalent has been placed in parenthesis for the reader's convenience. Apart from these considerations, no concession has been made in the text to the former units.

We wish to acknowledge the generous help and advice of colleagues and the many industrial organizations who have kindly provided us with information.

We dedicate this book to our respective wives, without whose monumental patience the enterprise would not have been possible.

C.V.C.
A.D.H.

1 System characteristics and standards of measurement

1.1 Measurement systems

Instrumentation is the science and technology of complete measurement systems with which physical quantities are measured so as to obtain data which can be transmitted to recording and display devices. Some important terms used in the technology of measurement systems are defined below.

Measurand

The measurand is the physical quantity to be measured, i.e. temperature, pressure, flow rate, strain, displacement, etc.

Transducer

A transducer is a detecting element which is used to convert the physical quantity being measured (measurand) into a signal of more usable form.

Transmission path

The output signal from a transducer must be conveyed to the display, data processing or recording device by various means, e.g. an electrical cable or pipe. The signal in the transmission path may be affected by various factors such as noise (unwanted signals). The range of frequencies which can be transmitted is known as the bandwidth of the transmission path. If this bandwidth is insufficient then some of the frequency components of the signal may be lost and the signal attenuated or reduced in power.

Signal processing

Between the transducer and the recording or display device the signal normally requires some form of processing. This processing can take a number of different forms and it can occur either before or after the transmission path. Some common forms of signal processing are discussed below.

Amplification

Small output voltages or currents are connected to the input of an amplifier; the output from the amplifier has an increased magnitude which is then more useful for recording or display purposes. An amplifier increases the overall sensitivity of the measurement system.

Filtering

Filters are used to remove or reduce interference which can be picked up from other equipment within the system. It should be noted that the use of screened cables in the signal transmission path will also reduce interference.

Modulation

Modulation is used where the transmission path is long. The measurand is used to control a parameter of an electric carrier signal. Examples of modulation techniques are amplitude modulation, where the size of the measurand is used to control the amplitude of an alternating voltage, and frequency modulation, where the size of the measurand controls the frequency of an alternating voltage. Modulation reduces the effect of attenuation and noise in the transmission path and allows more than one signal to be transmitted.

Analogue to digital conversion

Many display devices used in instrumentation require digital input signals and therefore it is necessary to convert analogue signals into an equivalent digital form using appropriate conversion equipment.

1.2 Complete measurement system

All measuring systems include three basic elements:

(a) A detecting and measuring element (transducer) which detects the physical variable to be measured (measurand) and converts the signal into a more usable form. In practice the transducer output is usually a mechanical, pneumatic, hydraulic or electrical signal.
(b) An intermediate stage which modifies the signal from the transducer so that a desirable output is available.
(c) An indicating or recording device.

A block diagram of the above system is shown in Fig. 1.1.

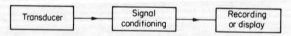

Fig. 1.1 Basic elements of a measurement system

The simple Bourdon tube pressure gauge discussed in Chapter 9 can be considered as an example of the general measurement system. The Bourdon tube itself represents the transducer as it converts the pressure signal into a mechanical displacement of the tube. The gearing constitutes the intermediate stage as a relatively small displacement at the end of the tube is amplified to give a relatively large displacement of the centre gear. Finally, the indicator scale consists of the pointer and a dial. The dial is calibrated in pressure units and thus the pointer gives an indication of the pressure acting on the Bourdon tube.

A second example is the piezoelectric pressure transducer also discussed in Chapter 9. In this case the crystal itself converts the pressure signal into an output voltage proportional to the pressure. Since it is necessary to indicate or record this voltage an amplification stage is also required. The final stage of the system may then be a voltmeter or recorder.

1.3 Recording and display devices

Recording and display devices may be broadly classified into two groups.

Indicating instruments

In these the value of the measured quantity is visually indicated but not recorded. These instruments may be analogue or digital and typical examples are as follows.

Analogue display
Scale- and pointer-type instruments, moving coil meters, Bourdon-type gauge, oscilloscopes.

Digital display
In this case the output is expressed in numbers. Examples are digital voltmeters, digital frequency meters, digital display of temperature.

Recording instruments

In these the values of the measured quantity are recorded on a chart, digital computer or data logger. Typical examples of chart recorders are pen recorders, $x-y$ plotters and ultraviolet light recorders. Magnetic tape recorders are also extensively used in instrumentation.

1.4 Characteristics of measurement systems

When faced with the task of trying to choose from commercially available measuring instruments the one most suited to a particular measurement application, the subject of performance criteria assumes major proportions.

The performance characteristics may be broadly divided into two groups, namely 'static' and 'dynamic' characteristics. Static characteristics are used to define the performance criteria for the measurement of quantities that remain constant, or vary only quite slowly. Dynamic characteristics are concerned with the relationship between the system input and output when the measured quantity (measurand) is varying rapidly.

In practice, the characteristics of the one group may well influence the characteristics of the other. In order to assess overall instrument performance, however, the two groups of characteristics are normally studied separately and then a semi-quantitative superposition is carried out. The general characteristics which apply to the majority of measuring instruments and systems will be considered in this chapter; more specialized characteristics which apply to a particular instrument will be discussed later in the book.

1.5 Static characteristics

Accuracy

This is the closeness with which the measuring instrument can measure the 'true value' of the measurand under stated conditions of use, i.e. its ability to 'tell the truth' (see Chapter 2).

Sensitivity

This is the relationship between a change in the output reading for a given change of the input. This relationship may be linear or non-linear. Sensitivity is often known as scale factor or instrument magnification and an instrument with a large sensitivity (scale factor) will indicate a large movement of the indicator for a small input change.

Linearity

Most instruments are specified to function over a particular range and the instruments can be said to be linear when incremental changes in the input and output are constant over the specified range. The amount of non-linearity accepted is normally quoted as a percentage of the operating range.

Resolution

This is defined as the smallest input increment change that gives some small but definite numerical change in the output.

Threshold

If the instrument input is very gradually increased from zero there will be a minimum value required to give a detectable output change. This minimum value defines the threshold of the instrument.

Repeatability

This is the ability of a measuring instrument to give identical indications, or responses, for repeated applications of the same value of the measurand under stated conditions of use. See Chapter 2.

Hysteresis

This is the algebraic difference between the average errors at corresponding points of measurement when approached from opposite directions, i.e. increasing as opposed to decreasing values of the input.

A system free of hysteresis will produce the same reading irrespective of whether the reading has been achieved by increasing from a lesser value or decreasing from a higher value. Because of the presence of hysteresis many instruments do not reproduce the same readings under these conditions and a typical hysteresis curve for a pressure gauge is shown in Fig. 1.2. Hysteresis is caused by strain energy stored in the system, slack motion in bearings and gears, bearing friction, etc.

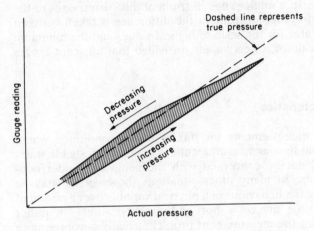

Fig. 1.2 Typical hysteresis loop for a pressure gauge

Drift

This is variation in the output of an instrument which is not caused by any change in the input; it is commonly caused by internal temperature changes and component instability.

Zero stability

This is a measure of the ability of the instrument to return to zero reading after the measurand has returned to zero and other variations such as temperature, pressure, vibration, etc. have been removed.

Dead band

This is the largest change in the measurand to which the instrument does not respond. This is produced by friction, backlash or hysteresis in the instrument.

Readability

This is defined as the ease with which readings may be taken with an instrument. Readability difficulties may often occur due to parallax errors when an observer is noting the position of a pointer on a calibrated scale.

Range

The 'scale range' is defined as the difference between the nominal values of the measured quantities corresponding to the terminal scale marks. This is normally expressed in the form 'A to B' where A is the minimum scale value and B the maximum scale value.

The 'instrument range' is the total range of values which an instrument is capable of measuring. In a single range instrument this corresponds to the scale range. In a multi-range instrument the difference is taken between the maximum scale value for the scale of highest values and the minimum scale value for the scale of lowest values, provided that adjacent ranges overlap.

1.6 Dynamic characteristics

Many experimental measurements are taken under conditions where ample time is available for the measurement system to reach steady state, and hence one need not be concerned with the behaviour under non-steady-state conditions. In many other situations, however, it may be desirable to determine the behaviour of a physical variable over a period of time. Sometimes the time interval is short and sometimes it may be rather extended. In any event the measurement problem usually becomes more complicated when the transient characteristics of a system need to be considered. The following section considers some of the more important characteristics and parameters applicable to a measurement system under dynamic conditions.

1.7 System response

The most important factor in the performance of a measuring system is that the full effect of an input signal (i.e. change in measured quantity) is not immediately shown at the output but is almost inevitably subject to some lag or delay in response. This is a delay between cause and effect due to the natural inertia of the system and is known as measurement lag.

An important dynamic characteristic used in assessing the performance of measurement systems is the response of the system when subjected to a sudden change in input signal (known as a step input). The resulting system response will depend on the type of system considered.

First order systems

Many measuring elements or systems can be represented by a first order differential equation in which the highest derivative is of the first order, i.e. dx/dt, dy/dx, etc. Examples of first order transducers are mercury in glass thermometers, thermocouples and thermistors used in temperature measurement (see Chapter 13).

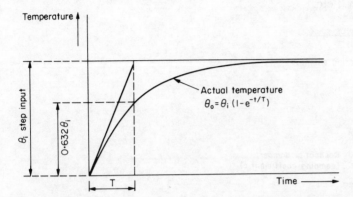

Fig. 1.3 Response of a mercury in glass thermometer to a step change in temperature

Consider as an example a mercury in glass thermometer which is suddenly dipped into a beaker of boiling water (i.e. a step change in input temperature is applied to the transducer). The response of the thermometer to this step input is exponential in form and is shown in Fig. 1.3. The actual thermometer response (θ_o) approaches the step value (θ_i) exponentially according to the relationship

$$\theta_o = \theta_i(1 - e^{-t/T})$$

where t is the time elapsed after immersion of the thermometer and T is the time constant of the instrument, which is a measure of the speed of response.

The time constant is defined as the time taken for the thermometer response to reach the final value of the step change if the initial rate of change of temperature is assumed constant, i.e. if a tangent is drawn to the initial slope. Mathematically the time constant can be shown to be the time taken for the thermometer response to reach 63·2% of the step change. The time constant is a measure of the speed of response of the instrument or system and it can be shown that after three time constants the response has reached 95% of the step change and after five time constants 99% of the step change. Hence the first order system can be said to respond to the full step change after approximately five time constants.

It should be emphasized that all systems which can be represented by a first order differential equation produce a similar response to that discussed above but the value of the time constant will obviously depend on the type of system considered.

Second order systems

Very many instruments, particularly all those with a moving element controlled by a spring, and probably fitted with some damping device, are of 'second order' type. Systems in this class can be represented by a second order differential equation where the highest derivative is of the form d^2x/dt^2, d^2y/dx^2, etc.

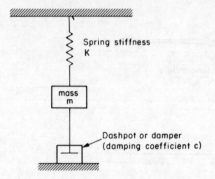

Fig. 1.4 Second order mechanical system

It is useful to represent second order systems by a mass, a controlling spring and a damper. Such a system is shown in Fig. 1.4. If the mass is suddenly disturbed the spring will exert a force (proportional to the displacement) to try to restore the mass to a position of equilibrium. The result will be an oscillation about the original equilibrium position of the mass, the oscillations gradually decreasing in amplitude until the system is at rest. This is characteristic of a second order system which has a natural frequency of oscillation. When the damping present is zero the system is said to be undamped and the natural frequency of oscillation is given by

$$f_n = \frac{1}{2\pi} \sqrt{\frac{K}{m}}$$

where f_n is the natural undamped frequency of the system, K is the stiffness of the spring (i.e. the ratio of force to extension) and m is the mass.

The value of the natural frequency becomes smaller, i.e. there are fewer oscillations per second, as the damping is increased. It should be noted, however, that the damping needs to be quite heavy before the reduction in frequency is appreciable.

Before considering the response of a second order system to a step input change it is useful to discuss the effects of damping in more detail. Damping is a method of absorbing the energy of vibration of a system and a damper may consist of a piston working in a fluid, the energy being absorbed in displacing fluid round and through the piston. A damper may also be called a dashpot and in the case of vehicle suspension systems is often called a 'shock-absorber'. In many instruments the damping fluid used is air; a metal vane moving in a magnetic field also produces a damper, owing to dissipation of energy in the flow of 'eddy' currents in the metal vane.

The amount of damping is normally specified by quoting a *damping ratio*, ζ, which is a pure number, or by quoting the 'frictional' resistance at unit velocity (since damping resistance may usually be assumed proportional to velocity).

The frictional resistance at unit velocity is referred to as the *damping coefficient*, c, where

$$c = \frac{\text{damping force}}{\text{velocity}}$$

the units of c being N per (m/s) or N s/m.

The *damping ratio* is the most useful figure, however, and is defined as follows:

$$\zeta = \frac{c}{c_c}$$

where c is the actual value of the damping coefficient and c_c is the critical damping coefficient. The damping ratio will therefore be unity when $c = c_c$, which occurs in the case of critical damping. A second order system is said to be *critically damped* when a step input is applied and there is *just* no overshoot and hence no resulting oscillation.

The magnitude of the damping ratio affects the transient response of the system to a step input change, as shown in Table 1.1.

Table 1.1 Effect of damping ratio on transient response

Magnitude of damping ratio	Transient response
Zero	Undamped simple harmonic motion
Greater than unity	Overdamped motion
Unity	Critical damping
Less than unity	Underdamped, oscillatory motion

The transient response of a damped second order system is shown in Fig. 1.5.

Overdamped motion (ζ greater than unity)
An instrument is said to be overdamped when the degree of damping is more than sufficient to prevent oscillation of the index after an abrupt or step change in the measured quantity. The output will approach the desired value exponentially and without oscillation (see Fig. 1.5). The motion is said to be 'dead-beat' under these conditions.

Critically damped motion (ζ equal to unity)
An instrument is said to be critically damped when it is subject to the minimum degree of damping which will suffice to prevent oscillation of the index after an abrupt change in the value of the measured quantity. The system behaves in a similar manner to the previous overdamped case with

the exception that the output increases much more rapidly. This represents the transition state between 'dead-beat' and oscillatory motion and is shown in Fig. 1.5.

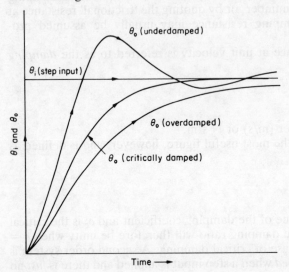

Fig. 1.5 Response of a second order system to a step input

Underdamped motion (ζ less than unity)

An instrument is said to be underdamped when the degree of damping is insufficient to prevent oscillation of the index after an abrupt change in the value of the measured quantity (Fig. 1.5). In this case the output overshoots the desired value resulting in oscillations which decrease exponentially with time.

The oscillatory motion is periodic and the periodic time of the damped oscillations can be found from the relationship

$$t_{pd} = \frac{2\pi}{\omega_n \sqrt{1 - \zeta^2}}$$

where t_{pd} is the periodic time of the damped oscillations (s), ω_n is the natural circular frequency of the system (rad/s) and is equal to $2\pi f_n$, and ζ is the damping ratio.

The percentage overshoot and number of oscillations of the system depend largely on the damping ratio. For example, a low damping ratio produces a large percentage overshoot and a large number of oscillations, whereas an increased damping ratio reduces both the percentage overshoot and the number of oscillations. In practice sufficient damping is required to prevent excessive oscillation but unfortunately an increase in the damping ratio also increases the response time of the system. An optimum damping ratio is therefore required which will produce a fast speed of response with a small number of oscillations. A damping ratio of about 0·6 is found to be satisfactory with a number of second order instruments.

1.8 Frequency response

If a sinusoidally varying input is introduced into a first order system, e.g. a thermometer subjected to a cycling temperature, the response will be such that the temperature indicated by the thermometer (or in general the output of the system) will also vary sinusoidally. The amplitude of the output signal will be reduced and the output will lag behind the input.

For example, if the input is of the form

$$\theta_i = a \sin \omega t$$

then the output will be of the form

$$\theta_o = b \sin (\omega t - \phi)$$

where b is less than a, and ϕ is the phase lag between input and output.

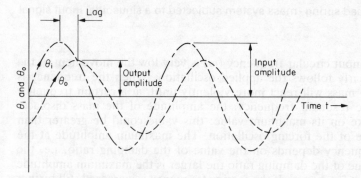

Fig. 1.6 Response of a first order system to a sinusoidal input

Figure 1.6 shows the response of a first order system subjected to a sinusoidal input signal. It should be noted that the natural frequency of both input and output signals is the same, $f_n = \omega/2\pi$, but the output lags behind the input by a phase angle ϕ.

If a sinusoidal input is applied to a second order system the response of the system is rather more complex and depends upon the relationship between the frequency of the applied sinusoid and the natural frequency of the system. The response of the system is also affected by the amount of damping present.

Consider the damped spring–mass system shown in Fig. 1.7. Practical examples of this system include seismic mass accelerometers and moving coil meters. The system may be represented by the differential equation

$$\frac{m d^2 x}{dt^2} + \frac{c dx}{dt} + Kx = Kx_1$$

where Kx_1 is the input force applied to the system or the forcing function.

Suppose that x_1 is a harmonic (sinusoidal) input, i.e. $x_1 = x_0 \sin \omega t$, where x_0 is the amplitude of the input displacement and ω is its circular frequency.

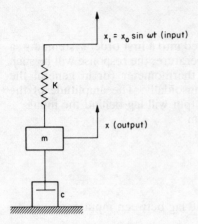

$x_1 = x_0 \sin \omega t$ (input)

K

m

x (output)

c

Fig. 1.7 Damped spring–mass system subjected to a sinusoidal input signal

When the input circular frequency (ω) is very low the movement of the mass very nearly follows the applied oscillation. When the frequency is increased the mass will react more violently until, at a certain frequency known as the resonant frequency, the amplitude of the mass displacement will take on its maximum value; this value could be greater than the amplitude of the forcing oscillation. The maximum amplitude at the resonant frequency depends on the value of the damping ratio, i.e. the lower the value of the damping ratio the larger is the maximum amplitude at the resonant frequency. If the forcing frequency is increased still further then the amplitude of the mass displacement will decrease rapidly and become very small at high forcing frequencies.

Clearly the displacement function x depends on the frequency of the forcing input x_1 and this behaviour is known as frequency response. A simple experiment with the system shown in Fig. 1.7 will show that the displacement of the mass (x) is not in phase with the forcing displacement, i.e. the maximum displacement of the mass does not occur at the same time as the maximum displacement of the forcing function. This phenomenon is known as phase shift.

If the amplitude of the mass movement (x) is X and the amplitude of the input displacement is x_0, the amplitude ratio is given by

$$\frac{X}{x_0} = \frac{1}{\{[1 - (\omega/\omega_n)^2]^2 + 4\zeta^2(\omega/\omega_n)^2\}^{\frac{1}{2}}}$$

where ω_n is the undamped natural circular frequency ($\omega_n = 2\pi f_n$), i.e.

$$\omega_n = \sqrt{\frac{K}{m}}$$

The ratio X/x_0 is sometimes referred to as the dynamic magnifier and is plotted in Fig. 1.8(a) for different damping ratios.

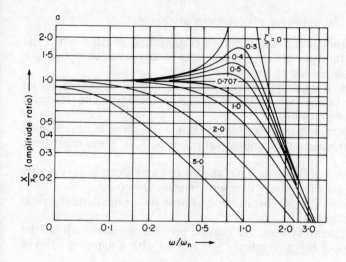

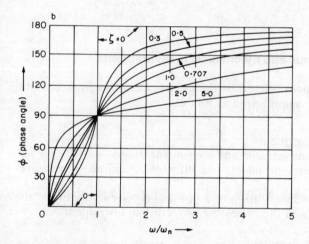

Fig. 1.8 Frequency response and phase shift characteristics of a second order system

Similarly, the phase shift between output and input displacements is given by

$$\phi = \tan^{-1} \frac{2\zeta\left(\dfrac{\omega}{\omega_n}\right)}{1 - \left(\dfrac{\omega}{\omega_n}\right)^2}$$

and the phase angle is plotted in Fig. 1.8(*b*) to illustrate the phase shift characteristics.

From Fig. 1.8 the following observations are evident:

(i) Resonance (maximum amplitude of response) is greatest when the damping in the system is low. The effect of increasing damping is to reduce the amplitude at resonance.

(ii) The resonant frequency coincides with the natural frequency for an undamped system but as the damping is increased the resonant frequency becomes lower.

(iii) When the damping ratio is greater than 0·707 there is no resonant peak but for values of damping ratio below 0·707 a resonant peak occurs.

(iv) For low values of damping ratio the output amplitude is very nearly constant up to a frequency of approximately $\omega = 0\cdot3\omega_n$.

(v) The phase shift characteristics depend strongly on the damping ratio for all frequencies.

(vi) In an instrument system the flattest possible response up to the highest possible input frequency is achieved with a damping ratio of 0·707.

1.9 Electronic methods and mechanical measurements

The particular advantages offered by the use of electronics in mechanical measurements may be summarized as follows:

(a) Speed of response is high.

(b) The instruments are versatile and convenient to use.

(c) The instruments may be adapted to difficult conditions of measurement.

(d) It is not always necessary to have a physical connection between the measuring device and the indicating or recording instrument.

The most significant advantage of electronic devices over other measuring systems is the exceptionally high speed of operation. Electronic instruments may be used for the measurement of rapidly changing functions of time where a mechanical system would be completely unsuitable.

With the application of radiotelemetry there is virtually no limit to the distance which may exist between the measuring device and the indicating or recording instrument. Thus measurements may be made in dangerous and hostile environments or inaccessible places. A good example of this application is that of space research.

Once the measured quantity has been converted into an electrical signal, the signal can be applied to indicate, record, or in the case of control systems perform a controlling function, thus indicating the versatility of electronic systems. Any one of a large range of instruments may be used provided the basic requirements of matching the inputs and outputs of the devices are carried out.

1.10 Elements of electronic measuring systems

The basic elements of an electronic measuring system are as shown in Fig.
1.1. The sensing element or transducer converts variations in the measured
quantity into corresponding electrical signals. In order to make the
electrical output from the transducer suitable for instrumentation purposes, signal conditioning is usually required. Many transducers give a very
small electrical output which must be amplified before it can be used to
operate an indicator or recorder. In other applications it may be necessary
to convert a d.c. signal into an a.c. signal or convert the signal into pulses
for digital indication, transmission of information or computer processing.

The third stage of the measuring system is that of indication or recording
and a number of methods are available depending on the type and accuracy
of the information required. Indication may be achieved by means of a
pointer and scale, digital display, teleprinting or a cathode ray oscilloscope. Recording of slowly changing variables may be achieved by means
of an ink trace on a paper chart. Ultraviolet light beam traces are normally
used for recording rapidly changing variables but other methods available
are:

(i) A camera used to photograph a cathode ray oscilloscope trace
(ii) Punched tape
(iii) Magnetic tape
(iv) Videotape.

1.11 Electronic control

In many applications a controlling function is required in addition to, or
instead of, measurement. The block diagram (Fig. 1.9) shows how the
controller uses the electrical output of the transducer to operate a
servosystem which controls the measured variable.

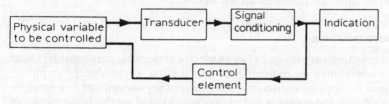

Fig. 1.9 Basic elements of an electronic control system

The controller compares the actual electrical output with the desired (or
reference) electrical output. The difference between the actual or measured output and the desired output is known as the error or deviation.
Thus error or deviation is used to operate a valve and adjust the measured
variable.

Consider as an example the temperature control of a furnace shown in

Fig. 1.10. If the temperature of the furnace is higher than the desired temperature then the measured electrical output from the thermocouple will be greater than the desired output and a positive deviation or error will occur. This error is used to close the main gas inlet valve to the furnace by an amount proportional to the error, thus causing the temperature to fall. If, however, the temperature falls below the desired value a deviation or error of opposite sign is produced which is used to open the gas valve and thus increase the temperature.

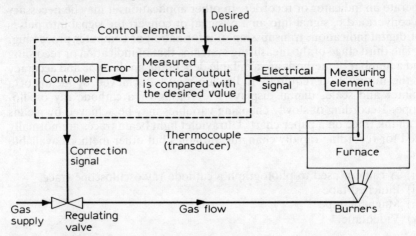

Fig. 1.10 Control of furnace temperature

1.12 Practical considerations for electrical instrumentation

It is often necessary to connect various items of electrical equipment such as a transducer, pre-amplifier and an indicating or recording instrument in order to obtain a complete measurement system. In practice certain precautions must be taken as shown below.

Impedance matching

When connections are made between electrical devices, care must be taken to avoid impedance mismatching. A signal from a transducer, amplifier, etc. cannot be applied indiscriminately to another instrument as it must be ascertained that the signal is not excessively loaded by the input circuit of the following instrument. The transducer can be replaced by an equivalent circuit consisting of the internal resistance R_i connected in series with a voltage source V_i, as shown in Fig. 1.11.

If the device is connected to a circuit of input resistance R_L then the voltage at the output terminals A and B will depend on the value of R_L (Fig. 1.12). The potential difference V_o across R_L is given by

$$V_o = \frac{R_L}{R_i + R_L} V_i \tag{1.1}$$

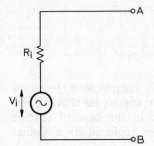

Fig. 1.11 Input impedance of a two terminal resistive device. A and B are the connecting terminals for the instrument

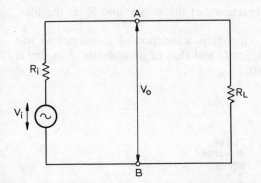

Fig. 1.12 Two terminal device connected to circuit of input resistance

There are two matching conditions:

(a) For maximum voltage transmission the internal voltage source V_i must equal the output voltage V_o at the terminals A and B.

Now $V_i \approx V_o$ when $R_i \ll R_L$.

Thus for maximum voltage transmission the resistance of the load must be very much greater than that of the signal source.

(b) If power is to be delivered from the device to the external load R_L the power dissipated in the load is given by

$$P = V_o^2/R_L$$

Using Eq. 1.1

$$P = \frac{R_L}{(R_i + R_L)^2} V_i^2$$

Differentiating P with respect to R_L

$$\frac{dP}{dR_L} = \frac{(R_i - R_L)}{(R_i + R_L)^3} V_i^2$$

For the power to be a maximum, $\mathrm{d}P/\mathrm{d}R_L = 0$ and

$$R_L = R_i$$

Thus for maximum power transmission the resistance of the external load must equal the internal resistance.

The internal impedance and external load of a complicated electronic device may contain inductive and capacitative components that will be important in a.c. transmission and dissipation. In the case of voltage transmission the expression given above may be replaced by a similar expression relating impedances:

$$V_o = \frac{Z_L}{Z_i + Z_L} V_i$$

where Z_i is the impedance or reactance of the source and Z_L is the load impedance or reactance.

Impedance matching in a.c. circuits is a function of frequency as the reactance of a capacitor C is $1/2\pi f C$ and that of an inductor L is $2\pi f L$ where f is the frequency in hertz.

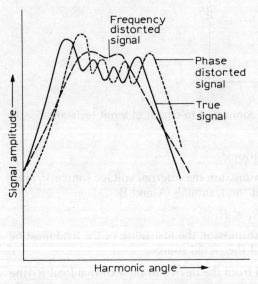

Fig. 1.13 Signal distortion produced by poor frequency response and poor phase shift response

Distortion

Distortion is a term which is used to specify the variation of a signal from its true form. Distortion of the signal may occur as a result of poor frequency response or poor phase shift response (Fig. 1.13). Various circuits are employed in electronic devices to reduce the effect of distortion to very small values.

1.13 SI system of units

Basic standards of measurement

The fundamental quantities of the SI system are mass, length, time, temperature, electrical current, luminous intensity and amount of substance. These together with some important derived quantities are realized at the National Physical Laboratory (NPL) and their multiples and sub-multiples are published for use throughout Great Britain in trade, industry and science.

Mass

The mass of a body is defined as the quantity of matter of which the body consists and can only be changed if matter is added to or subtracted from the body.

The fundamental unit of mass is defined as the kilogram (kg). The International Prototype Kilogram was legalized in 1889 at the First General Conference of Weights and Measures and remains the primary standard. It is housed at the International Bureau of Weights and Measures at Sèvres, France, and takes the form of a 90% platinum–10% iridium alloy cylinder of equal height and diameter. Duplicates are held by various countries including Great Britain and may be compared with the prototype on request. The comparison is made by means of accurate scales to a precision of at least 1 in 10^8.

Length

The fundamental unit of length is the metre (m). The first metre standard was defined at the time of the French Revolution as the distance between the ends of a platinum bar at 0 °C. The International Prototype Metre which replaced the original standard was defined in 1889 as the distance between two scribed lines on a 90% platinum–10% iridium bar at 0 °C.

Because of the unsatisfactory nature of this and other material standards such as the Imperial Standard Yard, also a line standard, the metre was defined in 1960 as a length equal to 1 650 763·73 wavelengths in vacuum of a particular radiation band emitted by the krypton 86 atom. This has the advantage of being easily reproducible to a precision of 1 part in 10^8 and avoids the difficulties of intercomparison between material standards used in the past, which suffered from progressive changes in length with time.

In Britain the metre is maintained through the 0·633 μm wavelength of an iodine stabilized helium–neon laser to about 3 parts in 10^{11}, equivalent to measuring the earth's mean circumference to about 1 mm.

Time

The fundamental unit of time is the second. The second was originally defined as 1/86 400 part of the mean solar day, but because of the variation of the solar day due to irregularities in the rotation of the earth at different periods of the year, and variations due to the movement of the earth's pole, a definition based purely on the mean solar day means that some days will consist of more or fewer parts of a second than the mean solar day.

Such a definition is not sufficiently accurate for many scientific purposes. By 1967, experimental work had shown that an atomic time standard could provide a very precise definition of the second independently of fluctuations in the earth's rotation, etc., and thus could fulfil the requirements of advanced metrology.

The 1967 General Conference of Weights and Measures adopted a definition, which may be understood as follows:

> *The second is the duration of 9 192 631 770 periods of oscillation of the radiation emitted by the caesium 133 atom under precisely defined conditions of resonance.*

Such precise oscillations can be reproduced electronically to an accuracy of 1 part in 10^{11} and such instruments are commercially available.

Time signals conform to a scale known as Co-ordinated Universal Time (UTC). In order that a day may contain 86 400 seconds (as defined above) and be approximately equal to the period of one rotation of the earth, the second as defined by the Co-ordinated Universal Time scale is shorter than that defined by the atomic time scale.

In 1966 the following offset was agreed:

$$\frac{1 \text{ second (UTC)}}{1 \text{ second (true)}} = 1 - 300 \times 10^{-10}$$

As the number of seconds in the day is constant at 86 400 and the period of rotation of the earth varies slightly, it may sometimes be necessary to increase or decrease the first minute of each month by one or more tenths of a second.

Both UTC and true time signals, synchronized to one microsecond throughout the world, are broadcast by radio so that precision clocks may be calibrated.

Thermodynamic temperature

In 1954 the General Conference of Weights and Measures selected the equilibrium point of water, water vapour and ice—the triple point—as the fundamental fixed point of the thermodynamic temperature scale.

In 1967 the name kelvin (K) was given to the unit of thermodynamic temperature (T) and the temperature 273·16 K was assigned to the triple point of water. The kelvin is therefore defined as the fraction 1/273·16 of the thermodynamic temperature of the triple point. The unit kelvin (K) is used to express an interval or difference in temperature.

The Celsius scale (t) is distinguished from the kelvin scale (T) in the International Practical Temperature Scale (IPTS) as follows:

$$t = T - 273 \cdot 15 \text{ K}$$

where the unit of t is the degree Celsius (°C), which is equal to the kelvin (K). A temperature difference expressed in kelvins may therefore be expressed in degrees Celsius.

triple point of water = 273·16 K
$t = 273 \cdot 16 - 273 \cdot 15 = 0 \cdot 01 \,°C$

Temperatures realized by triple point of water cells are accurate to $0 \cdot 1$ mK. Practical temperatures may be measured to a few millikelvins with platinum resistance and other NPL calibrated thermometers in the range $0 \cdot 5$ K to 3000 K.

Full details of the IPTS appeared in *Metrologia*, 1969, **5** (35).

Electric current

The General Conference of Weights and Measures in 1948 adopted the ampere as the fundamental unit of electric current according to the following definition:

The ampere (A) is that constant current which, if maintained in two straight parallel conductors of infinite length, of negligible circular cross-section and placed one metre apart in a vacuum, would produce between these conductors a force equal to 2×10^{-7} newtons per metre of length.

Luminous intensity

The fundamental unit of luminous intensity is the candela (cd) which is defined as follows:

The candela is the luminous intensity, in a given direction, of a source that emits monochromatic radiation of frequency 540×10^{12} hertz and that has a radiant intensity in that direction of (1/683) watt per steradian.

Amount of substance

The unit of amount of substance is the mole (mol) which is defined as follows:

The mole is the amount of substance of a system which contains as many elementary entities as there are atoms in $0 \cdot 012$ kg of carbon 12.

The related Avogadro constant ($6 \cdot 023 \times 10^{26}$/kg mol), the number of elementary entities per mole, is now known to about 1 part in 10^6.

The term 'entity' must be specified for this purpose, and may refer to atoms, molecules, electrons, etc.

In practice, the mass corresponding to one mole of substance, i.e. the molar mass, is calculated as follows:

$$M(X) = \frac{M(X)}{m(^{12}C)} \times 0 \cdot 012 \text{ kg/mol}$$

where $M(X)$ is the molar mass of substance X, $m(X)$ is the atomic mass of the substance X, $m(^{12}C)$ is the atomic mass of carbon 12 and $0 \cdot 012$ kg/mol is the molar mass of carbon 12.

For example, the atomic mass of oxygen (O_2) is 16.

$$M(O_2) = \frac{2 \times 16}{12} \times 0 \cdot 012 \text{ kg/mol} = 0 \cdot 032 \text{ kg/mol}$$

Supplementary units

The two supplementary units of the SI system are the radian (rad) for the plane angle and the steradian (sr) for the solid angle.

Plane angle
The radian is the angle which, having its vertex at the centre of a circle, cuts off an arc of the circle of length equal to its radius.

Solid angle
The steradian is the solid angle which, having its vertex at the centre of a sphere, cuts off an outline on the surface of the sphere having an area equal to the square of the radius of the sphere. Hence there are 4π steradians in one sphere.

The radian and steradian may, as convenient, be regarded as base units or derived units. Angle realization better than 0.1 seconds of arc can be achieved, which corresponds to an accuracy of about 4 parts in 10^7.

Derived units

Derived units are expressed in terms of the fundamental and/or supplementary units. Some important derived units are as follows.

Force
The newton is that force which, when acting on a mass of one kilogram, gives it an acceleration of one metre per second per second.

Work, energy, quantity of heat
The joule is the work done by a force of one newton when its point of application is moved through a distance of one metre in the direction of the force. The same unit is used for the measurement of every kind of energy including quantity of heat; thus the joule replaces the calorie and British thermal unit. Although the newton metre and the joule are identical in value, it is recommended that the newton metre is kept for the measurement of torque or moment and that the joule is used for quantities of work or energy (mechanical or electrical).

The unit of heat is no longer defined in terms of raising unit mass of water through unit temperature, and in consequence a figure must be assigned to the specific heat capacity of water. This varies with temperature, and the value at $16\,°C$ is $4.1868\,kJ/kg\,°C$. The word capacity is used to draw attention to the change.

Power
The watt is one joule per second.

Electric charge
The coulomb is the quantity of electricity transported in one second by a current of one ampere.

Electric potential
The volt is the difference of potential between two points of a conducting wire which carries a constant current of one ampere, when the power dissipated between these two points is one watt, or one joule per second.

Electric capacitance
A capacitance is one farad if a difference of potential of one volt appears between the plates of a capacitor when it is charged with a quantity of electricity equal to one coulomb.

Electric resistance
The ohm is the resistance between two points of a conductor when a constant difference of potential of one volt applied between these two points produces a current of one ampere in the conductor. The conductor must not be the source of any electromotive force at that time.

Magnetic flux
The weber is that flux which, when linking a circuit of one turn, and being reduced to zero at a uniform rate in one second, produces in the circuit an electromotive force of one volt.

Electric inductance
The henry is the inductance of a closed circuit in which an electromotive force of one volt is produced when the electric current in the circuit varies uniformly at the rate of one ampere per second.

Luminous flux
The lumen is the flux emitted within unit solid angle of one steradian by a point source having a uniform intensity of one candela.

Illumination
The lux is an illumination of one lumen per square metre.

Analysis of some derived units

Force

Force is defined as the product of mass and acceleration. If F is the force, m the mass and a the acceleration, then

$$F = ma$$

The unit of force is the newton, which is defined as the force required to produce an acceleration of $1\,\text{m/s}^2$ when applied to a mass of $1\,\text{kg}$. Therefore

$$1\,\text{N} = 1\,\text{kg} \times 1\,\text{m/s}^2$$

Weight

The force to which a mass is subjected by the presence of a gravitational field is its weight.

Let the mass of the body be m kg. The acceleration due to gravity is g m/s^2. Then the force on the body due to gravity (weight) is the mass times the acceleration due to gravity. Therefore

$$F = m\,\text{kg} \times g\,\text{m/s}^2 = mg\,\text{kg m/s}^2$$
$$F = mg\ \text{newtons}$$

Pressure and stress

Pressure and stress are defined as force per unit area. Thus the derived unit in both cases is the newton per square metre, and $1\,\text{N/m}^2$ has been assigned the name pascal (Pa).

Permitted non-SI units

The day, hour and minute are not decimal multiples of the second, which is the SI unit of time, but their use is so well established and universally adopted that their replacement is not practicable. They are therefore classified as 'permitted non-SI units'. Their use in calculations involving the basic units will, however, introduce numerical constants which are no longer multiples or sub-multiples of 10, e.g. $1\,\text{km/h} = 1/3\cdot6\,\text{m/s}$ and $1\,\text{kW h} = 3\cdot6\,\text{MJ}$.

Similarly the degree, minute and second are permitted non-SI angular measurements.

It is also recommended that decimal multiples and sub-multiples should be $10^{\pm3n}$ times the basic unit, where n is an integer. Permitted units which depart from this recommendation are the area unit known as the are ($1\,\text{a} = 10^2\,\text{m}^2$) and the hectare ($1\,\text{ha} = 10^4\,\text{m}^2$) and the pressure unit of the bar ($1\,\text{bar} = 10^5\,\text{N/m}^2$). In other permitted cases a fraction of the original unit can be used which will fit into the recommended pattern, e.g. the viscosity units of the centipoise ($1\,\text{cP} = 10^{-3}\,\text{N s/m}^2$) and the centistoke ($1\,\text{cSt} = 10^{-6}\,\text{m}^2/\text{s}$).

Units for pressure and stress

The SI unit for pressure and stress is the newton per square metre, but the use of the millibar ($1\,\text{mbar} = 10^2\,\text{N/m}^2$) for the measurement of atmospheric pressure is already well established.

Use of special names for units

The pascal (Pa) for one newton per square metre, the tesla (T) for a magnetic flux density of one weber per square metre, the tonne (t) for a mass of 1000 kilograms and similar names are convenient short terms which may be used if desired.

Multiples of SI units

The prefixes for use with SI units are given in Table 1.2.

Table 1.2 Prefixes for SI units

Multiplying factor	Prefix	
	Name	Symbol
10^{18}	exa	E
10^{15}	peta	P
10^{12}	tera	T
10^{9}	giga	G
10^{6}	mega	M
10^{3}	kilo	k
10^{2}	hecto	h
10	deca	da
10^{-1}	deci	d
10^{-2}	centi	c
10^{-3}	milli	m
10^{-6}	micro	μ
10^{-9}	nano	n
10^{-12}	pico	p
10^{-15}	femto	f
10^{-18}	atto	a

1.14 Non-SI instruments

Many existing instruments are calibrated in units other than SI units and for this reason it may be necessary to convert quantities expressed in one unit system to another. A convenient method which may be used for unit conversion is the Newton unity bracket technique. This is based on the understanding that a unit in one system is equal to its equivalent in any other system; thus the ratio between them is 1:1. For example, 1 pound force (lb f) = 0·454 kilogram force (kg f)

$$\therefore \quad 1 = \left[\frac{1\,\text{lb}\,\text{f}}{0\cdot454\,\text{kg}\,\text{f}} \right] = \left[\frac{0\cdot454\,\text{kg}\,\text{f}}{1\,\text{lb}\,\text{f}} \right]$$

Example 1.1
(*a*) The output torque (T_{fps}) from an engine shaft is measured in units of pounds force feet (lb f ft). Applying unity brackets express the torque in SI units.

$$T_{\text{SI}} = T_{\text{fps}}\,(\text{lb}\,\text{f}\,\text{ft}) \times \left[\frac{1\cdot36\,\text{Nm}}{1\,\text{lb}\,\text{f}\,\text{ft}} \right]$$

$$\therefore \quad T_{\text{SI}} = (1\cdot36\,T_{\text{fps}})\,\text{Nm}$$

(*b*) If the rated output torque from the engine is $10\,\mathrm{lb\,f\,ft}$ express this torque in SI units.

$$T_{\mathrm{SI}} = (1\cdot36 \times 10\,\mathrm{lb\,f\,ft})\,\mathrm{Nm} = 13\cdot6\,\mathrm{Nm}$$

Example 1.2
Using unity brackets convert sound intensity (S) expressed in $\mathrm{ft\,lb\,f/s\,ft^2}$ units into SI units.

$$S_{\mathrm{SI}} = S_{\mathrm{fps}} \left(\frac{\mathrm{ft\,lb\,f}}{\mathrm{s\,ft^2}} \right) \times \left[\frac{4\cdot45\,\mathrm{N}}{\mathrm{lb\,f}} \right] \times \left[\frac{0\cdot3048\,\mathrm{m}}{\mathrm{ft}} \right] \times \left[\frac{\mathrm{ft^2}}{0\cdot0929\,\mathrm{m^2}} \right]$$

$$\therefore \quad S_{\mathrm{SI}} = (14\cdot6\,S_{\mathrm{fps}})\,\mathrm{W/m^2}$$

Table 1.3 gives conversion factors, Table 1.4 some useful approximations to conversion factors and Table 1.5 some approximate values of common quantities.

Table 1.3 Conversion factors

Values are given to three figures except where marked† which signifies an exact figure.

	To convert	Into	Multiply by
Length	inches	millimetres (mm)	25·4†
	feet	metres (m)	0·3048†
	yards	metres (m)	0·9144†
	miles	kilometres (km)	1·61
Area	square inches	square millimetres (mm²)	645
	square feet	square metres (m²)	0·0929
	square yards	square metres (m²)	0·836
	acres	square metres (m²)	4050
	acres	hectares (ha)*	0·405
Volume	cubic inches	cubic millimetres (mm³)	16 400
	cubic feet	cubic metres (m³)	0·0283
	cubic yards	cubic metres (m³)	0·765
	pints	litres (l)‡	0·568
	gallons	litres (l)	4·55
	gallons	cubic metres (m³)	0·004 55
Mass	pounds	kilograms (kg)	0·454
	hundredweights	kilograms (kg)	50·8
	tons	kilograms (kg)	1020
Density	pounds per cubic foot	kilograms per cubic metre (kg/m³)	16·0
	pounds per cubic inch	megagrams per cubic metre (Mg/m³)	27·7
Mass flow rate	pounds per hour	kilograms per second (kg/s)	0·000 126

Table 1.3 (contd)

	To convert	Into	Multiply by
Volume flow rate	cubic feet per second	cubic metres per second (m³/s)	0·0283
	gallons per minute	cubic metres per second (m³/s)	0·000 075 8
Heat flow rate	Btu per hour§	watts (W)	0·293
Power	horsepower	watts (W)	746
Energy	foot pound force	joules (J)	1·36
	British thermal units§	kilojoules (kJ)	1·06
	kilowatt hour	megajoules (MJ)	3·6†
Force (weight)	pounds force	newtons (N)	4·45
	kilograms force	newtons (N)	9·81
	dynes	micronewtons (μN)	10†
	tons force	kilonewtons (kN)	9·96
Torque or moment of force	pounds force feet	newton metres (N m)	1·36
	pounds force inches	millinewton metres (mN m)	113
	tons force feet	kilonewton metres (kN m)	3·04
Second moment of area¶	inches⁴	millimetres⁴ (mm⁴)	416 000
	feet⁴	metres⁴ (m⁴)	0·008 63
Second moment of mass (moment of inertia)	pounds mass feet²	kilograms metres²	0·0421
	pounds mass inches²	kilograms metres² (kg m²)	0·000 293
Pressure and stress	pounds force per square inch	newtons per square metre (N/m²)	6890
	pounds force per square foot	newtons per square metre (N/m²)	47·9
	tons force per square inch	meganewtons per square metre (MN/m²)	15·4
	tons force per square foot	kilonewtons per square metre (kN/m²)	107
	'inches of water'	newtons per square metre (N/m²)	249
	'feet of water'	newtons per square metre (N/m²)	2990
Velocity	feet per second	metres per second (m/s)	0·3048†
	feet per minute	millimetres per second (mm/s)	5·08
	miles per hour	metres per second (m/s)	0·447
	miles per hour	kilometres per hour (km/h)	1·61

Table 1.3 (contd)

	To convert	Into	Multiply by
Acceleration	feet per second^2	metres per second^2 (m/s^2)	0·3048†
Momentum	pounds mass feet per second	kilograms metres per second (kg m/s)	0·138
Moment of momentum	pounds mass feet^2 per second	kilograms metres^2 per second (kg m^2/s)	0·0421
Kinematic viscosity	feet^2 per second feet^2 per second	metres^2 per second (m^2/s) centistokes (cSt)	0·0929 92 900
Dynamic viscosity	pounds force seconds per foot^2	newton seconds per metre^2 (N s/m^2)	47·9
Calorific value	Btu per cubic foot	kilojoules per cubic metre (kJ/m^3)	37·3
Latent heat or specific enthalpy	Btu per pound mass	kilojoules per kilogram (kJ/kg)	2·33
Specific thermal capacity	Btu per pound mass per degree Fahrenheit	kilojoules per kilogram per degree Celsius (kJ/kg °C)	4·19
Sound intensity	foot pounds force per second per square foot	watts per square metre (W/m^2)	14·6

* The hectare = 10^4 square metres = 1 square hectometre.

‡ The litre is mainly used for fluid capacity and was redefined in 1964 to be exactly 10^{-3} cubic metres. This is very slightly less than its previously defined value, the difference being only noticeable in high precision work. The litre is not therefore recommended for precise measurements (which should be expressed in m^3, mm^3, etc) in case some of the older litre measures are unintentionally used.

§ The British thermal unit is temperature dependent.

¶ The second moments of area of standard sections may be quoted in centimetres^4 as a more convenient unit for practical use.

Table 1.4 Useful approximations to conversion factors

Non-SI quantity	Approximation	More exact value
1 cwt	50 kilograms	50·8023 kg
1 ton	1 tonne = 1000 kg	1·016 05 t
1 ton force	10 kilonewtons	9·964 kN
1 lbf	4½ newtons	4·448 N
1 'thou'	25 micrometres	25·4 μm
100 cubic feet	3 cubic metres	2·83 m³
1000 ft/min	5 metres/second	5·08 m/s
1 mile/hour	0·5 metres/second	0·447 m/s
1 Btu	1 kilojoule	1·055 06 kJ
10 Btu/hour	3 watts = 3 joules/second	2·9307 J/s
1 therm	105 megajoules	105·506 MJ
10 acres	4 hectares	4·0469 ha
10 gallons	45 litres	45·46 l

Table 1.5 Approximate values of common quantities

Absolute zero	−273 °C
Range of normal room temperature	18 °C to 21 °C
Normal body temperature of human beings	36·9 °C
Height of average man (5 ft 8 in)	1·7 m
Diameter of earth	12 740 km
Acceleration due to gravity	9·81 m/s²
Speed of light	300 Mm/s
Speed of sound at sea level	341 m/s
Specific thermal capacities in kJ/kg °C	water 4·19
	copper 0·40
	steel 0·48
	concrete 0·84
	aluminium 0·92
Thermal capacity of air at constant pressure	1·01 kJ/kg °C
Atmospheric pressure	1 bar = 10⁵ N/m²
Mass of 1 litre of water	1 kg
Densities in kg/m³	steel 7830
	water 1000
	air at sea level 1·23
Weight per unit volume (on earth) in kN/m³	steel 76·8
	water 9·81
	concrete 22·6
Young's modulus in GN/m² = 10^9 N/m² = kN/mm²	steel 200 to 210
	copper 90 to 117
	aluminium about 69
	brass about 90
Tensile strengths in MN/m² = N/mm²	mild steel 450 to 600
	copper 300 to 350
	aluminium 150 to 190

Study problems

1.1   The density of a granite surface table is given as $2700 \, kg/m^3$. Using unity brackets express this density in fps units.

Answer: $D_{fps} = 168{\cdot}3 \, lb \, f/ft^3$

1.2   The units of angular momentum (H), sometimes referred to as the moment of momentum, are lb mass ft^2/s in the fps system. Derive an expression for angular momentum in SI units.

Answer: $H_{SI} = (0{\cdot}0421 \times H_{fps}) \, kg \, m^2/s$

1.3   The relationship between stress and strain is given by $\sigma = E\varepsilon$, where σ is the stress, E is Young's modulus and ε is the strain. Derive an expression for the constant E in SI units in the form MN/m^2 where σ is expressed in lbf/in^2.

Answer: $E_{SI} = \left(0{\cdot}0069 \left(\dfrac{\sigma}{\varepsilon} \right)_{fps} \right) \dfrac{MN}{m^2}$

1.4   (a) What is meant by the 'response' of an instrument or a system?

(b) Explain what is meant by the 'order' of a system.

(c) Name one example of a 'first order' system and one of a 'second order' system.

1.5   A thermometer is initially at a temperature of $21 \, °C$ and is suddenly placed in a liquid which is maintained at $149 \, °C$. The thermometer indicates $93 \, °C$ after a time interval of 3 seconds. Estimate the 'time constant' for the thermometer.

Answer: $3{\cdot}63$ seconds

1.6   A thermometer reading a steady $50 \, °C$ is plunged into liquid at $90 \, °C$. The rise of temperature with time (seconds) is given below:

t (s)	0·25	0·5	0·75	1·0	1·25	1·5	1·75	2·0	3·0	4·0	6·0
T (°C)	55	59	62·5	65·5	68·5	71·2	73·5	76·0	82·2	85·2	89·4

Plot a graph showing the response of the thermometer and hence determine the 'time constant' of the instrument.

Answer: $1{\cdot}93$ seconds

1.7   Why is the 'time constant' of a system important?

Suggest a reason why the forward movement of an instrument might be arranged to have a small time constant and the return movement a much larger time constant.

Approximately how many 'time constants' elapse before a first order system responds by 99% to a step input displacement?

1.8   (a) The damped spring–mass system shown in Fig. 1.14 is subjected to a harmonic disturbing force at the support. Describe with the aid of suitable diagrams the resulting changes in amplitude ratio and phase between the mass and the support as the frequency of the disturbing force is increased from zero.

(b) The system has $m = 5 \, kg$, $K = 650 \, N/m$ and $\zeta = 0{\cdot}614$. If the support is moved with amplitude $0{\cdot}5 \, mm$ at a frequency of $2 \, Hz$ find the amplitude of motion of the mass.

Answer: $X = 0{\cdot}36 \, mm$

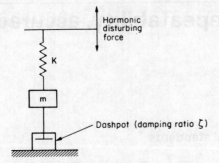

Fig. 1.14 Damped spring–mass system for Problem 1.8

1.9 (*a*) Distinguish between the quantities 'mass' and 'weight' and describe one primary standard of mass.

(*b*) Make a distinction between primary standards which depend on natural phenomena and primary standards which depend on material standards. State the advantages of defining primary standards in terms of natural phenomena.

(*c*) Why are secondary material standards used?

(*d*) State three different types of standards of length and give a typical example of the use of each standard.

1.10 Explain the differences and similarities between the degree Celsius and the kelvin.

2 Traceability, repeatability, accuracy

2.1 National and international standards

The National Physical Laboratory (NPL) at Teddington, England, and the National Engineering Laboratory (NEL) at East Kilbride, Scotland, are the primary laboratories which set UK national standards for measurement. In turn they intercompare their standards with the international standards housed at the International Bureau of Weights and Measures, Sèvres, France. Most of the world's nations subscribe to this system.

The NPL and NEL in their role as national authorities do not carry out routine calibration (i.e. proof of correctness of standards) for industry as this would require very large test house facilities and in any case it is vital that they should be free to concentrate on the highest quality of measurement.

To provide a calibration service the Minister of Technology in 1966 stated that existing laboratories would be authorized to calibrate gauges, measuring instruments and standards, and to issue an official British Calibration Certificate. These laboratories were initially vetted by a headquarters staff at the Ministry and this vetting has been continued to ensure that the required standards are maintained. British Calibration Services (BCS) laboratories are to be found in industry, educational establishments and in government research organizations.

2.2 Traceability

One of the tenets of the BCS scheme is that all measurements must be 'traceable', that is, the standard used must have been compared with some higher level of standard. A hierarchy of such standards exists, and ultimately most mechanical measurements are traceable back to NEL or NPL (Fig. 2.1). When the national length standards were line standards this was invariably the case but today, for example, length is defined in terms of wavelengths of light and some laboratories have a length interferometer for direct determination of length.

Procedure

A BCS laboratory must proceed broadly as follows:

(1) Each measurement must be recorded with details of the method and standards used to carry out the calibration.

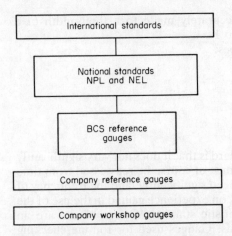

```
┌─────────────────────────────────┐
│      International standards     │
└─────────────────────────────────┘
              │
     ┌────────────────────┐
     │  National standards │
     │     NPL and NEL     │
     └────────────────────┘
              │
       ┌──────────────┐
       │ BCS reference │
       │    gauges     │
       └──────────────┘
              │
┌─────────────────────────────┐
│   Company reference gauges   │
└─────────────────────────────┘
              │
┌─────────────────────────────┐
│   Company workshop gauges    │
└─────────────────────────────┘
```

Fig. 2.1 Simplified traceability ladder

(2) The records must be available at all times to allow for independent arbitration in case of dispute with a client.

(3) Records must be kept so as to provide a history of gauges and standards which are calibrated at regular intervals.

(4) The laboratory must assess uncertainty of measurement and must quote them for each size or quantity given on a certificate.

Best and minimum uncertainties for each type of measurement are mutually agreed between the laboratory and headquarters before approval is given to the laboratory. The technique used to establish an uncertainty is based on statistical theory and is quoted as plus or minus three times the standard deviation. Assuming a normal distribution, the probability of the true size of the gauge or standard being outside the measured size plus or minus the uncertainty is less than 0·3%.

A BCS laboratory must also submit to an audit scheme which operates as follows. A selection of gauges is circulated to the laboratories and the measured sizes returned to the audit officer. Needless to say the gauge sizes are not known in advance. When the results have been received they are collated and published for all to see. The individual laboratories are not named so that it is only possible to identify one result. A laboratory where results are significantly different from the rest is usually invited to remeasure before the results are published.

2.3 Calibrators

The instrument or device used as a calibrator should be as accurately made as possible or its value should be known to a high degree of accuracy, and any variation with time or frequency of use should normally be between four and ten times better than the instrument to be calibrated. For example, a dial test indicator registering hundredths of a millimetre should be calibrated with gauge blocks accurately made to a thousandth of a millimetre or better, a ratio of 10 to 1.

Calibrators are of three basic types:

(1) Static standards
(2) Reference instruments
(3) Combination calibrators.

Static standards

The essential quality of a static standard is that it does not vary significantly from one test to another. Its value must of course be reassessed from time to time to ensure that it has not changed significantly, and the frequency of this reassessment will depend largely on experience gained in the use of the calibrator and on its own characteristic stability. Gauge blocks are an excellent example of static standards. Gauges used for routine checking and resetting of large numbers of gap gauges might need to be checked once per month whereas the factory master gauge blocks, which are held as an ultimate length reference and used at very infrequent intervals, might be recalibrated annually. The use of a calibrator of this type eliminates the need to assign an uncertainty to it, which very much simplifies matters.

Reference instruments

A reference instrument is an instrument or device capable of the same measuring function but of a higher accuracy than the instrument to be calibrated. The two are compared by measuring the same quantity so that the comparative performance of the instrument being calibrated can be assessed. In the final result, the repeatability of the reference instrument must be taken into account.

Combination calibrator

In this case, more than one quantity is measured so that a more complex calibration quantity may be derived. To ensure that the calibrator has an accuracy of the required higher order than the instrument under test the accuracy of the individual elements which go to make up the calibrator must be such that when they are combined to form the calibrator the order of accuracy required is achieved. For example, a torque meter may be calibrated by the application of a force through a lever, the product of force and effective lever length constituting an accurately known torque. By applying a suitable range of forces to the lever the applied torques could be compared with the output readings of the meter.

The reader is referred to Preston (1963) (see Bibliography) for a more detailed discussion of combination calibrators.

2.4 Error

The term 'error' if not used with care is open to various interpretations.

The following two definitions are both valid provided their contexts are kept clearly in mind.

Error of size or quantity

An error of size or quantity is the difference between the desired or specified size or quantity of an object and its measured size or quantity without reference to any uncertainty in the measurement.

This form of error may be expressed in absolute or relative terms. For the sake of brevity the term 'size' will be taken to include quantity.

absolute error = result of measurement − specified size

The following example illustrates both absolute and relative error:

$$\text{specified shaft diameter} = 40 \cdot 00 \, \text{mm}$$
$$\text{result of measurement} = 40 \cdot 10 \, \text{mm}$$
$$\text{absolute error} = 40 \cdot 10 - 40 \cdot 00 = +0 \cdot 1 \, \text{mm}$$

$$\text{relative error} = \frac{\text{absolute error}}{\text{specified size}}$$

$$= +\frac{0 \cdot 1}{40 \cdot 00} = +0 \cdot 0025 \quad \text{or} \quad +0 \cdot 25\%$$

In the latter case, the error is clearly related to the specified size and may be expressed as a percentage of that value.

Error of measurement

An error of measurement is the discrepancy or difference between the result of a measurement and the absolute true value of the quantity measured.

An error of measurement when considered in isolation is of little practical value; however, a number of similar measurements, each carrying an error, can be used to provide valuable information regarding the accuracy and repeatability of any measurements made.

2.5 Absolute true value and conventional true value

The absolute true value of a quantity is an ideal concept and, except in the simplest case when counting a number of discrete articles, cannot exactly be known. In practice, the term 'true value' is used as a short form for the term 'conventional true value' which, in turn, is defined as:

that value approximating to the absolute true value such that the difference between them is of no significance.

2.6 Uncertainty of a measurement

Uncertainty is not to be confused with error. Like error, it is an attribute of measurement and is not applicable to a measuring instrument. It may be defined as:

> *the range within which the true value of the quantity measured is likely to lie at a given level of probability.*

By its very nature it consists of the results of a number of measurements each of which carries an error; it expresses the variability which always occurs when more than one measurement is made.

2.7 Confidence level or level of probability

Assigning a confidence level as to the likelihood of an event occurring is part of human experience. For example, a traveller arrives every weekday at a railway station to catch a particular train. He notices that sometimes it is early, sometimes late and sometimes on time. By careful observation he finds that the train arrives within 5 minutes of the correct time 90 times in every 100 arrivals of the train. However, his observations also inform him that in a further 9 cases in every 100 the train arrives within plus or minus 8 minutes of the correct time. He is thus able to assign two levels of confidence to the arrival time of the train. If he wishes to be correct only 90% of the time he chooses the ±5 minutes confidence level, but if he wishes to be correct 99% of the time he chooses the ±8 minutes confidence level. He does not of course know at what time his train will arrive on a particular day and there is 1 chance in 100 that his prediction will be incorrect.

Table 2.1 Symbols used in Chapter 2

A:	accuracy of instrument
f:	frequency of occurrence of sample value x
K:	constant
N:	sample size
R:	U_r: repeatability of instrument
s:	sample standard deviation
σ:	estimated population standard deviation
t:	Student's t distribution
$2U$:	uncertainty of a measurement
U:	half range uncertainty of measurement
U_1, U_2, U_3, etc.:	half range component uncertainties
U_r:	half range random uncertainty of measurement
U_s:	half range systematic uncertainty of measurement
w:	sample range
x:	sample values (variates)
$\bar{X}$:	sample mean
$\overline{X^2}$:	mean of the sum of the squares of the various values of x

Similarly with the uncertainty of a measurement, the choice of a level of confidence must be made in the light of particular measuring circumstances. A 95% confidence level is often used in practice as this represents 19 chances in 20 that a measurement lies within this range of probability and has the added advantage that it is equal to plus or minus two standard deviations, assuming that the distribution of the measurements follows the normal curve of distribution. It should be noted that a choice of 99·73% confidence level provides less than 5% improvement for an increase of 50% in the distribution to $\pm 3\sigma$, where σ is the standard deviation of the population, but it must be emphasized that the choice depends on the degree of confidence demanded by the measuring situation.

2.8 Component uncertainties

The overall uncertainty of a measurement always consists of the summation of a number of separate uncertainties usually referred to as component uncertainties. Strain measurement using an electrical resistance strain gauge provides an illustration of the chain of component uncertainties which contribute to the overall uncertainty in this way. Measurements contributing to the overall uncertainty would include gauge position, operating temperature, gauge resistance, internal bridge resistance, linearity of system response, force or torque applied to the strained member and many others. Uncertainties are of two kinds, random and systematic.

2.9 Systematic uncertainty and bias

The assessment of a systematic uncertainty is illustrated in the following example. A hand micrometer used for measuring a diameter has a bias of 0·025 mm. A number of measurements are made on the diameter of a spindle and the readings recorded reveal scatter in a random manner about their mean value. The slight variations or random scatter of the readings could be caused by slight differences in measuring pressure, friction variations in the micrometer screw, discrepancies in reading the instrument and other sources. An acceptance of the mean value as the true value of the diameter clearly introduces a bias into the measurement. By checking the micrometer with a calibrator of a size as near as possible to the measured size the bias (0·025 mm) is revealed and could be reduced either by correcting the mean value or by readjusting the instrument. However, there is a limit to the accuracy with which the instrument could be corrected and consequently it must be assumed that there is a residue which remains undetected. This undetected residue is a systematic effect which constitutes a factor in all the measurements. An assessment of the magnitude of the systematic effect should be made and a value assigned to it in the light of the level of confidence chosen. This then is accepted as the systematic uncertainty. Such a systematic uncertainty might be defined, for example, as having a 99·73% ($\pm 3\sigma$) probability of lying within $\pm 0·0005$ mm of the calibrator size.

Strictly speaking, the estimation of this uncertainty applies only to one reading of the instrument, and if the micrometer screw has a systematic pitch error, this might be revealed as a bias at other points on the scale. A decision may then be made as to the suitability of the instrument to its purpose as it is clearly impracticable to recalibrate each time a measurement is made with this type of instrument.

An interesting example of correction of linear systematic bias appears on the Sigma screw thread pitch measuring instrument. When the instrument screw has been calibrated its calibration curve is examined and any progressive bias isolated. This is then eliminated by means of a straight line corrector cam set at a suitable angle, which rotates the instrument stationary dial through a cam follower attached to the dial in such a direction as to oppose bias.

2.10 Typical sources of systematic uncertainty

The following list indicates some typical examples of sources of systematic uncertainty; it must not in any sense be taken to be exhaustive:

(1) A discrepancy in a standard weight.
(2) A discrepancy in the length or diameter of a gauge.
(3) A scale zero setting discrepancy.
(4) Discrepancies in the lengths of an instrument's lever system.
(5) The assumption of perfect flatness in a reflecting surface.
(6) The cumulative discrepancies in an assembly. A sine bar provides an example where the magnitude of the effect of manufacturing and assembly discrepancies is value dependent; that is, its effect increases in a non-linear manner with the angle to which the sine bar is set.
(7) A small elastic deflection where perfect rigidity has been assumed.
(8) An assumption of linear response from an instrument which is not exactly linear.
(9) The use of values of physical constants such as the local value of gravity; the elastic and shear moduli for metals; the values of electrical conductivity; the use of density constants for liquids or gases which are slightly incorrect.
(10) When more than one dimension is measured, e.g. in the computation of volume, then the uncertainty of each measurement must be considered to be systematic.

Systematic uncertainties may also vary according to the magnitude of the quantity measured, for example the angle of a sine bar, or they may vary with time. The accuracy of an instrument is always evaluated at a specific point within its range and for a quantity dependent uncertainty the only requirement is that it be appropriate to that point.

Time dependent uncertainties are a different matter, however, as they take the form of long term random variations or steady trends or drifts. Instruments usually incorporate an adjustment mechanism which can be used to correct the effect of steady trends such as the increasing effect of wear in the instrument.

A series of adjustments of this kind changes a steady trend into what are effectively long term random variations, but a measurement is taken over a short period of time and consequently such uncertainties must be treated as systematic at the moment of measurement.

2.11 Random uncertainties

When a number of measurements of a given quantity are taken it soon becomes clear that, as they accumulate, there is a variation in the results. If sufficient measurements are taken it is found that the results tend to form a range about a mean value and the greater the number of readings the more clearly defined does this effect become. Such effects arise from a number of sources which contribute to variability each time a measurement is taken. For example, a micrometer measuring pressure varies slightly at each measurement, there is a parallax discrepancy each time the user reads the result, and the location of the micrometer on the workpiece varies slightly at each measurement. These and other causes contribute to the random nature of the readings about a mean value and only a number of readings can establish a developed random pattern or distribution.

As the source of this variability arises from uncertainties which change slightly as each measurement is taken and yet form a distinct and well defined range of results, it is necessary to use a technique which allows calculation of the expected uncertainty resulting from these random variations. It is usual to assume that random variability in measurement follows the Gaussian or normal curve of distribution although it is by no means certain that this distribution applies in all cases. Despite this limitation, however, the application of this technique is becoming common practice as it does allow the essential estimations to be made within a logical framework which is not seriously at variance from practical experience.

2.12 Combination of component uncertainties

When the sources of all the uncertainties have been defined and values assigned to them it is necessary to combine them. Combination involves two separate steps or stages.

Stage 1

(i) Combination of random components to form an overall random uncertainty;
(ii) Combination of systematic components to form an overall systematic uncertainty.

Stage 2

Combination of the random uncertainty with the systematic uncertainty if a combined value of uncertainty is required. Systematic and random uncertainties should not be combined prior to stage 2.

2.13 Methods for combining uncertainties[1]

Two methods for combining uncertainties are in general use—algebraic addition and addition in quadrature. Neither method gives entirely satisfactory results, algebraic addition tending to overestimation of the uncertainty and addition in quadrature tending to underestimation.

Addition in quadrature is the square root of the sum of the squares of the uncertainties, or the root sum square. For example, if three independent component half range uncertainties of measurement are defined as U_1, U_2 and U_3, then

$$\Sigma U = (U_1^2 + U_2^2 + U_3^2)^{\frac{1}{2}}$$

Example 2.1

Let $U_1 = 2$ units, $U_2 = 4$ units and $U_3 = 5$ units; then

$$\Sigma U = (2^2 + 4^2 + 5^2)^{\frac{1}{2}} = 6 \cdot 71 \text{ units}$$

Algebraic addition yields 11 units.

There are circumstances where uncertainties can be eliminated by a carefully designed measurement technique. A well known example occurs when measuring screw threads using calibrated pins. Screw thread measurement is based on the assumption that the vee of the thread forms an annular groove on the bolt, but in reality the thread is helical in form and the result is that the pins locate a little higher in the groove than the measuring theory postulates. However, the measuring pressure exerted on the pins causes a wedging action which tends to press the pins into the thread groove by an amount almost equal to the helix effect, and for all practical purposes the algebraic sum of the 'wedge' and 'helix' effects is virtually zero when the helix angle is small. When the helix angle is large, however, an allowance should be made before addition in quadrature.

Care must be exercised when assessing uncertainties which act in combination or unison. This is clearly demonstrated when two slip gauges are wrung together, one having an uncertainty of $\pm 1 \cdot 5 \times 10^{-4}$ mm and the other an uncertainty of $\pm 2 \cdot 5 \times 10^{-4}$ mm. It is much more likely that the combined uncertainty is of the order of

$$\pm [(1 \cdot 5 + 2 \cdot 5)^2]^{\frac{1}{2}} = \pm 4 \qquad \times 10^{-4} \text{ mm}$$

rather than

$$\pm [1 \cdot 5^2 + 2 \cdot 5^2]^{\frac{1}{2}} = \pm 2 \cdot 9 \qquad \times 10^{-4} \text{ mm}$$

[1] Throughout this chapter the assumption is made that uncertainty is bilateral in nature and equally disposed around a datum. It may well be that under certain circumstances this is not so, and in such cases separate unilateral assessments of uncertainty should be made and appropriate modifications to the calculations applied.

Example 2.2

Let U_1 and U_2 be independent half range uncertainties each having a value of 2 units. U_3 and U_4 act in combination but are not dependent upon U_1 and U_2, and each has a value of 2 units. The components should be combined as follows:

$$\Sigma U = (U_1^2 + U_2^2 + (U_3 + U_4)^2)^{\frac{1}{2}}$$
$$= (2^2 + 2^2 + (2 + 2)^2)^{\frac{1}{2}}$$
$$= (24)^{\frac{1}{2}}$$
$$= 4 \cdot 9 \text{ units}$$

Independent addition in quadrature yields 4 units; algebraic addition yields 8 units.

Note that the half range uncertainties which are in combination are first added before addition in quadrature.

A practical example of two mutually exclusive uncertainties occurs when a spring balance is used to find the difference between two weights. The systematic uncertainty of both the measurements remains the same, and because only the difference between the two weights is required these uncertainties can be ignored. Incidentally, bias is also eliminated. If the measurements were made using a different balance for each measurement, then the uncertainties would be independent and should be added in quadrature.

2.14 Repeatability of a measuring instrument

British Standard 5233:1975 defines repeatability as follows:

> *the ability of a measuring instrument to give identical indications, or responses, for repeated applications of the same value of the measured quantity under the same conditions of use.*

By definition, repeatability is a property of an instrument whereas uncertainty is a property of a measurement.

A quantitative statement of repeatability may be defined as:

> *the half range random uncertainty of a typical measurement under specific conditions of use and at a defined level of confidence.*

Repeatability (R) is then numerically equal to the half range random uncertainty (U_r) of the measurement.

2.15 Determination of repeatability

When the repeatability of a measurement is to be estimated the following factors must be taken into consideration:

(1) Sampling technique
(2) Sample size
(3) Level of confidence.

Sampling technique

Populations are either finite or infinite. For example, if samples of 10 spacers are successively drawn, without replacement, from a box containing 100 spacers then the population of spacers is said to be finite. However, if the sample is replaced in the box each time it is taken, then the finite population can be considered to be infinite as the population will never be exhausted. For many practical purposes, sampling from a finite population which is very large can be considered as sampling from an infinite population. Measuring instruments fall into this latter category as the number of measurements which could be taken with a measuring instrument can be considered to be very large.

When sampling, it is essential that the individual values recorded be not biased by such factors as preconceptions as to their magnitude, parallax, bias when reading scales, significant changes in ambient conditions and so forth.

Sample size

From a practical viewpoint it is advantageous to use only a small sample size in estimating the repeatability of an instrument. The dividing line between small sample size (N) and large sample size is $N = 30$, i.e. $N \geq 30$ constitutes a large sample and $N < 30$ constitutes a small sample.

It can be shown that by multiplying the sample standard deviation (s) by the factor $[N/(N - 1)]^{\frac{1}{2}}$, a good estimation of the standard deviation of the population can be obtained from a small sample. Incidentally, this holds good for both small and large samples, for as N increases, $[N/(N - 1)]^{\frac{1}{2}}$ approaches unity.

For the purposes of estimating repeatability a sample $N = 10$ is a convenient and economical number for non-automatic instruments, but for automatic instruments, where a larger sample may more rapidly be obtained, a sample $N = 20$ may be used.

Level of confidence: Student's t distribution

One further step is required before the repeatability of the instrument is estimated and that is to decide on the required confidence level. This may be determined by the application of the t distribution. For example, for a large population the 95% confidence level occurs at $\pm 1 \cdot 96$ standard deviations but small samples are biased to underestimate this level. The application of the appropriate value of the t distribution for a given sample size and confidence level corrects this and provides a better estimation of the 95% confidence level for the population.

Values of t for sample sizes $N = 10$ and $N = 20$ are shown in Table 2.2.

Table 2.2 Values of t for two sample sizes

$N = 10$

Confidence level (%)	99·9	99·73	99	98	95	90
Student's t	4·78	3·96	3·25	2·82	2·26	1·83
K	5·04	4·17	3·43	2·97	2·38	1·93

$N = 20$

Confidence level (%)	99·9	99·73	99	98	95	90
Student's t	3·88	3·36	2·86	2·54	2·09	1·73
K	3·98	3·45	2·93	2·61	2·14	1·77

The repeatability may now be stated as:

$$R = t\sigma$$

where t is the Student's t function, σ is the estimation of the population standard deviation, $s[N/(N-1)]^{\frac{1}{2}}$, s is the sample standard deviation and N is the sample size.

2.16 Standard deviation

The standard deviation of a set of numbers or a sample is denoted by s and is defined by:

$$s = \left[\frac{\sum_{1}^{N} f(x - \bar{X})^2}{N} \right]^{\frac{1}{2}}$$

where the x are the sample values (the variate), $\bar{X} = \Sigma(fx/N)$ is the arithmetic mean of the sample values, N is the sample size and f is the frequency of occurrence of the sample value x.

Example 2.3
A balance is calibrated against a standard mass of 250 g. The differences (in grams) from the 250 g scale reading were determined as $+10·5$, $-8·5$, $+9·5$, $+9·0$, $-10·0$, $+9·0$, $-9·5$, $+10·0$, $+10·0$ and $-8·0$. Find the repeatability (R) of the balance at 95% confidence level.

Method
(1) Calculate the sample arithmetic mean ($\bar{X}$) and standard deviation (s).
(2) Multiply (s) by $[N/(N-1)]^{\frac{1}{2}}$ to obtain σ.
(3) Read the Student's t value from Table 2.1 at 95% confidence level.

(4) Estimate repeatability from $R = \sigma t$.

$$\bar{X} = (+10\cdot5 - 8\cdot5 + 9\cdot5 + 9\cdot0 - 10\cdot0 + 9\cdot0 - 9\cdot5 + 10\cdot0 + 10\cdot0 - 8\cdot0)/10$$

$$= 2.2\,g$$

$$f(x - \bar{X})^2 = f(x - 2\cdot2)^2$$

$f = 1$	$x =$	$10\cdot5$	$68\cdot89$
$f = 2$	$x =$	$10\cdot0$	$121\cdot68$
$f = 1$	$x =$	$-10\cdot0$	$148\cdot84$
$f = 1$	$x =$	$+9\cdot5$	$53\cdot29$
$f = 1$	$x =$	$-9\cdot5$	$136\cdot89$
$f = 2$	$x =$	$+9\cdot0$	$92\cdot48$
$f = 1$	$x =$	$-8\cdot5$	$114\cdot49$
$f = 1$	$x =$	$-8\cdot0$	$104\cdot04$

$$840\cdot60 = \Sigma f(x - 2\cdot2)^2$$

$$s = \left[\frac{\Sigma f(x - \bar{X})^2}{N}\right]^{\frac{1}{2}} = \left[\frac{840\cdot60}{10}\right]^{\frac{1}{2}} = 9\cdot17\,g$$

$$\sigma = s\left[\frac{N}{N - 1}\right]^{\frac{1}{2}} = 9\cdot17\left[\frac{10}{9}\right]^{\frac{1}{2}} = 9\cdot66\,g$$

$$t(95\%) = 2\cdot26$$

Repeatability $(R) = 9\cdot66 \times 2\cdot26 = 21\cdot84\,g$.
Rounding to two significant figures, $R = 22\,g$.

It can be shown that

$$s = (\overline{X^2} - \bar{X}^2)^{\frac{1}{2}}$$

where $\overline{X^2}$ denotes the mean of the sum of the squares of the various values of x, while $\bar{X}^2$ denotes the square of the mean of the various values of x.

$$\overline{X^2} = [(10\cdot5)^2 + (-8\cdot5)^2 + (9\cdot5)^2 + (9\cdot0)^2 + (-10\cdot0)^2 + (9\cdot0)^2 + (-9\cdot5)^2 + (10\cdot0)^2 + (10\cdot0)^2 + (-8\cdot0)^2]/10$$

$$= 88\cdot9\,g^2$$

$$s = (88\cdot9 - 4\cdot84)^{\frac{1}{2}} = 9\cdot17\,g$$

The computation may be further simplified for given sample sizes and confidence levels. Let $K = t[N/(N - 1)]^{\frac{1}{2}}$ (Table 2.2). Then:

Repeatability $(R) = Ks = 2\cdot382 \times 9\cdot17 = 21\cdot84\,g$.
Rounding to two significant figures, $R = 22\,g$.

It should be noted that the mean value $(\bar{X})$ lies at $250 + 2\cdot2 = 252\cdot2\,g$, and as the calibrator is $250\,g$ then a positive bias of $+2\cdot2\,g$ occurs each time a measurement is taken. This bias may either be taken into account whenever a measurement is taken or, more usually, the instrument will be adjusted to reduce the bias as closely as possible to zero (see Section 2.9, on systematic uncertainty and bias).

The range (w) of the sample is the difference between the extreme values; thus $10 \cdot 5$ and $-8 \cdot 0$ yield a range of $18 \cdot 5$ mm, not greatly at variance with the computed repeatability ($22 \cdot 0$ g). However, it would be quite wrong to assume that the range of a sample represents an estimate of the repeatability, as a sample of two values from ten cannot provide information regarding the magnitude of the eight remaining values, which might vary considerably from Example 2.3 and yield a different estimation of repeatability.

2.17 Reliability of repeatability estimations

It is often the case that the repeatability of an instrument varies from time to time and, on occasion, by a considerable amount. This does not necessarily indicate that the instrument is faulty but rather that repeatability is a somewhat variable quantity. There is no complete answer to this problem available at the present time and only practical advice can be offered in terms of an empirical solution.

Some authorities advocate that three repeatability tests be carried out on three similar but not identical specimens in quick succession. If the ratio between the highest and lowest value is not greater than 2:1, then the root mean square (r.m.s.) value of the three results should be regarded as the repeatability of the instrument. This method of computation is justified on the grounds that repeatabilities are themselves square root quantities.

If the ratio obtained is greater than 2 then the instrument should be examined for faults, and on rectification further tests should be made.

Example 2.4
Three repeatability tests were carried out on the balance introduced in Example 2.3. The results obtained were as follows:

$$R_1 = 22 \text{ g} \qquad R_2 = 24 \text{ g} \qquad R_3 = 28 \text{ g}$$

$$\text{ratio } R_3 : R_1 = \frac{28}{22} = 1 \cdot 27$$

$$\text{r.m.s.} = \left(\frac{R_1^2 + R_2^2 + R_3^2}{3} \right)^{\frac{1}{2}}$$

$$= \left(\frac{22^2 + 24^2 + 28^2}{3} \right)^{\frac{1}{2}}$$

$$= 24 \cdot 79$$

Rounding to two significant figures, r.m.s. = $25 \cdot 0$.
Stated repeatability is 25 g.

2.18 Accuracy of a measuring instrument

The accuracy of a measurement made with an instrument is a function of the ability of the instrument to indicate the true value of the measured quantity under specific conditions of use and at a defined level of confidence. This is normally referred to as the accuracy of the instrument. It consists of a combination of the repeatability with the half range systematic uncertainty. The same method of combination will be used as before, i.e. addition in quadrature.

The accuracy (A) of the instrument is expressed by the following equation:

$$A = (R^2 + U_s^2)^{\frac{1}{2}}$$

where R is the instrument repeatability and U_s is the half range systematic uncertainty.

Example 2.5

The systematic uncertainty of a balance is estimated to be $\pm 5\,$g and the random uncertainty of its measurements is $\pm 25\,$g. State the repeatability and calculate the accuracy of the instrument.

$$R = U_r = 25\,\text{g}$$
$$U_s = 5\,\text{g}$$

$$A = (R^2 + U_s^2)^{\frac{1}{2}} = (25^2 + 5^2)^{\frac{1}{2}}$$

Instrument accuracy $(A) = 25 \cdot 49\,$g.

As the systematic uncertainty and the repeatability are both stated in grams, a practical statement of accuracy is $26\,$g.

It is usual to express the accuracy of an instrument in terms of its full scale deflection (f.s.d.). The following partial specification for a tachometer will serve as an example (left hand and right hand operation):

Range 1: 0–1000 rev/min directly.
Range 2: 0–5000 rev/min ($\times$ 5).
Range 3: 0–50 000 rev/min ($\times$ 50).
Accuracy: 0·5% f.s.d.

Hence on range 2 at an indicated 2500 rev/min the accuracy is

$$\frac{0 \cdot 5}{100} \times 5000 = 25\,\text{rev/min}$$

Example 2.6

A balance has a range of 0 to 1 kg and its estimated accuracy is 26 g when it is calibrated against a 1 kg standard mass. Express the accuracy of the balance in terms of percentage full scale deflection.

$$\text{accuracy } A = \frac{26}{1000} \times \frac{100}{1} = 2 \cdot 6\% \text{ f.s.d.}$$

2.19 Estimating the uncertainty of a measurement

The uncertainty of a measurement is given a qualitative definition in Section 2.6; however, a quantitative definition of uncertainty may be stated as:

> *the sum of the systematic and random uncertainties of a typical measurement, under specific conditions of use and at a defined level of confidence.*

In contrast to accuracy and repeatability estimations, uncertainty assessments must include the uncertainty of the calibrator itself and, specifically, take account of the confidence level upon which it is founded. If the calibrator is original to the assessor and its uncertainty has been assigned by him then all is well. However, if an external calibration has been applied to the calibrator then it is unlikely that the level of confidence will be stated on the calibration certificate, and indeed it is only fairly recently that the term 'accuracy of determination' has begun to be discarded in favour of 'uncertainty of measurement' on such certificates. In these circumstances it is necessary to ascertain the confidence level used from the calibrating authority concerned.

A British Calibration Service laboratory of long experience and high reputation known to the authors assigns a 'better than 95% level of confidence' to their measurements of plain cylindrical setting standards and this level will be used in the following examples of uncertainty estimation, there being little point in using a different level from that assigned to the calibrator itself.

Example 2.7
The diameter of the setting gauge used to calibrate a sensitive comparator was stated on its calibration certificate to be 60·0072 mm diameter and to have an accuracy of determination equal to ±0·0008 mm. Although not stated on the certificate the level of confidence was known to be 'better than 95%'. The sample standard deviation of ten instrument readings yielded a value (s) equal to 0·35 μm. Estimate the uncertainty of the measurement at better than the 95% confidence level.

From Table 2.2, $K = 2·38$.
Half range random uncertainty $U_r = Ks$:

$$U_r = 2·38 \times 0·35 = 0·833 \,\mu\text{m}$$

Half range uncertainty of setting gauge $U_1 = 0·8 \,\mu$m.
Half range uncertainty of measurement

$$= (U_r^2 + U_1^2)^{\frac{1}{2}}$$
$$= (0·833^2 + 0·8^2)^{\frac{1}{2}}$$
$$= 1·424 \,\mu\text{m}$$

This result must be rounded up to the first place of decimals as this is the order of the observations.

Uncertainty of measurement $2U = \pm1.5\,\mu\text{m}$ or $\pm0.0015\,\text{mm}$.
This estimate is given with better than 95% confidence owing to the necessary effect of rounding up.

2.20 Compound uncertainty

In many instances, the ultimate uncertainty of a measurement is dependent upon the uncertainty of a number of contributory measurements which are combined to determine the final quantity. For example, the uncertainty of determination of the volume of a cylinder depends on the uncertainty with which the length and diameter are measured.

Example 2.8
Consider a solid rectangular block $100 \times 10 \times 1\,\text{mm}$, as in Fig. 2.2(*a*). Its volume is $1000\,\text{mm}^3$; the equation to its volume may be stated as

$$V = L \times W \times T$$

where L is its length, W its width and T its thickness.

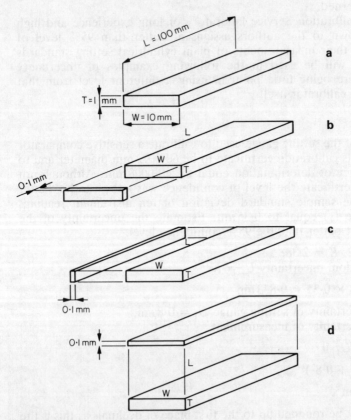

Fig. 2.2 Block for Example 2.8

If the uncertainty of length (L) determination is ± 0.1 mm [Fig. 2.2(b)], assuming for the moment that the width and thickness dimensions are perfect, then the uncertainty of volume determination is $\pm(0.1 \times 10 \times 1)$ $= \pm 1.0$ mm^3. Similarly, if the uncertainty of width (W) determination is again ± 0.1 mm [Fig. 2.2(c)], then the uncertainty of volume determination is $\pm(100 \times 0.1 \times 1) = \pm 10$ mm^3. Finally, if the uncertainty of thickness (T) determination is also ± 0.1 mm [Fig. 2.2(d)], then the uncertainty of volume determination is $\pm(100 \times 10 \times 0.1) = \pm 100$ mm^3.

The uncertainty of determination of the volume depends not only upon the accuracy of the instrument used for the measurement but also upon the effect of the uncertainty of measurement of a particular dimension on the overall determination of uncertainty.

Compound uncertainty problems may be solved by the technique of partial differentiation.

For the equation to the volume, $V = L \times W \times T$, it can be shown that:

$$dV = \pm \left[\delta L \frac{\delta V}{\delta L} + \delta W \frac{\delta V}{\delta W} + \delta T \frac{\delta V}{\delta T} \right] \tag{2.1}$$

where dV is the arithmetic sum of the uncertainties and δL, δW and δT are the half range uncertainties of L, W and T respectively.

$\delta V / \delta L$ is the differential coefficient (rate of change) of V with respect to L, all other variables being considered as constants in this term. $\delta V / \delta W$ and $\delta V / \delta T$ are similarly described.

In the present example, $\delta L = 0.1$ mm, $\delta W = 0.1$ mm and $\delta T = 0.1$ mm. If

$$V = L \times W \times T \tag{2.2}$$

then

$$\frac{\delta V}{\delta L} = WT \qquad \frac{\delta V}{\delta W} = LT \qquad \frac{\delta V}{\delta T} = LW \tag{2.3}$$

Substituting in Eq. 2.1,

$$dV = \pm [(\quad \delta L \, WT \quad) + (\quad \delta W \, LT \quad) + (\quad \delta T \, LW \quad)]$$
$$\therefore \quad dV = \pm [(0.1 \times 10 \times 1) + (0.1 \times 100 \times 1) + (0.1 \times 100 \times 10)]$$
$$= \pm [(\quad 1 \quad) + (\quad 10 \quad) + (\quad 100 \quad)]$$
$$dV = \pm 111 \text{ mm}^3 \tag{2.4}$$

Note that the measurement uncertainty of T contains approximately 90% of the sum total while W and L contain only 9% and 1% respectively although the individual uncertainties are equal.

The uncertainty of thickness determination plays a dominant role in the sum total in this case, and if a significant improvement is to be gained then the uncertainty of measurement of thickness must be improved. As instrument accuracy plays a major part in the establishment of uncertainty then either the accuracy of the instrument should be improved or another instrument having superior accuracy should be used. However, it is essential to recognize that instrument accuracy is not the only factor in the establishment of uncertainty, as clearly the physical characteristics of the quantity measured will also constitute a powerful factor in the final outcome. A well understood example of such physical constraints occurs in the length measurement of gauge blocks, where it is essential to control flatness and parallelism to a very high level of quality, if a meaningful measurement of length is to be obtained.

Let the uncertainty of thickness measurement (T) be improved from $\pm 0 \cdot 1$ to $\pm 0 \cdot 02$ mm; then

$$\mathrm{d}V = \pm [(0 \cdot 1 \times 10 \times 1) + (0 \cdot 1 \times 100 \times 1) + (0 \cdot 02 \times 100 \times 10)]$$

$$= \pm [(\qquad 1 \qquad) + (\qquad 10 \qquad) + (\qquad 20 \qquad)]$$

$$= \pm 31 \, \mathrm{mm}^3$$

The contribution of uncertainty of measurement of T now falls to $(20/31) \times (100/1) = 65\%$; L and W are 3% and 32% respectively, while the compound uncertainty has improved by the ratio $31 : 111 = 3 \cdot 6$.

It is of great importance that in the computation of compound uncertainties the choice of instrument used to make individual measurements should be given careful consideration, and that performance be matched to the final required uncertainty. For purposes of discussion the uncertainties in Example 2.8 have been combined by simple addition; however, each of the components should be considered to be independent (see Section 2.10) and the compound uncertainty of measurement finally arrived at by addition in quadrature.

In the first case:

$$2U = \pm (1^2 + 10^2 + 100^2)^{\frac{1}{2}} = \pm 100 \cdot 5 \, \mathrm{mm}^3$$

In the second case:

$$2U = \pm (1^2 + 10^2 + 20^2)^{\frac{1}{2}} = \pm 22 \cdot 4 \, \mathrm{mm}^3$$

Study problems

2.1 (a) A floating carriage diameter measuring instrument was calibrated at its nominally 5 mm scale position against a cylindrical setting standard and the following results were recorded (in micrometres): $+1 \cdot 6$, $+1 \cdot 6$, $+1 \cdot 0$, $+1 \cdot 0$, $+1 \cdot 0$, $+1 \cdot 4$, $+1 \cdot 6$, $+0 \cdot 8$, $+1 \cdot 6$ and $+1 \cdot 4$.

Calculate the repeatability (R) and the accuracy (A) of the instrument at this scale position to yield a better than 95% level of confidence in the result, when the systematic uncertainty ($2U_s$) for each sample reading is estimated to be $\pm 0 \cdot 2 \, \mu$m.

(b) The diameter of the plain cylindrical setting gauge used for setting the instrument was stated on its calibration chart to be $40 \cdot 0061$ mm, with an uncertainty of measurement of $\pm 0 \cdot 0005$ mm at a confidence level of 95%. When a cylindrical plug gauge was mounted to the instrument for checking, the mean of a number of readings was found to be $4 \cdot 9952$ mm. State the mean diameter of the plug gauge and the uncertainty of the measurement.

Answers

(*a*) $R = 0.0008$ mm; $A = 0.0008$ mm

Because of the high quality of this instrument both repeatability and accuracy are of the same order. This is of course a very desirable condition for any measuring instrument.

(*b*) Uncertainty of measurement $2U = \pm 0.001$ mm at a level of confidence better than 95%; mean plug gauge diameter $= 40.0000$ mm.

2.2 Two tests were carried out on a 0–1 inch micrometer having thimble graduations in 0.001 inch units and barrel vernier graduations in 0.0001 inch units. The first test employed the vernier graduations and the second test the thimble graduations only, to establish accuracy and repeatability in both cases.

Calculate the probable values of accuracy and repeatability at better than 95% confidence level from the following observations and estimations:

Thimble readings sample (10^{-3} in): +2.7, +2.8, +2.8, +2.7, +2.7, +2.7, +2.8, +2.7, +2.6 and +2.6.

Vernier readings sample (10^{-3} in): +2.6, +2.5, +2.6, +2.6, +2.6, +2.7, +2.7, +2.6, +2.7 and +2.7.

Micrometer zero setting half range systematic component uncertainty (10% of graduation value) U_1 is 0.1×10^{-3} in.

Micrometer thimble half range systematic component uncertainty of readings between graduations (20% of graduation value) U_2 is 0.2×10^{-3} in.

Micrometer vernier half range systematic component uncertainty U_3 is 0.1×10^{-3} in.

N.B. The readings were taken over a nominally 0.5 in diameter setting disc and the micrometer and disc were hand held.

Answers

Test 1: $R = 0.0002$ in; $A = 0.0005$ in

Test 2: $R = 0.0002$ in; $A = 0.0003$ in

It would appear from these results that the use of the vernier scale may give the user a false impression of the instrument's accuracy and repeatability.

2.3 A well known straightness measuring instrument of 100 mm stroke was calibrated against a 150 mm diameter optical flat, having a stated maximum flatness error of 0.05μm and mounted to ensure minimum deflection in accordance with a kinematic support arrangement suggested by G. D. Drew of the NPL.

The flat was sampled ten times across different diameters and the deviation from a straight line of each 100 mm long trace estimated against a straight edge in terms of the 0.0002 mm units of the recorder paper. An electronic thermometer was employed to monitor temperature which varied within the range 19.7 to 19.9 °C during the test.

Sample values (0.2μm units): 0.25, 1.00, 1.00, 0.00, 0.50, 0.25, 0.00, 0.25, 0.25 and 0.25.

Estimated positioning error of straight edge at ends of trace line is 0.2 units $= 0.2 \times 0.2 \mu$m $= 0.04 \mu$m.

Calculate the accuracy of the instrument at the 98% confidence level.

Answer: accuracy = $0 \cdot 21 \, \mu$m

This result conformed closely to the manufacturer's specification.

2.4 A well known technique used when measuring large bores is to place a pin gauge in the bore and measure the swing of the pin across the bore. Provided that the pin length is precisely known and reasonable care is taken when measuring the swing, it is possible to estimate the bore diameter with good precision. From Fig. 2.3 it can be shown that

$$D = L + \frac{S^2}{8L}$$

by applying the approximation $x \approx S/2$ where L is the length of the pin, S is the swing, and the diameter D is $L + \delta L$.

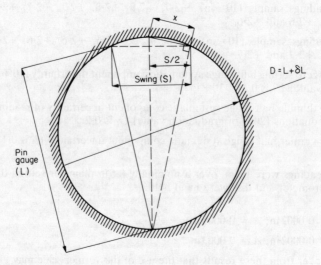

Fig. 2.3 Bore diagram for Problem 2.4

(*a*) Calculate the bore diameter (D) and the compound uncertainty of its measurement.

(*b*) Explain why much greater care must be taken when measuring the length of the pin gauge than when measuring the swing.

$L = 500$ mm is the pin length, $\delta L = 0 \cdot 02$ mm is the half range uncertainty of the pin measurement, $S = 30$ mm is the swing and $\delta S = 1 \cdot 0$ mm is the half range uncertainty of the swing measurement.

Answers
(*a*) $D = 500 \cdot 225$ mm; $2U = \pm 0 \cdot 025$ mm

(*b*) The rate of change of D with respect to L is approximately 67 times greater than the rate of change of D with respect to S.

2.5 (a) A method used for checking a large radius is shown in Fig. 2.4. Show that the equation to the radius may be stated as

$$R = \frac{c^2}{8(d - h)} - \frac{h}{2}$$

Find the value of R and calculate its uncertainty of measurement.

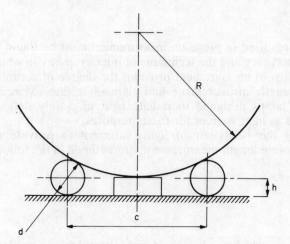

Fig. 2.4 Radius checking diagram for Problem 2.5

(b) Establish what action is required to reduce the uncertainty of measurement of R by an order of 9.

Dimension	Nominal size (mm)	Uncertainty (mm)
c	125	±0·05
d	25	±0·001
h	1·25	±0·0005

Answers
(a) $R = 81\cdot612\,$mm; $2U = \pm0\cdot066\,$mm

(b) Uncertainty of $C = \pm0\cdot005\,$mm

3 Interferometry

The length of standards used in precision measurement must be found to the highest possible accuracy and the technique of interferometry in which light is used as a means of measurement provides the degree of accuracy required for both length measurement and flatness testing. Mercury vapour and sodium lamps designed to radiate light of closely defined wavelengths are used as light sources for these purposes.

Certain aspects of the behaviour of light, sufficient to provide an understanding of absolute length measurement, are outlined in the following sections.

3.1 White light

Light is a form of energy which can be considered to travel from one place to another in the form of electromagnetic sinusoidal waves. The wavelength λ determines the colour, and the amplitude a determines the intensity of the light. White light is a combination of all the colours of the visible spectrum, red, orange, yellow, green, blue, indigo and violet, each colour band consisting of a group of similar wavelengths. Because white light is a combination of light of all colours and is therefore a combination of all the wavelengths of the visible spectrum, it is not in a form suitable for length measurement by interferometry. To overcome this difficulty a substantially monochromatic light source such as a mercury isotope 198 discharge lamp is used, the light produced having an average wavelength of $0.53(4)\mu$m to an accuracy of about one part in one hundred million.

3.2 Monochromatic light

A beam of monochromatic light can be considered as an infinite number of rays all having the same wavelength. When the waves are emitted from the lamp they are in phase, and the intensity of the light, which increases as the square of the amplitude of the waveform, depends upon the power of the light source. If one half of the waves are displaced a distance equal to one half wavelength, the algebraic sum of the amplitudes, assuming that they are all of equal value, will be zero and any object in the path of light in this condition will not be illuminated. This effect is known as interference. At any intermediate condition the interference effect will be lessened and the light will be of reduced intensity (Fig. 3.1).

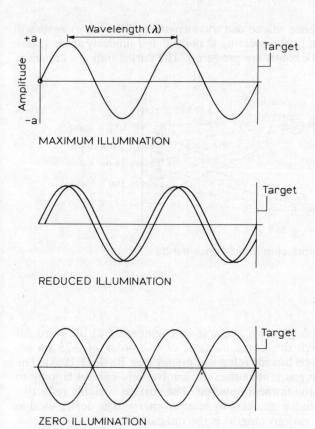

Fig. 3.1 Interference at a target

3.3 Interference of light

To produce the clearest and most stable interference effects the following conditions should be observed:

(1) The light must be of uniform frequency and wavelength.
(2) Any phase differences existing should not vary with time.
(3) The amplitudes should be equal or nearly equal.

A method for producing bands of interference is shown in Fig. 3.2. Light passes through the very narrow slit A and thence through the slits B and C which are close together. Thus two separate beams of light are formed which for the purposes of this explanation may be assumed to be in phase. If the ray paths BO and CO are exactly equal then the waves on these paths will be in phase at the screen and a band of light will occur at point O. At some point M the ray path difference will be equal to one half wavelength, i.e. $CM - BM = \frac{1}{2}\lambda$. Thus, at the screen, the waves will be 180° out of phase and a band of darkness will occur at M, and similarly at N. At point

P, the ray path difference will be one wavelength, and the waves again will be in phase, a band of light appearing at point P and similarly at Q. Thus a series of light and dark bands are produced. The dark bands are known as interference fringes.

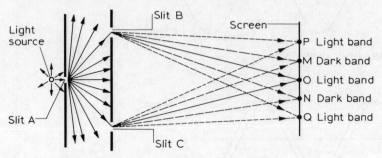

Fig. 3.2 Method for producing interference bands

3.4 Flatness testing

Slip gauges are the best known example in engineering of the need for surfaces of a very high degree of flatness, of the order of $0·25\,\mu$m for workshop grades to $0·08\,\mu$m for reference grades (see BS 4311:1968). The final processes of slip gauge manufacture involve very careful lapping to produce a surface of the flatness required. The surface is highly reflective which makes it suitable for checking by interferometry. The device used to produce ray paths of various lengths is the optical flat.

An optical flat is a circular piece of unstressed glass or quartz which is usually about 5 cm diameter but may be 30 cm in diameter or more. The thickness is sufficient to prevent significant flexure under its own weight. The upper and lower surfaces are ground optically flat so that they become reference planes. Consider an optical flat placed upon a flat metal surface so that a thin wedge film of air is entrapped between them (Fig. 3.3). When suitably illuminated, interference fringes will appear at the metal surface. The behaviour of a ray of light as it passes through the flat to the surface and thence to the observer's eye may be understood as follows. Ray L_1 follows the path AB. At B part of the ray is reflected to follow path BF while the remainder continues along the path BC and is reflected from the metal surface C along the path DE. Both parts of the ray are recombined at the eye, having traversed unequal distances.

If the waves reaching the eye are 180° out of phase a straight dark band or fringe will be seen to lie across the surface. The fringe is straight because the surface is flat as fringes always follow a line of constant distance between the surface and the lower face of the flat. They are, in a sense, contour lines. Straight fringes always lie parallel to the line of contact or line of minimum displacement of the optical flat from the surface.

Referring again to Fig. 3.3, at some point J to the right of C the gap between the two surfaces has increased such that the difference between the distance traversed by the two portions of ray L_2 has increased by one half wavelength. The waves will then be in phase and a bright band will be seen. A further increase of one half wavelength will produce a second dark band at Q. In this way successive light and dark bands are produced which follow the contour of the surface, each band indicating a path of constant separation between the optical flat and the surface under examination. If the surface is curved then the bands will follow the line of constant

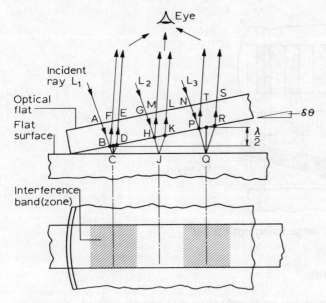

Fig. 3.3 Use of optical flat

separation and the curvature in one plane will be faithfully reproduced by the fringes, although the type of curvature, i.e. concave or convex, will not be clear from simple visual observation (see Section 3.5).

The rate of separation of the lower surface of the flat and the surface under test depends on the angle ($\delta\theta$) of the air wedge. If this angle is too large the rate of separation is correspondingly too great and the fringes will be so close together that they cannot be distinguished one from another. If the angle is too small the fringes will be so far apart as not to appear in sufficient numbers or not at all. Thus the pitch of the fringes varies inversely as the angle $\delta\theta$, increasing as $\delta\theta$ decreases and decreasing as it increases. Consequently it may be necessary to perform a number of trial placings with the optical flat before satisfactory results are obtained. Since the path difference from one fringe to the next similar fringe is one whole wavelength, then PQR − BCD = λ. When the angle $\delta\theta$ is very small the vertical displacements of the surface from the points Q and C are seen to be very nearly ½PQR and ½BCD respectively; thus

$$\tfrac{1}{2}PQR - \tfrac{1}{2}BCD = \tfrac{1}{2}\lambda$$

The change in elevation between the optical flat and the surface can be calculated by counting the number of fringes and multiplying by the length of one half wavelength of the light used (Fig. 3.4).

Incident light: wavelength $\lambda = 0.5\,\mu m$, i.e. $\frac{1}{2}\lambda = 0.25\,\mu m$.
Number of fringes is 3. Thus, separation is $3 \times \frac{1}{2}\lambda = 0.75\,\mu m$.

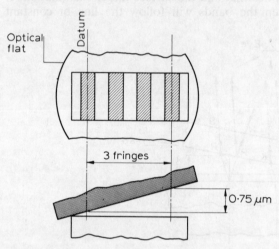

Fig. 3.4 Elevation change using optical flat

3.5 Contour testing

Consider a surface which is uniformly convex in one plane, and upon which is mounted an optical flat as shown in Fig. 3.5(a).

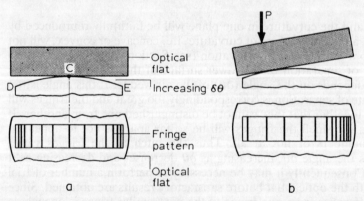

Fig. 3.5 Uniformly convex surface

The angle between the two surfaces is no longer constant as it was for the flat surface but increases at all points between CD and CE, reaching a maximum value at the outer edges D and E. From the previous discussion it will be appreciated that the fringes will be closer together towards the outer edges. To test whether the surface is concave or convex, a light pressure P is applied towards one edge of the flat. If the surface is convex then the flat will roll over the surface to a new line of contact, the bands taking up a new configuration similar to that shown in Fig. 3.5(b).

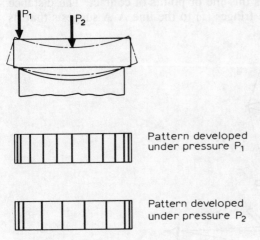

Pattern developed under pressure P_1

Pattern developed under pressure P_2

Fig. 3.6 Uniformly concave surface

The pattern for a uniformly concave surface in one plane is shown in Fig. 3.6.

If a light pressure is applied at point P_1 then little or no change in fringe pattern will occur as there is virtually no distortion of the optical flat. If now a pressure P_2 is applied at the centre of the flat it will bend slightly as shown in chain dot outline, becoming more nearly parallel to the surface under test. Thus the rate of separation of the surfaces will decrease and the number of fringes appearing will be less numerous. If the surface tested is spherically concave or convex then a 'bull's eye' fringe pattern will appear. The same method of testing is used.

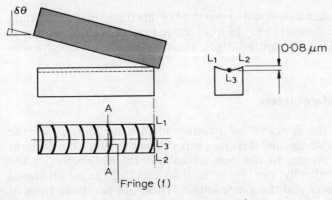

Fig. 3.7 Curved surface: contact at two points

Figure 3.7 shows a curved surface with contact at points L_1 and L_2. The fringes curve away from a line through the points of contact, and keeping in mind that the fringes are contour lines, which indicate that the surface is at a constant distance from the flat along their path, it will be seen that a concave surface will produce this fringe pattern. A convex surface would reveal fringes curving towards the line or points of contact. The distance from the centre of one of the fringes (f) to the line A-A suggests that its

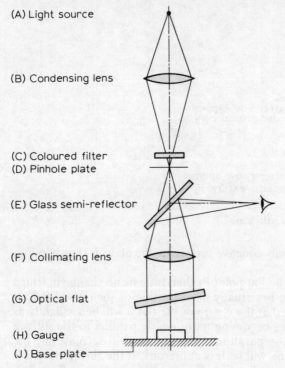

(A) Light source

(B) Condensing lens

(C) Coloured filter
(D) Pinhole plate

(E) Glass semi-reflector

(F) Collimating lens

(G) Optical flat

(H) Gauge
(J) Base plate

Fig. 3.8 Flatness interferometer (NPL type): optical system

curvature is approximately equal to one third of one fringe pitch, indicating that the curvature is equal to $\frac{1}{3} \times \frac{1}{2}\lambda$ from centre to edge. Thus the centre is approximately $0.08\,\mu$m below the edges, assuming a half wavelength equal to $0.25\,\mu$m.

3.6 Optical interferometers

When an optical flat is placed on a surface there is no control over the position of the air wedge, and it is often very difficult to adjust the flat so as to orientate the fringes to the best advantage. Interferometers, while overcoming this difficulty, can also be used for checking the parallelism of opposed gauge faces and the gauge length. There are two basic types of interferometer, the flatness interferometer and the length interferometer.

The fundamental difference between them is that the latter incorporates a constant deviation prism which splits the light into a number of parallel beams each having a different and closely defined wavelength of known value.

3.7 Flatness interferometer

The optical layout of a flatness interferometer of the NPL type is shown in Fig. 3.8.

Light from the mercury vapour lamp (A) is condensed by lens (B) through the green filter (C) to the pinhole (D) providing an intense point source. The green filter ensures that all light other than green of known wavelength is excluded. The light then diverges, passing through the glass semi-reflector (E) and on to the collimating lens (F) which transforms it into a parallel beam. The beam passes through the optical flat (G) which is independently mounted on three adjustable legs so that its angle can be varied to obtain fringes and orientate them at will. The lapped flat rotatable base plate (J) on which the gauge (H) is wrung will also show a fringe pattern when the flat and the base are fairly near to each other. The glass semi-reflector enables a vertical view of the fringes to be obtained while viewing from the side of the instrument. A number of examples of fringe patterns are shown in Fig. 3.9.

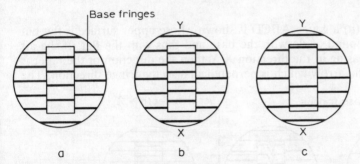

Fig. 3.9 Examples of fringe patterns

In Fig. 3.9(a) the supper surface of a gauge block which is both flat and parallel to the base is shown. The fringes are straight, parallel to the base fringes and equispaced, and their spacing is the same as the base fringe spacing. Thus the angle $\delta\theta$ is the same for both the gauge and the base. The displacement of the gauge fringes relative to the base fringes is entirely a function of the gauge length and the wavelength of the light used and is of no concern in flatness testing.

The fields of view in Figs. 3.9(b) and (c) show a gauge which is flat but not parallel to the base in the direction X-Y. The difference between the number of gauge and base fringes multiplied by $\frac{1}{2}\lambda$ will give the amount of taper present.

Beyond a gauge length of about 25 mm the fringe pattern on the base plate becomes more difficult to observe and the following method may then be used to estimate the degree of taper present.

The number of fringes on the workpiece are counted, the base is rotated through 180° without disturbing the instrument setting, and another fringe count is taken. Half the difference between the two counts multiplied by $\frac{1}{2}\lambda$ will give the amount of taper present (see Fig. 3.10). The need to halve the difference is caused by the rotation of the base through 180° and is similar to the effect on the bubble reading when using the level comparator (see Section 4.13).

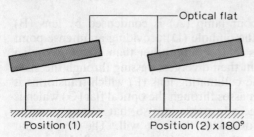

Fig. 3.10 Taper estimation
Fringe count position (1): 5
Fringe count system (2): 11
Difference ÷ 2 = 3 and $\frac{1}{2}\lambda$ = 0·25 μm
Gauge taper = 3 × 0·25 = 0·75 μm

In Fig. 3.11(a) a gauge ABCD is shown whose upper surface is flat but makes a compound angle with the base and thus with the flat. If the air wedge is increasing in the direction X-Y then the direction of the taper is indicated by the arrow which is perpendicular to the fringe direction. The

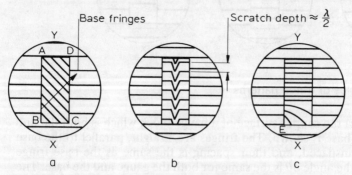

Fig. 3.11 Fringe patterns for a reference gauge

fringe spacing on the gauge is less than the base fringe spacing; thus corner D is the lowest point on the gauge. Because the surface is flat, corner B is the highest point. The intermediate points A and C are determined by the fringe count along AB and BC. The number of fringes along AB is 7 and along BC is 3. Thus A is lower than C. The order of descending height from B is C, A, D.

The effect of a scratch on the gauge surface is shown in Fig. 3.11(*b*) and an estimation of its depth can be made. A gauge which is flat but not parallel to the base at one end and curved towards point E is shown in Fig. 3.11(*c*).

Example 3.1

A reference gauge X of known length is wrung to a surface and is in close contact with a cylinder of known size which in turn abuts gauge Y. The measuring surfaces of gauge Y are flat but not parallel and the optical flat makes contact at corner A (Fig. 3.12).

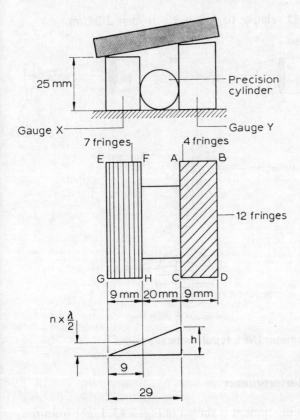

Fig. 3.12 Diagram for Example 3.1

Let *h* be the height of corner A above gauge X, *n* be the number of observed fringes on gauge X and λ be 0·5 μm. The length of gauge X is 25·000 mm and the cylinder diameter is 20·000 mm. Thus

$$\frac{h}{29} = \frac{7 \times \lambda}{2 \times 9}$$

$$h = 5 \cdot 63 \, \mu\text{m}$$

The height of corner A above the reference gauge is $+5\cdot63\,\mu$m. Since there are three fringes fewer on AB than there are on EF, B is higher than A by

$$(7 - 4)\lambda/2 = 3\lambda/2 = +0\cdot75\,\mu\text{m}$$

Point C is lower than A by

$$(0 - 12)\lambda/2 = -6\lambda = -3\,\mu\text{m}$$

Point D is higher than C by

$$(7 - 4)\lambda/2 = 3\lambda/2 = +0\cdot75\,\mu\text{m}$$

Therefore the height of D relative to A is $-3 + 0\cdot75 = 2\cdot25\,\mu$m.

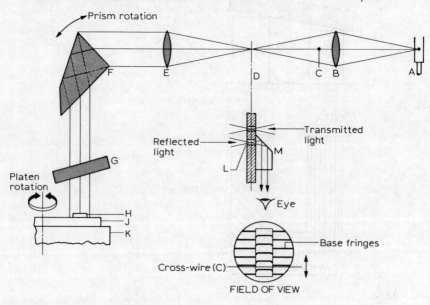

Fig. 3.13 Length interferometer (NPL type): optical system

3.8 NPL-type length interferometer

The optical system of this instrument is shown in Fig. 3.13. Light from the hot cathode cadmium lamp (A) is focused by the condensing lens (B) at the plane of the pinhole plate (D) thus giving an intense point source of light. An adjustable cross-wire is located at (C) and its reflected image will be seen in the field of view. This wire is a useful aid for estimating the displacement of the gauge fringes relative to the base fringes (see Section 3.9). The collimating lens (E) projects a parallel beam of light on to the constant deviation prism (F) which splits the light into its component colours; these, on leaving the prism, are in the form of separated parallel beams. The prism can be rotated so that beams of different wavelengths (colours) may be brought to bear on the reference plane (optical flat G), the gauge (H) and the rotatable platen (J). The light is reflected through the system by the gauge and platen surfaces and is brought to focus at the plane of the pinhole but slightly displaced to one side. This displacement is caused by the angle of tilt of the reference plane which determines the angle of reflection. A second pinhole (L) allows the light to pass on to a 45° reflecting prism (M) which enables observations to be made from the side of the instrument. For convenience the reflecting prism is shown in plan but in the instrument it lies in the horizontal plane. A further point to note is that focusing at (L) reverses the image; thus the reference plane position in the diagram will produce an image of the gauge as shown. The slight curvature on the gauge edges results from carefully stoning a small radius to give protection from damage.

3.9 Absolute length measurement

The following conditions must be observed in absolute length measurement:

(1) The gauge must be fully wrung to the platen.
(2) The gauging surfaces must be flat and parallel to each other.
(3) The position of the reference surface must be adjusted so that the gauge and platen fringes are parallel and square to the sides of the gauge.
(4) Sufficient time must be allowed for temperature equalization.
(5) The temperature at which the measurement is made must be known. When this temperature differs from standard temperature ($20 \pm \frac{1}{2}°C$), then the length obtained must be corrected to standard temperature.
(6) For highest accuracy, correction must also be made for humidity and atmospheric pressure. The standard conditions are 760 mm barometric pressure with water vapour at a pressure of 7 mm and containing 0·03% by volume of CO_2.

The measuring scale unit used in absolute length interferometry is one half wavelength of the monochromatic light used for observation. Therefore, the length of a gauge can be expressed as a number of half wavelengths plus or minus a fraction of one half wavelength. For example, the length of a slip gauge exactly 2 mm long when observed under light of 0·5 μm wavelength is

$$(2 \times 10^3 \times 2)/0·5 = 8000 \quad \text{half wavelengths}$$

where 2×10^3 is the gauge length expressed in micrometres. The same gauge observed under a wavelength of 0·51 μm is approximately 7843·13 half wavelengths long.

A little thought will indicate that when the gauge is an exact number of half wavelength units long the fringes observed on the gauge should be exactly in line with the fringes observed at the platen [Fig. 3.14(a)]. It follows that the fringes observed on any gauge will be displaced relative to the platen fringes when the gauge length is any number of half wavelengths plus a fraction and that such displacement will be directly proportional to the fraction. The displacement fraction expressed as a proportion of one platen fringe spacing may be determined as shown in Fig. 3.14(b), where it is seen to be approximately 0·7 when using platen fringe P as a datum.

Although the nominal length of a gauge can be expressed in terms of half wavelength units, its true length cannot be determined from observation under one beam of monochromatic light alone.

If a gauge of a given nominal length, say 2 mm, is exactly 2 mm long then the half wavelength fractions successively observed when the gauge is viewed under a number of monochromatic beams will be equal to the calculated fractions in each case, but if the observed fractions differ from the calculated fractions then an error in gauge length is indicated. The fractions observed, taken as a group, can be assumed to be unique to the length of the gauge under observation; that is, no other gauge error can produce the same group of fractional values within the region of the expected error in gauge length. This is a valid assumption provided that a sufficient number of observations are made (three or four), as absolute length interferometry is concerned only with small deviations from nominal length and under these circumstances the probability of more than one result from this number of readings is virtually zero.

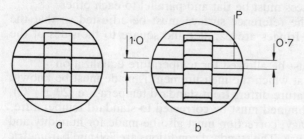

Fig. 3.14 Fringe spacing in absolute length measurement

The method outlined in the following example demonstrates how an error in length may be determined when measurement is made using a number of different scales. For the purpose of the example the error is assumed, as the observed fraction cannot otherwise be stated.

Example 3.2
Nominal length   31 mm
Actual length   32 mm
Error   +1 mm

Measuring scales
Scale 1   3 mm units
Scale 2   4 mm units
Scale 3   5 mm units
Scale 4   7 mm units

	Nominal length	Scale fraction
Scale 1	$31/3 = 10\cdot33$	$0\cdot33$
Scale 2	$31/4 = 7\cdot75$	$0\cdot75$
Scale 3	$31/5 = 6\cdot20$	$0\cdot20$
Scale 4	$31/7 = 4\cdot43$	$0\cdot43$

	Actual length	Observed fraction
Scale 1	$32/3 = 10\cdot66$	$0\cdot66$
Scale 2	$32/4 = 8\cdot00$	$0\cdot00$
Scale 3	$32/5 = 6\cdot40$	$0\cdot40$
Scale 4	$32/7 = 4\cdot57$	$0\cdot57$

The difference between the two groups of fractions when added algebraically to the nominal length yields the actual length.

The evaluation of the error from the calculated and the observed fractions is shown in Table 3.1. The results obtained from scales 1, 3 and 4 shown in column 5 directly indicate a $+1\,\text{mm}$ error. The coincidence of these results alone is sufficient to confirm the error, but an analysis of the result from scale 2 (column 4) also yields a coincident value (Fig. 3.15).

Table 3.1 Evaluation of error for Example 3.2

Column 1	2	3	4	5
Scale	Calculated fraction	Observed fraction	Obs. – Cal. col. 3 – col. 2	Calculated error (from col. 4) (mm)
1	$0\cdot33$	$0\cdot66$	$0\cdot33$	$0\cdot33 \times 3 = +1$
2	$0\cdot75$	$0\cdot00$	$-0\cdot75$ or $\bar{1}\cdot25$	$-0\cdot75 \times 4 = -3$ or $0\cdot25 \times 4 = +1$
3	$0\cdot20$	$0\cdot40$	$0\cdot20$	$0\cdot20 \times 5 = +1$
4	$0\cdot43$	$0\cdot57$	$0\cdot14$	$0\cdot14 \times 7 = +1$

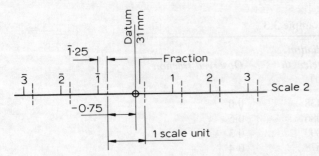

Fig. 3.15 Analysis for scale 2, Example 3.2

By adding one scale 2 unit, the position of the fraction relative to the datum is seen to coincide with the positions obtained from scales 1, 3 and 4, i.e. its position is inferred from the other results. A diagram of the scales and the fraction coincidences is shown in Fig. 3.16.

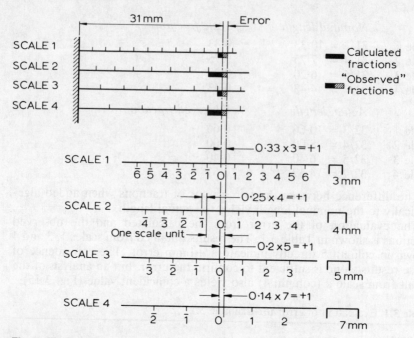

Fig. 3.16 Scales and fraction coincidences for Example 3.2

Example 3.3

This example illustrates the measurement of a 9 mm block gauge using the NPL-type interferometer shown in Fig. 3.13. In practice the calculated fraction would be obtained from a table, but for the purpose of this example the fractions are obtained by calculation.

The light source is a cadmium–mercury discharge lamp; wavelength details are given in Table 3.2.

Table 3.2 Data for Example 3.3

Colour	Radiation wavelength (μm)	Observed fraction
Red (λ_1)	0·6438	0·0
Green (λ_2)	0·5086	0·5
Blue (λ_3)	0·4800	0·3
Violet (λ_4)	0·4678	0·4
Nominal slip gauge length is 9 mm		

Nominal gauge length in terms of half wavelength units

Let N be the number of half wavelengths, F the fractional half wavelengths and L the nominal gauge length (μm).

$$Red \quad N_1 + F_1 = 2L/\lambda_1 = (9 \times 10^3 \times 2)/0{\cdot}6438 = 27\,958{\cdot}\underline{99} \quad \lambda_1$$

$$Green \quad N_2 + F_2 = 2L/\lambda_2 = (9 \times 10^3 \times 2)/0{\cdot}5086 = 35\,391{\cdot}\underline{27} \quad \lambda_2$$

$$Blue \quad N_3 + F_3 = 2L/\lambda_3 = (9 \times 10^3 \times 2)/0{\cdot}4800 = 37\,500{\cdot}\underline{00} \quad \lambda_3$$

$$Violet \quad N_4 + F_4 = 2L/\lambda_4 = (9 \times 10^3 \times 2)/0{\cdot}4678 = 38\,477{\cdot}\underline{98} \quad \lambda_4$$

The evaluation of the error from the calculated and observed fractions is shown in Table 3.3. The fraction differences shown in column 4 may now be tested for coincidence on the half wavelength rule designed for this purpose; a simplified diagram of such a rule is shown in Fig. 3.17.

Table 3.3 Evaluation of error for Example 3.3

Column 1	2	3	4	5
			Fraction	
	Calculated	Observed	difference	Calculated
Wavelength	fraction	fraction	col. 3 − col. 2	error (μm)
1	0·99	0·0	−0·99	$1{\cdot}01 \times \frac{1}{2}(0{\cdot}6438)$
				$= 0{\cdot}325$
			or $\overline{1}{\cdot}01$	
2	0·27	0·5	+0·23	$1{\cdot}23 \times \frac{1}{2}(0{\cdot}5086)$
				$= 0{\cdot}313$
3	0·00	0·3	+0·3	$1{\cdot}3 \times \frac{1}{2}(0{\cdot}48)$
				$= 0{\cdot}312$
4	0·98	0·4	−0·58	$1{\cdot}42 \times \frac{1}{2}(0{\cdot}4678)$
				$= 0{\cdot}332$
			or $\overline{1}{\cdot}42$	
				Mean error
				$= 0{\cdot}32$

Only the positive part of the fractions need be considered as the negative ($\overline{1}$) part represents one half wavelength unit. A first attempt at finding coincidence is shown under A (Fig. 3.17). In these positions the fraction spread is about $0{\cdot}1\,\mu$m. To test for a closer grouping one half wavelength is added (or subtracted) to each of the fractions. In the case under consideration the addition of one half wavelength is found to provide almost exact coincidence as shown under B. Further additions or subtractions as shown at C and D indicate that the fraction divergence increases. Thus the readings at B represent the true error of about $0{\cdot}32\,\mu$m. The average error is shown in column 5, Table 3.3.

3.10 Laser measurement

A laser (Light Amplification by Stimulated Emission of Radiation) produces an intense emergent beam of light which can be almost parallel or

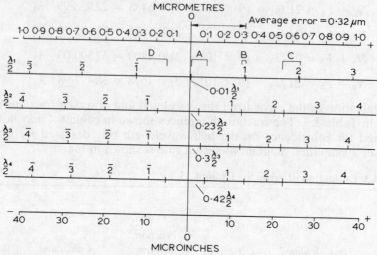

Fig. 3.17 Fraction difference coincidence for Example 3.3 using half wavelength rule

focused onto a very small area. Although lasers bear a superficial resemblance to autocollimators and similar instruments in so far as a beam of light is emitted and received, the resemblance ends there as the power of the beam emitted by a laser is many times greater than that of normal light and output occurs at specific wavelengths, i.e. monochromatically. Because of its very high power the laser beam can be used to penetrate metals, jewels, ceramics, etc. and from the point of view of human welfare, flesh—the laser has been used for welding detached eye retinas. (Under no circumstances must the beam be observed along its axis by the human eye as certain damage will result.) Although a number of materials may be used in developing the laser effect, for the purposes of metrology the helium–neon gas laser is the most common.

The simplest form of laser measuring system consists of a laser, an interferometer, a reflector and a receiver as shown in Fig. 3.18. The laser, interferometer and receiver remain stationary while the retroreflector senses the variables to be measured, e.g. the straightness of a machine slideway. The laser output beam has two frequency components, one polarized vertically and the other horizontally (see Section 6.20) with reference to the laser feet. At the interferometer the beam is divided into its two component frequencies f_1 and f_2; the measurement beam f_1 is transmitted to the retroflector while the reference beam f_2 is returned via the interferometer to the receiver. The difference between the reference signal from the laser $(f_1 + f_2)$ and the combined measurement signal from the receiver $[f_2 + (f_1 + \delta f_1)]$ constitutes the displacement of the retroreflector caused by the change in quantity measured, δf_1, sensed at the retroreflector. The comparison of the reference and measurement signals is processed electronically to generate displacement information appropriate to the specific application.

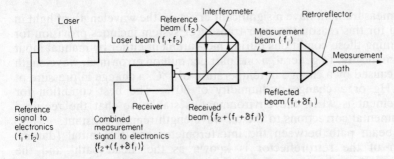

Fig. 3.18 Laser transducer system

A laser transducer measures only the relative change of position between the interferometer and the retroreflector and is thus not an absolute measurement technique. If required, the reflector may remain stationary and the interferometer constitute the moving element.

Laser transducers can measure up to six independent axes of displacement using one transducer head. A three axis configuration is shown in Fig. 3.19.

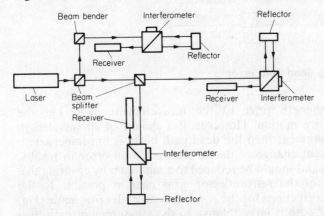

Fig. 3.19 Laser three axis configuration

The transducer produces signals in the form of interference fringes (see Section 3.3) and the light emitted by the widely used He–Ne gas laser manufactured by Messrs Hewlett–Packard has a wavelength of $0·633\,\mu m$ in a vacuum. The system is so arranged that it is able to resolve motion of the order of one quarter of a wavelength and to count the number of quarter wavelengths of relative motion between the interferometer and retroreflector.

3.11 Environmental stability

Variations in temperature, barometric pressure and relative humidity during measurement have a significant effect on the wavelength of light in air, and for this reason the laser transducer system includes provision for determining these conditions during measurement either by manual input or automatically. In general, a one part per million error in air wavelength will be caused by a change in temperature of 1 °C, a change in pressure of 2·5 mm Hg or a change in humidity of 30%. The best condition for measurement is when the environment is stable, so that the required environmental corrections to the air wavelength remain constant.

The beam path between the interferometer and the initial (datum) position of the retroreflector is known as the 'dead path' and the displacement of the retroreflector from its datum to any measurement position is known as the 'measurement path' [Fig. 3.20(a)]. Corrections

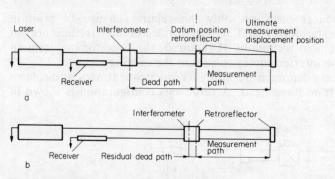

Fig. 3.20 Minimizing dead path error

made for air wavelength refer to the measurement path, i.e. the wavelengths of relative motion. However, if a change of air wavelength occurs during measurement then the dead path beam is uncompensated, leading to an apparent change of datum and hence an error in results. Dead path error can and should be reduced to a minimum by ensuring that the datum position of the retroreflector is as near as possible to the interferometer and corrections for the residual dead path error made [Fig. 3.20(b)]. If the dead path is large relative to the measurement path then the uncertainty in determining dead path error will predominate in the measurement and this cannot be eliminated.

3.12 Changes in the measured part

Changes in the shape of the part or machine element being measured as a result of temperature variations or for other reasons have a marked effect on the accuracy of the results. For example, error due to a change of 1 °C in the temperature of a measured part made from steel may be of the order of 8:1 in relation to an air temperature change of 1 °C affecting the laser beam, and the magnitude of the error increases in proportion to the length of the measurement path. Ideally, all elements in the measurement situation, the transducers, the air and the measured part or machine element should be held at standard temperature (20 °C); alternatively, if this control is not possible, all temperatures should be held at the same stable known value. If this cannot be achieved then tests should be devised to determine the magnitude of the changes so that allowances can be made. Any deviation from controlled conditions must increase the uncertainty and reduce the accuracy of the final result.

3.13 Laser beam alignment

To fulfil the requirements of Abbé's principle of alignment (Section 4.8), it is essential that the optical axis of the laser beam be as nearly as possible co-axial with the axis of motion of the measured element. The effect of inclination of the laser beam to the axis of measurement is to cause an apparent increase in the beam wavelength, so that a greater distance is

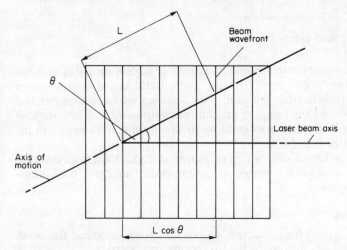

Fig. 3.21 Laser alignment error

moved by the measured part for a given wave count response than would otherwise be the case. This is a further example of cosine error in which movement is in excess of that recorded. The effect of alignment error is shown in Fig. 3.21.

If θ is the angle of laser beam misalignment and L is the actual motion, then $L \cos \theta$ is the recorded motion. If e is the induced error, then $e = L - L \cos \theta = L(1 - \cos \theta)$.

There are circumstances when measurement is made along an axis or line parallel to, but displaced from, the axis or line of motion of the element to be measured. This introduces what is generally termed Abbé offset error. For example, for practical reasons it may not be possible to check the movement of a machine tool element directly along its axis of motion, and consequently rotations of the element as it traverses its slideway will be magnified by a factor proportional to the laser offset from the axis of motion (Fig. 3.22). In such cases the error introduced to the measurement must be compensated for if best accuracy is to be achieved. As a guide, one second of angular motion introduces an approximate error of $5 \mu m/m$ offset.

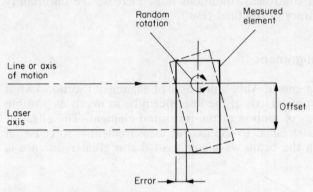

Fig. 3.22 Abbé offset error

Laser interferometers are capable of extremely high accuracy as they are able to resolve displacements of $0 \cdot 16 \mu m$, and with the use of a plane mirror instead of a retroreflector, $0 \cdot 08 \mu m$. The accuracy of measurement is 5 parts per million and the range of measurement up to 60 m. They are able to measure at velocities of movement up to $18 \cdot 3$ m/min and operate in the temperature range 0 to 50 °C.

Translations and rotations can be measured in a vast variety of contexts and they are particularly valuable in the control of machine tool movements and calibration.

Study problems

3.1 (a) Sketch typical fringe patterns observed through an optical flat which illustrate surfaces that are (i) flat (ii) concave (iii) ridged.

(b) Explain and illustrate two simple tests on an optical flat which will reveal whether a surface is concave or convex.

(c) The length of a gauge block is 10 mm. Its length, expressed in terms of half wavelength units of 'red' and 'green' monochromatic light, is 31 065·55 units and 39 323·63 units respectively. With reference to Table 3.2, calculate its length in these units if it is (i) decreased by 0·0001 mm (ii) increased by 0·00015 mm.

Answers
 (i) 31 065·24; 39 323·24
 (ii) 31 066·02; 39 324·22

3.2 The mean error in length of a block gauge is +0·0012 mm. Express this error in absolute length measurement units for the wavelengths given in Table 3.2 and illustrate the error in terms of these scales to three significant figures in diagrammatic form.

Answers: 0·386 28 units; 0·288 00 units; 0·305 16 units; 0·280 68 units

3.3 The length of a gauge measured at 25 °C was found to be 25·0000 mm. Calculate its length, in millimetres, at standard temperature. The coefficient of linear expansion of the gauge material is 12 μm °C/m.

Answer: 24·9985 mm

3.4 Observation of a slip gauge on a flatness interferometer produced fringe counts numbering 10 and 14 for the two observation conditions. Assuming that both faces of the gauge are flat, calculate the error in parallelism if the radiation wavelength (λ) is 0·5086 μm.

Answer: 0·000 51 mm

3.5 (*a*) Show that two similar adjacent interference fringes represent a change of separation between surface and optical flat of one half wavelength of the light used for observation.

(*b*) Using diagrams, discuss the reasons why variations of air wedge angle between an optical flat and a finely finished surface increase or reduce the spacing of observed interference fringes.

3.6 The following results were obtained using an NPL-type absolute length interferometer with a slip gauge of nominal length 3 mm at 20 °C. Ignoring environmental corrections such as barometric pressure, calculate the length of the gauge.

Colour	Radiation wavelength (μm)	Observed fraction	Calculated fraction
Red	0·6438	0·91	0·66
Green	0·5086	0·66	0·09
Blue	0·4800	0·66	0·00
Violet	0·4678	0·70	0·99

Answer: 3·0004 mm

3.7 (*a*) A slip gauge (gauge block) having a nominal length equal to 12 mm is to be checked by the method of coincidences. Observations at the interferometer yielded the fractional values listed below. Utilizing the radiation wavelength values given in Problem 3.6 determine the mean error in the gauge length in micrometres.

Colour	Observed fraction
Red	0·4
Green	0·3
Blue	0
Violet	0

(*b*) List the corrections which should be applied to the calculated value in order to obtain the correct size.

Answer: +0·24 μm

3.8 (*a*) A nominally 10 mm slip gauge was observed on an absolute length interferometer under a cadmium light source having the monochromatic radiation wavelengths listed in Table 3.2. If the observed fractions were 0·93, 0·85, 0·83 and 0·46 respectively, determine the error in the gauge length in micrometres.

(b) If the temperature at which the observations were made was 18·5 °C, show that the error is essentially zero at standard temperature. The coefficient of linear expansion is 12 μm °C/m.

Answers
(a) −0·2 μm
(b) 0·000 02 mm

3.9 A flatness interferometer is fitted with a light source having a radiation wavelength 0·5 μm. Sketch the interference pattern which would be observed when testing a gauge block:

(i) When a scratch of depth 1 μm is present along the length of the gauge surface;
(ii) When a chamfer is present along a longitudinal side of width 2·5 μm and angle 45°.

Answers
(i) Penetration is 4 fringes.
(ii) Penetration is 10 fringes.

3.10 Slip gauges viewed through a flatness interferometer exhibited the interference patterns shown in Fig. 3.23. State the probable magnitude and form of

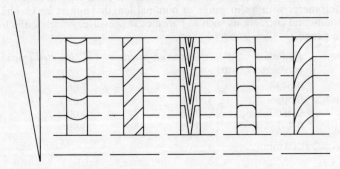

Fig. 3.23 Interference patterns for Problem 3.10

the errors in flatness and/or parallelism of the gauges and sketch their expected shapes. The radiation wavelength of the instrument lamp may be taken to be 0·5086 μm and the air wedge disposition is as shown.

Answers: 0·06 μm concave; 0·13 μm slope down right to left; 0·51 μm concave; 0·06 μm convex; 0·51 μm convex

3.11 (a) A 10 mm gauge block is to be checked by the method of coincidences. Observations at the length interferometer provided fractional values of 0·5, 0·3, 0·7 and 0·9 using radiation wavelengths of 0·64, 0·51, 0·485 and 0·46 μm respectively. Determine the actual gauge length.

(b) If the measurement temperature was 23 °C find the gauge length in micrometres and state its allowable tolerance with respect to standard temperature. α = 12 μm °C/m.

Answers
(a) 10·000 15 mm
(b) 9999·79 ± 0·06 μm

4 Dimensional and angular measurement

The fundamental datum in engineering metrology is provided by the flat surface. Flatness is defined as 'the total permissible variation between two parallel planes a given distance apart'.

4.1 Surface plates and tables

Surface plates are produced by machining, hand scraping or lapping, depending on the order of accuracy and surface finish required. Scraped and lapped surfaces are produced in sets of three by the Whitworth method of flat surface generation which does not involve the use of a master surface. A variety of materials are used—cast iron, steel, glass and granite—and plates are available in a range of sizes to suit requirements. The most widely used materials are cast iron, steel and granite, which has become more popular partly because it does not burr when damaged.

Steel plates of uniform thickness up to 200 mm diameter are called toolmakers' flats or platens. They allow slip gauges to be wrung to their surface and exhibit straight interference fringes when viewed under an optical flat. Lapped cast iron plates are also available up to 450 mm diameter (see BS 869:1978).

Square or rectangular hand scraped cast iron surface plates are flat to a few micrometres; they are heavily ribbed and deep in section to reduce deflections to a minimum. The same order of accuracy is available in granite plates which are square or rectangular and of uniform thickness. For marking out purposes, etc. planed surface plates and tables are used as the order of accuracy required is less. The present standard for surface plates is BS 817:1972 which provides three grades of accuracy, AA, A and B, for scraped, planed and lapped surfaces. This standard is soon to be replaced.

4.2 Straight edges

The straight edge is the material standard which represents the straight line and the following three types are available:

(a) Steel and granite straight edges of deep and narrow rectangular cross-section are available in a range of lengths. Both narrow faces are straight and parallel to each other to a close tolerance. Three grades, AA, A and B, are specified in BS 5204:2:1977.

(*b*) Cast iron straight edges which are in effect long narrow surface plates. They are made in the form of a deep I-section or are strengthened by a deep parabolic web so that resistance to bending along the edge is proportional to the bending moment due to the self-weight of the material. These are manufactured in lengths up to 8 m for use in checking the straightness of long narrow machine slideways, etc. Full details of cast iron edges are given in BS 5204:1975.

(*c*) High precision toolmakers' straight edges up to about 200 mm in length which have a 'knife' edge of small radius and are finished by grinding and lapping. Such edges are straight to about 1 μm. For further details see BS 852:1939.

Straight edges three feet long or longer when used edge downwards are subjected to significant deflection owing to their own self-weight. For example, a rectangular edge 2 metres long when supported at its ends sags at its centre approximately 0·096 mm. A surface having the same curvature would appear to be straight if the edge were placed directly upon it as the edge would follow the contour. The deflection can be reduced in this case to a maximum of 0·015 mm by supporting the edge at two points equidistant from each end and 0·554L apart, where L is the length of the beam (Fig. 4.1).

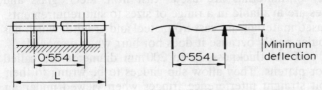

Fig. 4.1 Supporting a uniform cross-section beam for minimum deflection

4.3 Material standards of length

The material standards used for length measurement are available in two forms:

(*a*) Line comparison standards (rules, tapes).
(*b*) End comparison standards (gauge blocks or slip gauges and length or end bars).

Rules may be used for direct measurement of length or indirectly when, for instance, a length is first transferred to dividers and then measured. Similarly, gauge blocks may be used directly to measure the width of a slot, or indirectly when an instrument reading is first standardized using gauge blocks, and the reading over the measured part is then compared with the standardized reading.

4.4 Line measurement and end measurement

A summary of the characteristics of line and end standards indicates that line standards do not readily provide high accuracy while end standards are more suited to accuracy requirements of a high order.

Line standards

(1) Scales can be accurately engraved but it is difficult to take full advantage of this accuracy, e.g. a steel rule can be read to about ±0·2 mm of true dimension.
(2) A scale is quick and easy to use over a wide range since only one is required.
(3) The scale markings are not subject to wear although significant wear on the leading end leads to 'undersizing', i.e. a bias towards negative component error.
(4) A scale does not possess a 'built-in' datum which would allow easy scale alignment with the axis of measurement; this again leads to 'undersizing'.
(5) Scales are subject to the parallax effect, a source of both positive and negative reading errors (see Section 4.8).
(6) Scales are not convenient for close tolerance length measurement except in conjunction with microscopes.

End standards

These consist of sets of standard blocks or bars and are used to build up a required length.

(1) End standards are highly accurate and are well suited to measurements of close tolerance.
(2) They are time consuming in use and provide only one dimension at a time.
(3) Dimensional variations as small as 0·0005 mm can be obtained.
(4) They are subject to wear on their measuring faces.
(5) Groups of blocks are 'wrung' together to provide a given size; faulty wringing leads to damage.
(6) End standards have a 'built-in' datum because their measuring faces are flat and parallel and can be positively located on a datum surface.
(7) They are not subject to the parallax effect as their use depends on 'feel'.

The accuracy of end and line standards is affected by temperature change and both are originally calibrated at 20 ± ½ °C. Also, care is taken in manufacture to ensure that change of shape with time, secular change, is reduced to negligible proportions.

4.5 Comparison of line and end standards

With the abolition of the Imperial Standard Yard as the British standard of length, there is now no national line standard. Precision scales, however, are still widely used and techniques have been devised for comparing line standards with end standards, and thus indirectly with the ultimate standard of length, light waves.

Precision scales are often made of 58% nickel–iron alloy which has the same coefficient of linear expansion as steel and is highly corrosion resistant. Equally effective but cheaper scales are made of chromium plated mild steel.

4.6 Gauge blocks and length bars

Gauge blocks and length bars provide the material standards of length for industry. Their existence makes possible the manufacture of interchangeable components as they are made to such a high degree of accuracy and stability that, provided they are used correctly, their stated nominal length is accepted as their true length for most purposes.

Gauge blocks (slip gauges)

Metric gauge blocks are through-hardened high carbon steel rectangular blocks. They are 9 mm × 30 mm in sizes up to 10 mm length and 9 mm × 35 mm in sizes greater than 10 mm length. Their lengths range up to 100 mm and they are available in five grades, 00, calibration, 0, I and II.

Grade 00

This grade is accompanied by a calibration chart which lists the departure from nominal size of each gauge in the set. They are used as standards by gauge block manufacturers and in industries where work of a similar nature is produced and by the National Physical Laboratory and its associated organizations; there is thus little call for such gauges as their grade of accuracy is beyond normal requirements.

Calibration grade

This grade provides the highest level of accuracy required in normal engineering practice and is intended for calibrating other blocks in conjunction with suitably accurate comparators. They are used where tolerances are $2 \mu m$ or less, and are not intended for general gauge inspection.

The essential difference between 00 and calibration gauges lies in their length tolerance; calibration gauges have broader tolerances than 00 gauges, whereas the geometrical tolerances, that is flatness and parallelism of measuring faces, are the same in both cases. The values shown in Table 4.1 illustrate the tolerances of a selection from the two grades.

A calibration chart is supplied with the gauges. Thus, for nearly all length determination requirements, calibration grade gauges are of sufficient accuracy provided that true gauge length is known. Because of their broader length tolerances calibration gauges are cheaper than 00 gauges.

Grades 0, I and II

These grades are intended for general use without reference to their

Table 4.1 Block gauge tolerances
Tolerance unit is 0·01 μm.

| Gauge length (mm) | | | Gauge tolerances | | |
Over	Up to and inc.	Flatness	Parallelism	Length	Grade
—	20	5	5	± 5	00
—	20	5	5	± 25	cal
80	100	5	10	± 15	00
80	100	5	10	± 50	cal
—	20	10	10	± 10	0
80	100	10	15	± 25	0
—	20	15	20	+ 20 / − 15	0 / 0
80	100	15	25	+ 60 / − 30	I / I
—	20	25	35	+ 50 / − 25	I / I
80	100	25	35	+ 140 / − 100	II / II

For full details of gauge block tolerances see B.S. 4311:1968, *Metric gauge blocks*.

calibrated values, grade 0 providing the inspection grade for gauges and work of high precision. Grade I is the general purpose manufacturing gauge used for measurement in gauge, tool and component production, while grade II may be used for rough setting purposes and for checking components having fairly wide tolerances. The values shown in Table 4.1 illustrate the tolerance difference of a selection from the three grades.

The length tolerances of grades I and II are biased towards positive values to allow for wear on the measuring faces which will occur particularly during the early period of use. Grades 00, calibration and 0 have tolerances equally disposed about the nominal size, suggesting that they are not expected to suffer wear to any significant degree. Grade 0 has closer length tolerances than the calibration grade as it is not intended for use with a list of its calibrated values.

Length bars

Metric length bars are steel cylinders approximately 22 mm in diameter and through-hardened or hardened only at their ends, depending on their length. They range in size up to 1·2 m and are available in four grades—reference, calibration, inspection and workshop.
They are manufactured to the same high quality with regard to their

length, flatness and parallelism of their measuring faces as block gauges. The bars take one of two forms depending on their grade. Reference and calibration bars have plain ends whereas inspection and workshop grades have screwed holes at one or both ends and can be fixed together by means of loose fitting studs. Plain 25 mm bars may be wrung on if required.

Reference grade
This grade is sometimes used in laboratories or standards' rooms under temperature controlled conditions (20 ± ½°C) when length determination of the very highest order of accuracy is required. They are used only in conjunction with the most sensitive comparators, e.g. Brookes level comparator. Their function is similar to that of 00 block gauges.

Calibration grade
This grade has somewhat larger length tolerances than the reference grade, but is the same in all other respects. Because their length tolerances are larger, calibration bars are cheaper than reference bars and their function is more broadly based, i.e. they may provide the standard of length required in a factory against which inspection grade bars may be checked from time to time using suitably sensitive comparators. Strict regard for temperature control is required if full advantage of their accuracy is to be taken.

Both reference and calibration bars are supplied with an NPL certificate which lists the difference from nominal size of each gauge in the set; thus the larger length tolerance on calibration bars is no disadvantage.

Inspection grade
These bars have virtually the same length tolerance as the calibration grade but are biased towards positive values to combat the effect of wear. The flatness tolerances are rather larger than those of the calibration grade and the parallelism tolerance is about the same or larger. They are intended for use in inspection and tool rooms.

Workshop grade
This grade is intended for accurate length measurement in the workshop in built-up lengths and in conjunction with block gauges. All tolerances are larger than the inspection grade and the length tolerance is also biased to combat wear. Length tolerances are determined as shown in Table 4.2, suitable rounding off being applied where required.

Table 4.2 Basis for length bar tolerance

Length bar grade	Part per million	Minimum tolerance (0·01 μm)
Reference	± 2	± 8
Calibration	± 5	±15
Inspection	+ 7	±18
	− 3	
Workshop	+10	±30
	− 5	

Supporting length bars

Length bars may be used as standards in both the horizontal and vertical positions. When vertically mounted a tiny reduction in length occurs owing to the gravitational effect on the mass of the bar, but no correction for this is applied in assessing the length of the bar and parallelism and flatness of the measuring faces is not affected.

A different situation arises when a bar is used as a horizontal beam as it is then subject to deflection over its length, because however it is supported a deflection is always present. The solution to the problem lies in supporting the beam in such a manner that, although the beam is still subject to deflection, the slope of the beam at its ends is zero. This being the case, the end faces must be parallel. To ensure this condition the beam is simply supported at two points equidistant from each end (the Airey points) and $0.577L$ apart, where L is the length of the beam. In Fig. 4.2 the Airey positions are indicated on all grades of length bars 250 mm in length and over. When a number of length bars are wrung together the position of the Airey points for the composite bar must be calculated. The shortening caused by the sag in the bar is negligible.

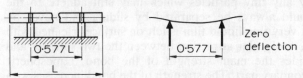

Fig. 4.2 Airey point support providing parallel end faces

Length tolerance accumulation

The length tolerances on both blocks and bars increase with increase in length, e.g.

Grade	Length		
	25 mm	100 mm	1000 mm
00 block	±8	±15	—
Reference bar	±8	±20	±200

Tolerance unit $0.01 \mu m$

For full details of length bar tolerances see BS 1790:1961.

The increase in manufacturing tolerance ensures as far as possible that any group of gauges built to a given size shall carry the same total tolerance as any other group from the same set. In practice the smallest total tolerance is obtained for a given size by using the smallest possible number of gauges in combination; thus a 175 mm inspection grade end bar has a total tolerance of $1.7 \mu m$ and the same length built from a combination of three bars $(100 + 50 + 25)$ has a tolerance of $1.89 \mu m$, an increase of 11%.

An analysis of gauge block tolerances presents a similar picture. Selecting from a grade 0, M88/2 set, i.e. an 88 piece set of 2 mm base size, a minimum of four gauges is required to build the length 45·061 mm and a minimum of five from the remainder to build the same length. In the first case the total tolerance is $0.9\,\mu$m and in the second $1.10\,\mu$m, an increase of 22%. The smallest measuring step for this set is 0.001 mm ($1\,\mu$m) which is about twice the upper or lower accumulated tolerance limit of the gauges in question. In certain circumstances slip gauge tolerance accumulation introduces small errors in measurement, for example in sine bar settings. When circumstances warrant it, calibrated gauges should be used.

Wringing

The ability to build up accurate lengths using gauge blocks and length bars depends on the flatness of their measuring faces. The final stages of manufacture involve lapping the faces to such a high degree of flatness that the act of rubbing two faces together causes adhesion. The faces must be cleaned with a solvent such as carbon tetrachloride, and wiped with a soft chamois leather or cloth. Placing two block gauges together to form a cross, and then rotating them under light pressure until they are parallel, provides a bond involving the least rubbing between the faces, and also tends to sweep away any tiny particles which may still adhere to the surfaces. Gauges should always be separated by sliding and never by breaking the bond. A very thin liquid film is left on surfaces cleaned with solvents, and it is intermolecular attraction between the two surfaces and the film which provides the main strength of the bond, atmospheric pressure playing a secondary part. The strength of the bond increases with time and gauges should not be left wrung together for more than a few hours as otherwise they may be damaged when separated. The wringing interval between correctly wrung gauges has a thickness of about 5 nm (5×10^{-9} m) but this may be as large as $1\,\mu$m if wringing is not fully effective; thus for maximum accuracy careful wringing is essential. The stated length of block gauges and length bars includes one wringing interval.

Damage prevention

To prevent loss of accuracy arising from incidental and accidental damage the following precautions should be adhered to as closely as possible:

(a) Protect from and remove dust, dirt and moisture.
(b) Avoid magnetization.
(c) Handle lapped faces as little as possible to prevent etching from finger acid. Remove all finger marks as soon as possible.
(d) Wipe faces immediately before use even when use is continuous.
(e) Always replace clean gauges in their box and close the lid after use. If gauges are not in frequent use they should be coated to prevent corrosion.
(f) Do not handle gauges above the open box, they may cause damage to other gauges if dropped.
(g) Gauges discarded for a moment during use should be laid on a soft cloth.

Building a known length

Gauge blocks are normally supplied in sets ranging from 32 pieces to 112 pieces at suitable intervals and in two base sizes, 1 mm and 2 mm. A 1 mm base auxiliary set comprising 27 pieces is also available. Grades 0, I and II may include two 2 mm protector blocks made of steel or tungsten carbide so that wear is confined to their faces alone. For purposes of illustration an M88/2 gauge set is used comprising the following gauges:

Size (mm)	Increment (mm)	Number of pieces
1·005	—	1
2·001– 2·009	0·001	9
2·01 – 2·49	0·01	49
0·5 – 9·5	0·5	19
10 –100	10·0	10
	Total	88

The size to be built is 45·061 mm and two lengths are required using the minimum number of blocks in each case. Each increment of size is successively eliminated beginning with the smallest, i.e. 0·001 mm.

45·061			45·061	
−2·001	(1)		−1·005	(1)
43·060			44·056	
−2·06	(2)		−2·006	(2)
41·000			42·050	
−1	(3)		−2·05	(3)
40·000			40·000	
−40	(4)		−10	(4)
00·000			30·000	
			−30	(5)
			00·000	

4 gauges required   5 gauges required

Finding an unknown length

Gauge blocks are sometimes used to find an unknown length and the following approach which involves the systematic division of an assigned tolerance is to be recommended. For the purposes of explanation it is necessary to assume the unknown length although in practice it will only be known approximately. The length to be found, 44·92 mm, is the distance between two parallel faces.

The length is estimated using rule, calipers, etc., as nearly as possible assigning a suitable zone within which the size must certainly lie, e.g. 45 ± 0·4 mm, and by trial and error converging on to the final size as follows:

Trial length (mm)	Result	Action
45	NOT GO	Try 44·8
44·8	GO	Try 44·9
44·9	GO	Try 44·95
44·95	NOT GO	Try 44·92
44·92	GO	Try 44·93
44·93	NOT GO	Accept 44·92

The final size is seen to lie within the range 44·92 and 44·93 mm. The same process of elimination applied to the 0·001 mm value will provide a more precise measurement.

4.7 Reference discs

Block gauges are not always suitable or convenient to use as standards when setting measuring instruments, particularly when the work is manufactured on centres and is intended to be measured using the centres as a datum. Standard sets of reference discs are supplied with a calibration certificate which lists the differences from nominal size of each disc in the set. Thus it is a simple matter to standardize such instruments as the floating carriage diameter measuring machine. A typical set consists of 22 discs ranging in size from 3 mm to 100 mm in diameter having a calibrated size determined to within a few ten millionths of a metre. For example, a disc of 30 mm nominal size has a calibrated size determined by the manufacturers of 29·9958 mm to an uncertainty of ±0·0005 mm (±0·5 μm). This determination applies to that part of the disc lying between two circumferential bands marked on the disc. The purpose of this limitation is to reduce the possibility of error arising from taper on the disc (Fig. 4.3).

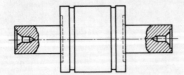

Fig. 4.3 Precision reference disc

4.8 Sources of error in precision measurement

Failure to consider the following factors may introduce errors in measurement:

(a) The alignment principle
(b) Location of the measured part
(c) Temperature
(d) Parallax
(e) Elastic deformation.

Alignment principle

Abbé's principle of alignment states that:

> *The axis or line of measurement of the measured part should coincide with the measuring scale or the axis of measurement of the measuring instrument.*

The effect of simple scale alignment error is shown in Fig. 4.4.

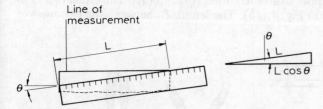

Fig. 4.4 Scale misalignment

If θ is the angle of scale misalignment and L is the apparent length, then $L \cos \theta$ is the true length. If e is the induced error, then

$$e = L - L \cos \theta = L(1 - \cos \theta)$$

An alignment error of 2° over 1 m introduces an error of approximately 0·6 mm.

Error is introduced to dial indicator readings if the plunger axis does not coincide with the axis or line of measurement [Fig. 4.5(a)].

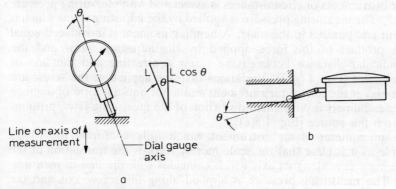

Fig. 4.5 Axis misalignment

If e is the induced error and L is the change in indicator reading, then $L \cos \theta$ is the surface displacement and

$$e = L(1 - \cos \theta)$$

To ensure correct displacement readings on the dial indicator the plunger must, of course, be normal to the surface in both mutually perpendicular planes.

Some dial indicators are fitted with a ball-ended stylus. The stylus arm is connected to the dial gauge operating mechanism in such a way that whatever the angle of the arm the gauge records the vertical displacement of the ball end [Fig. 4.5(b)].

The measuring jaws of the vernier caliper are in effect extensions of the scale markings on the instrument; thus the jaws of an instrument in good condition are parallel and remain so at any measurement within the instrument range. The length L indicated on the scale corresponds to the displacement of the jaws from each other [Fig. 4.6(a)]. The effect of a bent scale beam is shown in Fig. 4.6(b). The length L_1 between the extremes of

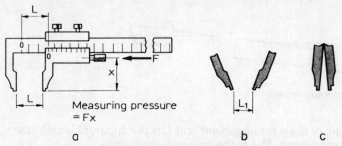

Measuring pressure = Fx

Fig. 4.6 Errors from measuring pressure

the jaws has now become smaller than the length indicated on the scale. It is also evident that the error introduced is proportional to the length of the jaws and is at its minimum along the line of the scale.

A second source of error well illustrated by the vernier caliper and similar instruments or circumstances is associated with measuring pressure or 'feel'. The measuring pressure is applied by the adjusting screw which is adjacent and parallel to the scale. A bending moment is introduced equal to the product of the force applied by the adjusting screw and the perpendicular distance between the screw centre line and the line of measurement [Fig. 4.6(a)]. Variations of force applied at the screw are augmented at the line of measurement and a not unusual form of damage to vernier calipers is permanent distortion of the measuring jaws, presumably from this source [Fig. 4.6(c)].

The micrometer is an instrument which fully conforms to Abbé's principle as it is clear that the scale merely records the translation of the measuring screw along its axis which coincides with the line of measurement. The measuring pressure is applied along the screw axis and the torque introduced is small; thus although variations in measuring pressure can and do occur, the 'feel' of the instrument is much easier to judge.

Errors in measuring diameter

Cylinders are often measured between centres on a diameter measuring machine (floating micrometer) and it is essential that the micrometer spindle and anvil measuring surfaces be parallel to the cylinder axis and the micrometer axis perpendicular to the cylinder axis. Figure 4.7 illustrates the effect of angle error between the micrometer and cylinder axis.

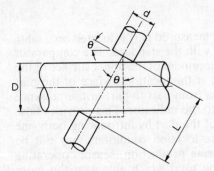

Fig. 4.7 Effect of angle error between micrometer and cylinder axis

If D is the true diameter, L the apparent diameter and d the micrometer anvil diameter, then

$$D = L \cos \theta - d \sin \theta$$
$$\text{error} = L - (L \cos \theta - d \sin \theta) = L(1 - \cos \theta) + d \sin \theta$$

When θ is small, $L \approx L \cos \theta$ and $\sin \theta \approx \theta$ radians; therefore

$$\text{error} = d\theta$$

The reading error introduced by 1 minute angle error when $d = 6\,\text{mm}$ is approximately $1\cdot7\,\mu\text{m}$. Floating micrometers are set by using calibrated discs; thus the effect of this error source is eliminated. It is particularly

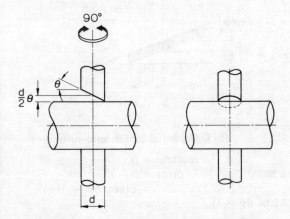

Fig. 4.8 Effect of the micrometer measuring face not being square to spindle axis

important that the measuring face of a micrometer spindle be square to the spindle axis, otherwise an error of the form shown in Fig. 4.8 is introduced and has a maximum value of $\frac{1}{2}d\theta$. This error source is overcome in the floating carriage micrometer by having a non-rotating spindle.

Location

When using a sensitive comparator the measured part is located on a table which forms the datum for comparison with the standard. The comparator reading is thus an indication of the displacement of the upper surface of the measured part from the datum. Faults at the location surface of the part through damage, geometrical variations from part to part or the presence of foreign matter are also transmitted to the indicator. This provides false information regarding the true length of the part by introducing both sine and cosine errors [Fig. 4.9(a)]. Where location conditions may not be ideal, e.g. interstage measurement during production, sensors operating on each side of the component can be used which eliminate the more serious sine-type error. A two probe system measures length rather than surface displacement and highly sensitive electronic comparators of this type are used for slip gauge measurement [Fig. 4.9(b)].

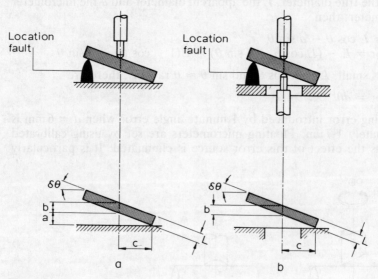

Fig. 4.9

(a) Surface displacement

reading = $a + b$
= $c \tan \delta\theta + L \sec \delta\theta$
error = $a + b - L$
= $c \tan \delta\theta + L(\sec \delta\theta - 1)$

(b) Differential length measurement

reading = b
error = $b - L$
= $L(\sec \delta\theta - 1)$

Temperature

The standard reference temperature at which line and end standards are said to be at their true length is $20 \pm \frac{1}{2}$°C, and for highest accuracy in measurement this temperature should be maintained. When this is not possible and the length at reference temperature must be known, a correction is made to allow for the difference between ambient and reference temperature. The correction value required is $-0.001\,375\,\text{mm}$ ($-1.375\,\mu\text{m}$) when a steel object exactly 25 mm long at 20 °C and coefficient of linear expansion $11\,\mu\text{m}\,°\text{C/m}$ is measured at 25 °C, which is rather larger than the increment step of the M88/2 slip gauge set referred to earlier. However, for less stringent measuring requirements it is not essential that correction to reference temperature is made provided that the following precautions and conditions are observed:

(a) The temperature at which measurement is made is not changing significantly;
(b) The gauge and work being compared are at the same temperature and this temperature is the same as ambient temperature;
(c) The gauge and work have the same cofficient of linear expansion.

Conditions (a) and (b) can be met if gauge and work are allowed sufficient time to reach equal temperature with their surroundings after being arranged in the measuring positions. If measurement can be carried out on the surface of a large mass, e.g. a surface plate, then temperature equalization will be fairly rapid as heat will be conducted away from the work and gauge but will not contribute any significant temperature change to the plate.

A component having a coefficient of linear expansion significantly different from the gauge may be said to be correct to size only at a given temperature, e.g. an aluminium component found to be exactly 30 mm long when compared with block gauges at 20 °C would exhibit a size differential of $+0.0036\,\text{mm}$ if measured against the same gauges at 30 °C ($\alpha_{\text{steel}} = 11\,\mu\text{m}\,°\text{C/m}$; $\alpha_{\text{al}} = 23\,\mu\text{m}\,°\text{C/m}$).

Significant temperature changes can easily be caused simply by handling gauges and this source of error should not be ignored.

Parallax effect

On most dials the indicating finger or pointer lies in a plane parallel to the scale but displaced a small distance away to allow free movement of the pointer. It is then essential to observe the pointer along a line normal to the scale otherwise a reading error will occur. This effect is illustrated in Fig. 4.10(a) where a dial is shown observed from three positions when the pointer is set at zero on the scale. Observed from position (i), i.e. from the left, the pointer appears to indicate some value to the right of zero, and from position (ii) some value slightly to the left of zero, while only at position (iii) will the pointer coincide with zero on the scale. Rules and micrometer thimbles are bevelled to reduce this effect; on dials the indicator may be arranged to lie in the same plane as the scale (Sigma comparator), thus completely eliminating parallax, or a silvered reflector may be incorporated on the scale so that the line between the eye and pointer is normal to the scale only when the pointer obscures its own image in the reflector [Figs. 4.10(b) and (c)].

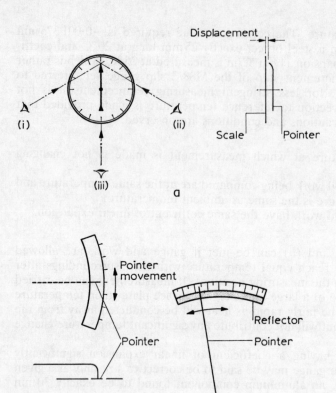

Fig. 4.10 Parallax effect

Elastic deformation

It is well known that all materials deflect and deform when subjected to external forces including the force of gravity. Such deformations are fairly obvious sources of error when the forces involved are large but there is a tendency to neglect them as being of little or no consequence when they are small. In fact, despite the extremely low measuring forces associated with many modern measuring instruments, they remain just as much a problem when calibrating standards, as the resulting deformation can quite easily be of the order of one half a micrometre or more.

The deformations caused by a measuring force applied through a spherical stylus to a ball mounted to a table are shown in Fig. 4.11. Deformation occurs at four contact points; 1 and 2 at the stylus/ball interface, and 3 and 4 at the ball/table interface.

It should also be noted that the ball will generally deform in shape, i.e. it is compressed; however, this effect is usually so small that it may be neglected. Even so, measurement techniques should be so designed as to

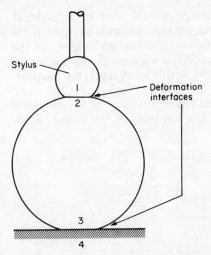

Fig. 4.11 Deformations in ball/stylus system

negate the effects of errors resulting from general deflections or distortions of this type whenever possible.

Virtually all solid materials behave to some extent elastically and consequently return to their original shape when external loading is removed. It is of the greatest importance that plastic deformation of the surface interfaces of measurements be avoided, which means that all the materials must remain within their range of elastic behaviour. It is not widely enough appreciated that, although a measuring force may be small, the areas developed at the measuring surface interfaces may also be small. This results in the development of high contact stresses and it is these which must be carefully assessed if uncertainty is to be kept to a minimum.

Some examples of different probe/surface combinations are shown in Fig. 4.12 and their order of increasing deformation for a given measuring force and stylus or probe shape is indicated.

In general, deformations involving spherical probes will lead to greater deformations than those involving flat faced probes and the smaller the probe diameter the greater the deformation for a given load. It may be thought that, this being the case, the flat probe should always be favoured, but a little thought will make clear that this is not always practical, practicable or desirable. For example, when a flat probe is used against flat work mounted to a flat datum it is virtually certain that the probe face will not be parallel to the datum surface or the work surface. This condition can only increase the uncertainty of measurement in cases where very high precision is required.

As it is not possible to eliminate elastic deformation altogether, careful consideration must be given to equalizing or balancing its effects wherever possible. An important factor in achieving this end is to compare like with like, geometrically speaking, during measurement. A simple example occurs during comparator operations. If the component is a cylindrical gauge then the instrument setting gauge should also be cylindrical. Furthermore, the setting gauge should be closely equal in size to the component so that the measuring pressure remains unchanged. In this context, although the deformation still occurs, it is almost exactly similar for both the gauge and component and consequently its effect on the measurement is negligible.

A factor which reduces the significance of deformation in measurement is the hardness of the workpiece and the hardness of the probe. Probe

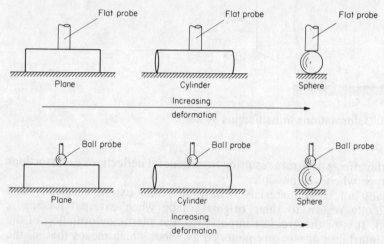

Fig. 4.12 Probe/surface combinations

deformation is reduced in the progression steel, carbide and diamond, and similarly aluminium, steel and carbide for the component. Hence measurements are likely to be less influenced by deformation when hard materials are in contact.

There are circumstances where it is not possible to compare 'like with like'. In such cases a larger margin of uncertainty may be allowed, or, if this is not permissible, a careful analysis of all the variables in the situation must be made and an appropriate correction factor applied. The quantitative treatment of such factors is beyond the scope of the present text but reference may be made to the equations developed by the mathematician Heinrich Hertz, and the work of Nichols and Oakley (see Bibliography).

A very important source of error in measurement results from variations in surface finish. The rougher the finish on a surface, the greater the uncertainty of measurement. This is illustrated in Fig. 4.13, where the probe position depends on its relationship to the peaks and valleys appearing on the surface of the work. A second factor which influences uncertainty is the variation in surface deformation from measurement to measurement owing to surface roughness. If measurements are to be of a high quality then careful attention must be paid to the surface finish of the probe and work.

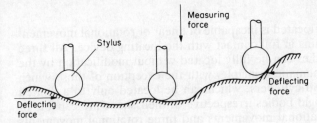

Fig. 4.13 Roughness error

4.9 Measuring instruments

In measurements and in the design of measuring instruments it is necessary to apply principles and techniques which allow the following requirements to be fulfilled:

(1) Accurate location of one element upon another
(2) Accurate translation (linear movement) and rotation of elements in the measuring instrument or system
(3) Freedom from unnecessary constraints or restraints which might introduce strains between component parts
(4) Elimination of clearances, e.g. in instrument bearings
(5) Transmission of thrust
(6) Freedom from unnecessary friction
(7) Elimination of backlash
(8) Low and constant measuring pressure
(9) Reduction of inertia to an acceptable level.

Kinematics and instrument design

Kinematics as applied in metrology is the study of the location and movement of three dimensional rigid bodies. Kinematic instrument design requires that all contacts between the component parts of a system should be point contacts. In many cases a close approximation to this requirement is easy to achieve in practice and even the introduction of line contacts to a limited degree does not significantly change the effectiveness of the technique. As examples of kinematic (point) and semi-kinematic (line) contact, a ball in a vee groove and ball in a conical hole are shown in Fig. 4.14.

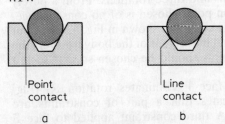

Point contact

Line contact

a

b

Fig. 4.14 (a) Kinematic (b) Semi-Kinematic

Location

A body which is fully located is incapable of linear or rotational movement provided that it remains in full contact with the locating device. All three dimensional rigid bodies can be fully located without modification by the application of the kinematic principle, with the exception of those which can roll, e.g. balls and cylinders, which can be located only to a limited extent. Further, all rigid bodies irrespective of their shape are capable of three linear or translational movements and three rotational movements

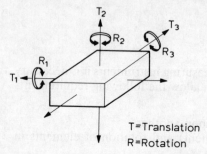

T = Translation
R = Rotation

Fig. 4.15 Six degrees of freedom of a rigid body

either singly or in combination. Each of these possible movements is termed a degree of freedom; thus all rigid bodies have six degrees of freedom. The translational degrees of freedom correspond to three mutually perpendicular axes passing through the body and the rotational degrees of freedom correspond to rotation about those axes. The six degrees of freedom are shown in Fig. 4.15 as they apply to a simple rectangular block; the letters T and R indicate translation and rotation.

The body can only be fully located in a given position by eliminating all six degrees of freedom and to do so kinematically requires the application of no more than six suitably applied point locations, each location eliminating one degree of freedom.

Constraint

Any rigid point location applied to a body is a constraint. Thus one constraint applied at face F [Fig. 4.16(a)] reduces the degrees of freedom of the block to five—two translations and three rotations. From a purely theoretical point of view the location point chosen is of no consequence, e.g. the block could be located at one corner as shown in Fig. 4.16(b), but this is not practical as any translational movement of the body transfers the location to a new axis. Location points should be chosen so that such a transfer cannot occur.

A second constraint applied to face F eliminates rotation R_3 [Fig. 4.16(c)] and a little thought indicates that a pair of constraints are necessary to eliminate a rotation. A third constraint applied to face F completes the points required to form a plane and eliminates rotation R_1

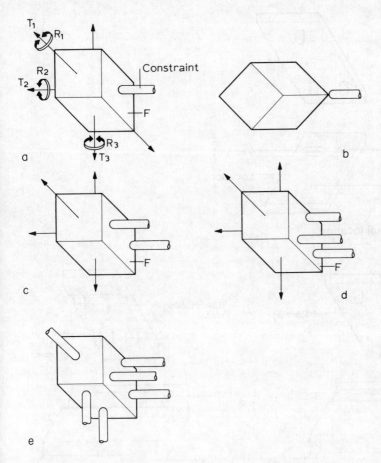

Fig. 4.16 Constraints

[Fig. 4.16(d)]. More constraints applied to face F create redundancies as no further degrees of freedom would be eliminated, and in any case they would not automatically lie in the same plane as the other three. The fully located block is shown in Fig. 4.16(e). It may be removed and replaced in exactly the same position without fear of translation along or rotation about any axis while it remains located. This result is achieved without application of external force (which includes friction force). The locating device upon which the constraints are mounted is not required to be highly accurate and the constraints themselves are simply domed studs screwed or otherwise fixed in position.

A method used in instruments to fully locate one component upon another is shown in Fig. 4.17. The hole should ideally provide three point location for its corresponding peg and this can be done by providing a hole or hollow of trihedral form. In practice, a conical hole is used which although it introduces line contact to the peg is much easier to manufacture

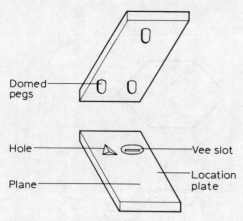

Fig. 4.17 Full location

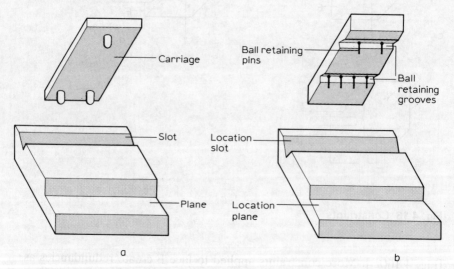

Fig. 4.18 Five constraints, one degree of freedom

and is just as effective. The vee slot can be produced by means of a simple formed cutter.

The location pegs contact the plate at six points: the slot eliminates two translations, the hole eliminates one translation and two rotations, and finally the plane eliminates the remaining rotation, a total of six.

Very often in metrology an instrument pair is required to have one degree of freedom, e.g. it may be necessary to provide a translation in one direction only. A simple method is shown in Fig. 4.18(*a*), where a slot and a plane are used to provide five constraints. The slot must of course be accurately machined and free from 'wind' or twist, and the plane must not rise or fall in relation to the slot if straight line motion is to be achieved, otherwise rotations will be introduced.

Such a motion having very low friction characteristics can be achieved by substituting balls for the location pegs [Fig. 4.18(b)]. The balls are held captive in vee grooves machined in the carriage so that they are able to roll; their point contacts in these grooves should not be mistaken for the locations required. Retaining pins provide a limit to the distance that the balls can roll, thus preventing the system from becoming unstable. This method is used on the upper slide of the floating carriage diameter measuring machine manufactured by Coventry Gauge and Tool Co. Ltd, where it is essential that the micrometer mounted on the carriage should adjust to the measured component along a line perpendicular to the component axis and with almost complete freedom from friction.

Metal strip springs

Metal strip springs provide a simple and effective method of flexible connection between two elements allowing frictionless relative motion in desired directions. A number of such devices used in measuring instruments where small movements are required are shown in Fig. 4.19.

The springs range from 0·05 to 0·1 mm in thickness depending on the stiffness required. Reinforcing plates which prevent buckling may be used to allow the elements to be placed the desired distance apart [Fig. 4.19(a)]. The crossed strip hinge [Fig. 4.19(b)] is widely used in comparators and gauging fixtures where small rotary motions are required. In Fig. 4.19(c) rotary motion is obtained as a result of the distortion introduced to the two flexure springs by relative parallel movement of parts A and B, while in Fig. 4.19(d) linear movement of a stylus is obtained. The twisted strip shown in Fig. 4.19(e), when placed in tension, causes the pointer to rotate. In all these examples sufficient stiffness, accuracy of movement, elasticity and stability, coupled with virtually zero friction and low inertia, are obtained along with the elimination of backlash. An ingenious application of the flexible metal strip is found in the design of the fiducial indicator on the NPL-type pitch measuring machine. Without going into details of screw thread pitch measurement, which is beyond the scope of this chapter, it is sufficient to state that the stylus which engages the thread to be measured must be moved from pitch to pitch on the thread, and an exact indication when one pitch has been moved is essential. The indicator, which consists of a stylus mounted on a block supported by a flexible steel strip and a strut having conical end bearings, is shown in Fig. 4.19(f). When the stylus is located in the centre of the groove it is subject to exactly equal pressures on both sides but as soon as it is moved parallel to the screw axis it begins to climb the thread flank, which causes the flexible strip to bend and twist. A fork fitted to the block transmits the twist to a cranked pivot upon which a light pointer is mounted. The pointer is immediately deflected from its index mark and will only return to the mark when the pressure is equal on each side of the stylus. This occurs first at the transition of the stylus over the crown of the thread and again when the stylus is exactly at the centre of the next groove, thus indicating one pitch movement.

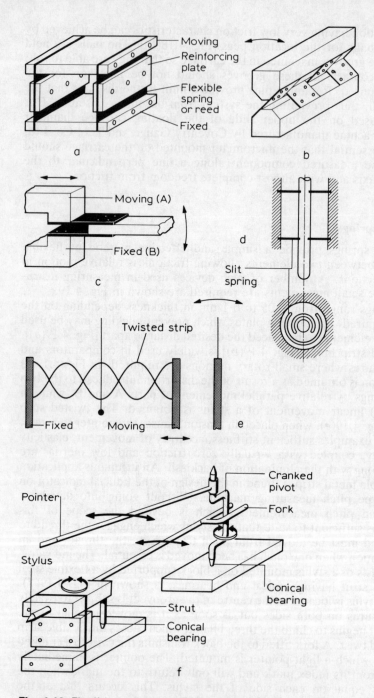

Fig. 4.19 Flexible connections allowing small movement

Thrust bars and bearings

The thrust bar (Fig. 4.20) provides a simple method for transmitting thrust and eliminating errors which might arise from a more rigid connection between two parts. A practical example is used on the pitch measuring machine where it is necessary to measure the movement of the fiducial indicator by means of a micrometer.

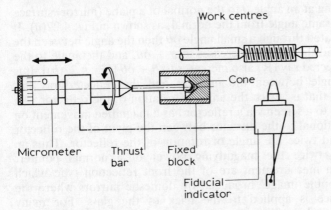

Fig. 4.20 Thrust bar

The micrometer and fiducial indicator are mounted on a kinematic carriage having one degree of freedom and the work is mounted on separate fixed centres parallel to the motion of the carriage. The thrust bar shown is a modification of the Lucas thrust bar which has two ball ends and is located in conical or trihedral seatings. The Lucas bar can also be used to provide true axial rotation [Fig. 4.21(a)]. This is not easy to achieve with the normal circular bearing and spindle as the clearance and geometrical errors produce 'path rotation' in which the axis of rotation does not remain in a fixed position [Fig. 4.21(b)]. A simple method for eliminating bearing clearances is to mount a cylindrical spindle in vee blocks instead of a circular bearing, the block acting as the bearing cap being spring loaded [Fig. 4.21(c)].

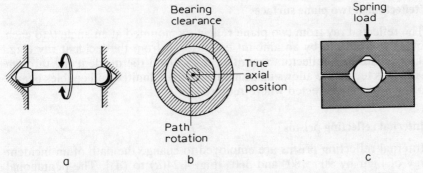

Fig. 4.21 Lucas bar for true axial rotation

4.10 Reflectors, prisms and lenses

Reflectors, prisms and lenses are incorporated in many measuring instruments to provide frictionless magnification and transmission systems.

Reflection at a plane surface

A ray of light falling at an angle θ to the normal of a plane (mirror) surface is reflected at the same angle from the normal, as shown in Fig. 4.22(a). If the reflector is rotated through a small angle $\delta\theta$ then the angle between the incident ray (I) and the normal increases to $\theta + \delta\theta$, and the angle to the normal of the reflected ray (R) also increases to $\theta + \delta\theta$ [Fig. 4.22(b)]. It is clear that the angle between the incident and the reflected ray has increased by $2\delta\theta$, that is, twice the angle of rotation of the reflector. An image transmitted to a screen via a reflector has a magnified movement on the screen proportional to the distance between the pivot of the reflector and the screen and twice the angle of rotation of the reflector. Thus an optical lever has twice the magnifying power of a normal pointer. Reflectors used in measurement are of the front reflection type which eliminates the 'double image' produced by domestic mirrors where the reflecting substance is applied to the back of the glass. For many applications, such as the reflectors used with autocollimators, the reflector is a lapped and polished steel plate.

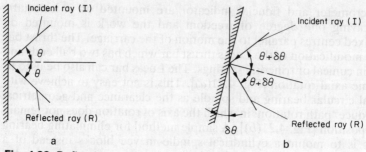

Fig. 4.22 Reflection at a plane surface

Reflection at two plane surfaces

The reflected ray from two plane reflectors mounted at an angle θ to each other will deviate by an amount equal to 2θ from the incident ray (Fig. 4.23). Thus two reflectors mounted at 45° bend the incident ray through 90°. This technique allows instrument size to be limited and enables beams of light to be redirected where required.

Internal reflecting prisms

Internal reflecting prisms are employed to change the path of an incident ray of light by 90°, 180° and 360° [Fig. 4.24(a) to (d)]. The pentagonal prism [Fig. 4.24(d)], commonly known as the constant deviation prism, has

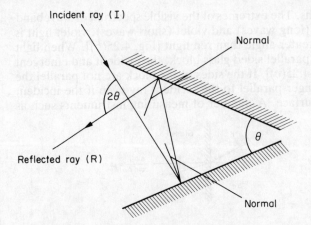

Fig. 4.23 Reflection at two plane reflectors

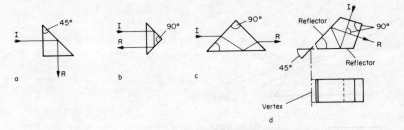

Fig. 4.24 Prisms

the advantage that if it is correctly positioned the right angle between the incident and reflected ray remains constant. Only in one condition is the right angle not reflected and this occurs when the plane of the incident ray is not perpendicular to the vertex of the prism, which may be defined as the plane in which the line of intersection of the two reflecting surfaces lies.

Refraction

Light bends when it passes from one transparent medium to another. When a ray passes from a less dense to a more dense medium, for example from air to glass, the light is always refracted or bent toward the normal; conversely, when the ray passes from glass to air the ray is bent away from the normal. The incident ray, the refracted ray and the normal to the surface at the point of incidence all lie in the same plane. The sines of the angle of incidence and the angle of refraction are always in constant ratio for any pair of media, and this ratio is termed the refractive index, μ [Fig. 4.25(a)]. Hence $\mu = \sin i/\sin r$. The refractive index varies according to the specification of the glass and also in accordance with the wavelength of light used. A ray of white light passing through a prism is separated into its constituent wavelengths. The extremes of the visible spectrum or waveband of white light are red (long waves) and violet (short waves); violet light is refracted through a greater angle than red light [Fig. 4.25(b)]. When light is refracted through a parallel sided glass block, the incident and emergent rays are parallel [Fig. 4.25(c)]. If the sides of the block are not parallel the emergent ray is no longer parallel to the incident ray even if the incident ray is normal to the surface. A number of measuring instruments such as

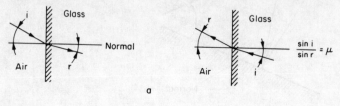

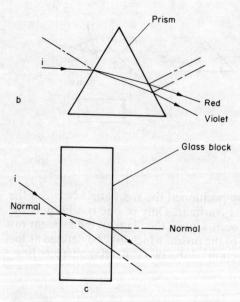

Fig. 4.25 (a) Refraction of light (b) Refraction of constituent wavelengths (c) Parallel glass block

microscopes and telescopes utilize the parallel glass block to form the basis of an optical micrometer. In one type of micrometer the block is mounted between the objective lens and the eyepiece of the instrument and is pivoted at, but at right angles to, the optical axis. Movement of the block is effected by a segment and pinion connecting it to a micrometer drum. In addition to the micrometer drum the instrument incorporates a scale in the field of view of the instrument eyepiece which enables whole revolutions of the micrometer drum to be counted. In operation the instrument is sighted at the datum position of the object (A) to be displaced [Fig. 4.26(a)] and the scale value of the eyepiece scale and micrometer drum is noted. After displacement of the object to position A' the instrument is resighted by rotating the micrometer drum until A' is positioned at the original position held by A [Fig. 4.26(b)]. The difference between the initial and final scale readings represents the displacement of the object.

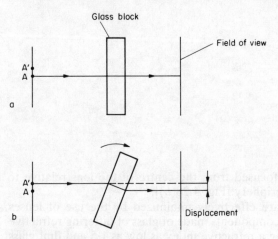

Fig. 4.26 Optical micrometer

Lenses

Lenses can be considered to be an infinite number of prismatic units of constantly changing angle, which is a maximum at the outer edge and zero at the centre. Lenses take a variety of forms but they may be classified into two main groups—concave or negative lenses and convex or positive lenses. Convex lenses cause parallel rays to converge on a single point known as the principal focus. They are able to transmit an image to an opaque or translucent screen, enabling the image to be viewed externally to the lens system; the image so projected is referred to as a 'real' image. Convex lenses which transmit a parallel beam of light are known as collimating lenses, but when such a lens is used to transmit a magnified image of the object then it is referred to as a projection lens [Fig. 4.27(a)].

Concave lenses cause to diverge a parallel beam of light, which then appears to come from a focal point behind the lens. The image produced by this type of lens is referred to as a 'virtual' image, which may be seen only along the axis of the lens [Fig. 4.27(b)].

Two main forms of error occur in simple lenses—chromatic aberration and spherical aberration. Chromatic aberration in simple lenses arises as a result of the refraction of the wavelengths of the component elements of white light at slightly different angles; the elements are then focused throughout a range of focal lengths. The aberration manifests itself as a coloured fringe on the image being viewed [Fig. 4.28(a)]. Spherical aberration results in a blurred image which arises from the focal plane

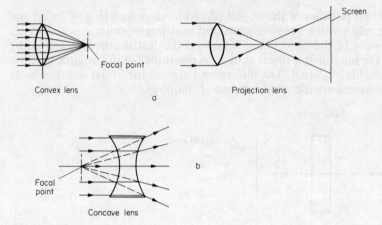

Fig. 4.27 Lenses

displacement of the rays focused from the centre of the lens relative to those focused from the periphery [Fig. 4.28(b)].

Both these conditions are effectively minimized by the use of lenses consisting of two or more components made of glass of differing refractive indexes, crown glass having a refractive index as low as 1·5 and flint glass having a refractive index as high as 1.9. A special adhesive known as canada balsam is used for cementing the lenses together.

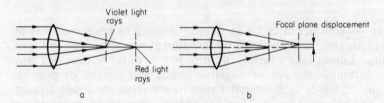

Fig. 4.28 Chromatic and spherical aberration

4.11 Precision comparators

The function of the comparator is to detect to a high degree of precision the small difference, if any, between a suitable length standard and the measured part.

In construction, a comparator consists of three essential elements:

(1) A sensing device (usually a plunger) which faithfully senses the input signal represented in this case by a change of length or a surface displacement.
(2) A magnifying or amplifying system to increase the signal to a suitable magnitude. Mechanical, optical, pneumatic, hydraulic and electronic methods are utilized for this purpose.

(3) A display system (usually a scale and pointer) which utilizes the amplified signal to provide a suitable readout.

The design criteria of comparators are broadly as follows:

(a) The comparator should at least be able to record variations of 0·0025 mm.
(b) The recording scale should be linear.
(c) The system should not be subject to variance, i.e. the instrument reading should not vary when repeated measurements of a given quantity are made.
(d) The scale indicator (pointer, liquid column, etc.) should be clear and free from oscillation ('dead-beat').
(e) The system should be free from backlash, unnecessary friction and clearances, and inertia should be low.
(f) The measuring pressure should be low and constant.
(g) The supporting frame should be rigid and able to withstand reasonable ill usage without permanent harm.
(h) The instrument should be capable of a wide measuring range.

4.12 Mechanical comparators

The essential details of two mechanical comparators are shown in Fig. 4.29 and Fig. 4.30.

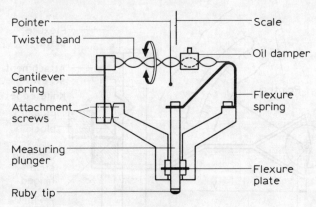

Fig. 4.29 Johansson Mikrokator

Johansson Mikrokator

This instrument, shown in Fig. 4.29, makes use of the Abramson movement to provide a virtually frictionless system. The plunger is supported at its lower end by a flexure plate and its upper end by the foot of a flexure spring. The end of the twisted metal band wraps round the knee of the spring and is firmly attached through its vertical leg. Vertical movement of the plunger is transformed into rotational movement of the vertical leg, thus stretching the twisted band which partially unwinds and rotates the attached pointer against the scale. This system provides a large angle of rotation for a small plunger movement which is further amplified by the pointer. Damping is provided by immersing a portion of the twisted band in a spot of oil. The cantilever spring fulfils two functions:

(a) The band can be brought to the correct tension by adjustment of the attachment screws.
(b) The magnification can be varied by increasing or reducing the length of the cantilever. An increased length reduces the force available to unwind the strip thus reducing magnification. The cantilever is preset in its correct position by the manufacturer.

A large range of Mikrokators are available, the most sensitive having a scale division of 0·000 01 mm, for closely controlled calibration work, while the least sensitive has a scale division of 0·1 mm. The range of instruments having magnifications up to ×5000 are available for industrial use.

Sigma comparator

This instrument is shown in Fig. 4.30. The plunger is attached to a rectangular bar which is supported at its upper and lower ends by flexure plates. The vertical movement of the bar is limited by stops. A knife edge is fixed to the side of the bar which bears on a sapphire block attached to the

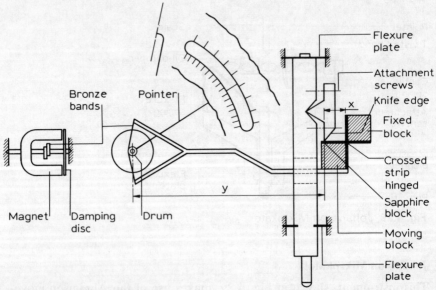

Fig. 4.30 Sigma comparator

If R is the pointer radius and r is the drum radius

$$\text{magnification} = \frac{y}{x} \times \frac{R}{r}$$

moving member of a crossed strip hinge. The hinge is suitably pre-tensioned to allow it to rotate within the range of the instrument scale. A forked arm attached to the moving member of the hinge transmits rotary motion to the indicator driving drum through a bronze band wrapped round the drum. The magnification preset by the manufacturer is varied by adjustment of the knife edge attachment screws.

The instrument is damped by a horseshoe magnet fixed to the frame and a non-ferrous (aluminium) disc fixed to the pointer spindle. Rotation of the disc in the magnetic field of the magnet sets up eddy currents which are proportional to the rotational velocity and in opposition to motion.

The range of instruments available provides magnifications of ×300 to ×5000, the most sensitive models allowing scale estimations of the order of 0·0001 mm (0·1 μm) to be made.

4.13 Mechanical–optical comparators

Mechanical–optical comparators utilize reflectors, lenses and prisms (Section 4.10) to provide frictionless magnification systems.

A simplified outline of a mechanical–optical comparator which incorporates a pivoted reflector to transmit an image and provide an optical lever is shown in Fig. 4.31.

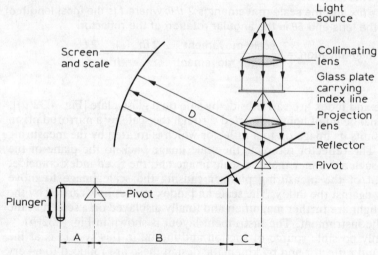

Fig. 4.31 Mechanical–optical comparator

Mechanical magnification = $A \times B \times C$
Optical magnification = $2D$
Total magnification = $2ABCD$

OMT Omtimeter

This is a well known comparator based on optical magnification. The instrument is designed to provide a moving scale against a fixed index line.

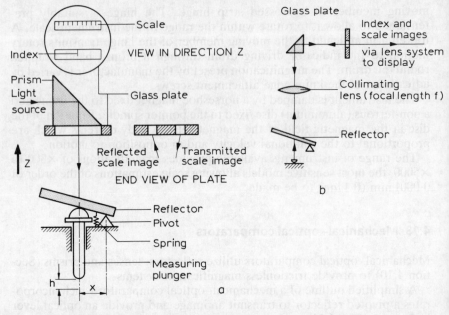

Fig. 4.32 OMT omtimeter

$\delta\theta = h/x$ and the scale movement is $2f\delta\theta$, where f is the focal length of the lens and $\delta\theta$ is the angular rotation of the reflector.

$$\text{magnification} = \frac{\text{scale movement}}{\text{plunger movement}} = \frac{2fh}{x} \times \frac{1}{h} = \frac{2f}{x}$$

The scale and index are carried side by side on a glass plate [Fig. 4.32(a)]. An external beam of light is directed through the scale by a mirrored prism and transmits its image on to a reflector which is rotated by the measuring plunger. The reflector redirects the scale image back to the plane of the index in such a manner that the scale image and the fixed index coincide, movement of the measuring plunger causing the scale image to move vertically against the index. The scale and index images now carried by the beam of light are further magnified and finally displayed on a screen at the side of the instrument. The instrument layout is shown in Fig. 4.32(b).

The only possible source of friction and inertia in this system is at the plunger and reflector and by kinematic design these are reduced to a very low level. The tension spring eliminates backlash, and the problem of damping does not arise. The scale range of the Omtimeter is ±0·125 mm in 0·001 25 mm graduations and the measuring force is between 3 and 4 N.

Eden–Rolt comparator

This mechanical–optical comparator (Fig. 4.33) was originally designed for slip gauge calibration and is an excellent example of instrument design in which the accuracy of measurement is not directly dependent on the accuracy of manufacture. The mechanical part of the instrument is a combination of the flexure spring systems shown in Figs. 4.19(a) and (c).

A long light beam terminates in a ring across which is mounted a thin strand or web of material. The plunger movement is magnified about 400 times at the web, and the web movement is magnified a further 50 times by an optical projection system, giving a total magnification of 20 000 at the scale. With this instrument it is possible to estimate size differences of the order of 0·000025 mm (0·025 μm).

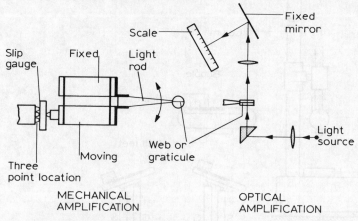

Fig. 4.33 Eden–Rolt comparator

Brookes level comparator

This comparator, essentially a highly sensitive spirit level, provides an excellent though rather slow means for measuring long gauges, e.g. length bars. A rotatable disc or platen having mutually parallel surfaces is located on a massive base provided with three levelling screws. The upper face of the platen is a plane lapped surface while the lower face is a lapped annular ring allowing easy rotation on the base. A bracket which kinematically supports the level and allows it to be raised and lowered during measurement is mounted to the main column of the instrument. A scale is provided so that bubble displacement may be measured (see Fig. 4.34).

In operation the end of the bubble is first brought approximately to the centre of the scale by allowing the two ball feet attached to the level to rest on a surface parallel with the platen while adjusting the levelling screws on the base. A block gauge or combined block gauge and length bar may be wrung to the platen for this purpose. The standard (S) and gauge to be compared (G) are now wrung to the platen, and the ball feet which are at approximately 20 mm centres rest on the gauges forming a bridge [Fig. 4.34(b)]. The position of the end of the bubble against the scale is noted, the level is raised, the platen rotated through 180°, and a second reading taken [Fig. 4.34(c)]. The displacement of the bubble along the scale represents twice the difference in length between the gauges; thus

$$\delta h = \tfrac{1}{2} L$$

where δh is the difference in length between the gauges and L is the bubble displacement.

The level comparator has several advantages:

(a) The gauges are compared together thus making temperature equalization easier. It is usual to allow 20 min per 25 mm gauge length for this purpose.

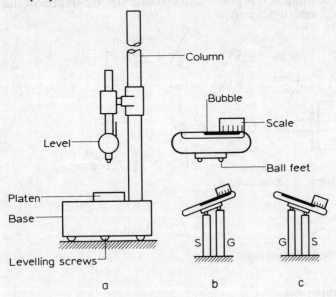

Fig. 4.34 Brookes level comparator

(b) The rotation of the platen provides twice the bubble displacement required and at the same time eliminates the need to bring the platen exactly to the horizontal plane.
(c) Slight errors in scale reading are halved in the final computation of length.
(d) The gauges are vertically mounted and any shortening under their own weight is the same for both gauges.

Differences as small as 0.00002 mm ($0.02\,\mu$m) can be detected, and gauges up to 1 m in length can be measured. The basic design of the precision spirit level is discussed in Section 4.24.

4.14 Principle of the pneumatic transducer

Since pneumatic transducers were first introduced in the 1930s they have found ever widening fields of application owing to their simplicity, sensitivity, robustness and versatility. Their function is to convert changes of length or surface displacement into changes of pressure.

The principal features of the pneumatic transducer are shown in Fig.

4.35(a). It consists of two chambers in series separated by an orifice plate or control orifice (C) of geometrical area A_c. Air passes from the first to the second chamber through the control orifice and thence to atmosphere via a second orifice, the measuring orifice or jet (M), of effective area A_m.

A continuous flow of clean dry air is supplied to the transducer through a pressure regulator which ensures that the pressure in the first chamber remains constant at all times. The pressure in the second chamber can be changed by varying the restriction applied to the measuring jet. When the measuring jet is completely closed the variable pressure p rises until it

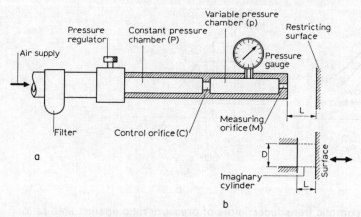

Fig. 4.35 Pneumatic transducer

equals the operating pressure P, but if it is completely unrestricted then the variable pressure falls towards atmospheric pressure. In practice variations in p are obtained by moving a restricting surface towards or away from M.

In a correctly designed transducer the ratio of the orifice areas is so proportioned that within a limited range of restriction the rate of change of p is uniform, i.e.

$$\mathrm{d}p/\mathrm{d}L = \text{constant}$$

where L is the displacement of the restricting surface.

The effective area A_m of air escapement from the measuring jet is determined by the displacement of the restricting surface and the geometrical area of the orifice, i.e. the surface area of the imaginary cylinder so formed [Fig. 4.35(b)]; thus

$$A_m = \pi DL \tag{4.1}$$

where D is the diameter of the measuring orifice.

Investigations have shown that when the pressure ratio p/P and the area ratio (A_m/A_c) are plotted over a wide range of supply pressures (15 to 500 kN/m^2), curves having similar characteristics are obtained, each curve representing the results for a given supply pressure. The extremes of the family of curves are shown in Fig. 4.36(a).

That portion on all the curves where p/P lies between 0·6 and 0·8 is linear to within 1% and the intercept on the p/P axis is almost exactly 1·10 in all cases. The slope depends upon the supply pressure and ranges from 0·6 at $500\,\text{kN/m}^2$ to 0·4 at $15\,\text{kN/m}^2$. From Fig. 4.36(b) the general linear equation may thus be stated

$$\frac{p}{P} = E - b\frac{A_m}{A_c} \tag{4.2}$$

where E is the intercept on the p/P axis, $E = 1·10$, b is the slope ($0·4 < b < 0·6$) and A_c is the geometrical area of the control orifice.

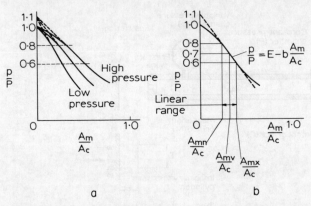

Fig. 4.36 Pneumatic transducer: plots of pressure ratio against area ratio

It is evident that for a given supply pressure there must be maximum and minimum values of A_m/A_c and thus of A_m, beyond which 1% linearity does not apply; this constitutes the linear range. By substituting the values of E and b into Eq. 4.2 it can be shown that

$$A_{mx} - A_{mn} = \tfrac{1}{2}A_{mv} \tag{4.3}$$

where A_{mn} is the minimum value of $A_m\,(p/P = 0·8)$, A_{mx} is the maximum value of $A_m\,(p/P = 0·6)$ and A_{mv} is the average of $A_m\,(p/P = 0·7)$.

The operating pressure P does not appear in Eq. 4.3; thus the linear range of A_m is equal to half the average value of A_m and is independent of the supply pressure.

Pneumatic sensitivity

As p and A_m are the only variables in Eq. 4.2, differentiating p with respect to A_m provides an expression for pneumatic sensitivity:

$$\frac{dp}{dA_m} = -\frac{b}{A_c}P \tag{4.4}$$

When $A_m = A_{mv}$, $p/P = 0·7$, i.e. the average value of p/P (1% linearity). Substituting in Eq. 4.2,

$$0·7 = 1·10 - b\frac{A_{mv}}{A_c} \qquad \text{i.e.} \quad \frac{b}{A_c} = \frac{0·40}{A_{mv}}$$

Substituting in Eq. 4.4,

$$\frac{\mathrm{d}p}{\mathrm{d}A_{\mathrm{m}}} = -0.40\frac{P}{A_{\mathrm{mv}}} \tag{4.5}$$

From Eq. 4.5 the pneumatic sensitivity is seen to vary directly as P and inversely as A_{mv}. The negative sign may be omitted as only the numerical value is of interest.

Magnification of a pneumatic system

The overall magnification is the rate of change of output with respect to input. The output variable is a pressure gauge or water column reading and the input variable is surface displacement. Three factors combine to produce the overall magnification in a pneumatic system:

(a) The pneumatic sensitivity: $\mathrm{d}p/\mathrm{d}A_{\mathrm{m}}$.
(b) The output gauge magnification where G is the gauge reading: $\mathrm{d}G/\mathrm{d}p$.
(c) The rate of change of A_{m} with respect to the displacement of the restricting surface: $\mathrm{d}A_{\mathrm{m}}/\mathrm{d}L$.

Thus the overall magnification is given by

$$\frac{\mathrm{d}G}{\mathrm{d}L} = \frac{\mathrm{d}p}{\mathrm{d}A_{\mathrm{m}}} \times \frac{\mathrm{d}G}{\mathrm{d}p} \times \frac{\mathrm{d}A_{\mathrm{m}}}{\mathrm{d}L} \tag{4.6}$$

Mention has already been made that the effective area of M is equal to πDL, where D is the diameter of the measuring jet [Fig. 4.35(b)]:

$$A_{\mathrm{m}} = \pi DL \qquad \text{and} \qquad \frac{\mathrm{d}A_{\mathrm{m}}}{\mathrm{d}L} = \pi D$$

As the linear range of L corresponds to the linear range of A_{m} then

$$L_{\mathrm{x}} - L_{\mathrm{m}} = \tfrac{1}{2}L_{\mathrm{v}}$$

where L_{x} is the maximum value of L, L_{m} is the minimum value of L and L_{v} is the average value of L.

If the linear scale of length R provides readings of p over the range 0 to P, i.e. atmospheric to supply pressure, then

$$\frac{\mathrm{d}G}{\mathrm{d}p} = \frac{R}{P}$$

Substituting in Eq. 4.6,

$$\frac{\mathrm{d}G}{\mathrm{d}L} = 0.40\frac{P}{\pi DL_{\mathrm{v}}} \times \frac{R}{P} \times \pi D$$

$$\frac{\mathrm{d}G}{\mathrm{d}L} = 0.40\frac{R}{L_{\mathrm{v}}} \tag{4.7}$$

where R and L_{v} are expressed in the same units, e.g. millimetres. From Eq. 4.7 the overall magnification is seen to vary directly as R and inversely as L_{v}.

Example 4.1
In a pneumatic measuring system the scale length R is 500 mm. Find the overall magnification if the linear range is to be 0·02 mm.

$$\frac{dG}{dL} = 0\cdot4 \times \frac{500}{0\cdot04} = 5000$$

Equations 4.5 and 4.7 indicate that increased magnification could be obtained by increased operating pressure and scale length but in practice this is inconvenient if the scale is to be kept to a reasonable length. But increased magnification can be obtained by reducing the linear range and this is achieved by careful proportioning of the orifice areas. The diameters of the orifices are also a factor in determining the order of magnification; thus, for high magnifications small orifice diameters are used, e.g. 0·5 mm, while larger, more easily manufactured orifices are used when lower magnifications are required.

Speed of response

It is difficult to measure surface displacements at frequencies greater than 2 Hz with a pneumatic transducer as time is required to establish each new value of p, but for a very wide range of measuring requirements this is not an important factor. Where speed of response must be optimized then the volume of the variable pressure chamber (which includes any volume required to operate the pressure measuring device, e.g. a Bourdon tube) should be kept to a minimum.

Pressure control

Pneumatic transducers may be operated at low, high and medium pressures, the last being of the 'flow velocity' type.

Low pressure
A pressure of about 7 kN/m² is maintained in the constant pressure chamber. Variations of pressure p are recorded on a manometer tube against a scale about 500 mm long.

Earlier versions use water in the manometer tube and excess air from the supply is allowed to bubble from a dip tube; the disadvantage of this method is the relatively high evaporation rate of the water in the system. Current models employ low viscosity oil in a manometer connected to a small chamber in which the lower end of a weight-type valve is immersed. The oil smoothes the valve movement preventing 'flutter' while excess air can blow through the valve (Fig. 4.37).

A feature of interest in these systems is the interchangeable control orifice which provides the easiest means for reproportioning the orifice areas and thus changing the magnification. A variety of scales are supplied for various requirements, each scale being accompanied by its corresponding control orifice.

The Sigma differential pressure system operating at about 30 kN/m² is shown in Fig. 4.38. In this case a constant operating pressure is applied to both sides of the manometer, pressure control being maintained by a diaphragm pressure regulator. One side of the manometer is used to zero the system by adjustment of p_2. Because of the relatively higher operating pressure the movement of water in the tube is restricted by means of a diaphragm which maintains the scale at a reasonable length while provid-

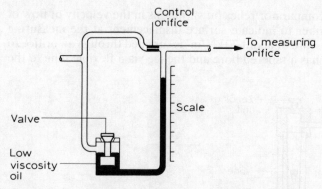

Fig. 4.37 Low pressure control for pneumatic transducer

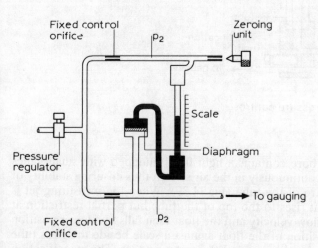

Fig. 4.38 Sigma differential pressure system

ing high magnification. An advantage of the differential system is that the full scale reading can be made to represent the linear range of p_1, i.e. $0.6P < p_1 < 0.8P$. This can be done because the zeroing facility allows zero on the scale to represent $p_1 = 0.6P$, and the length of the scale can be so designed that its maximum reading is $p_1 = 0.8P$.

High pressure
These systems use a Bourdon-tube pressure gauge instead of a liquid

column. They have the advantage of longer range and, for measurements where swarf and coolant are present, the jet is powerful enough to break through the liquid film to the measured surface. High pressure dial-type instruments have the added advantage of being easily portable. Differential systems are also available.

Medium pressure

The flow velocity comparator relies on variations in the velocity of flow of air through a chamber to indicate surface displacement at the measuring jet. A constant pressure of about $70\,kN/m^2$ is supplied through an orifice to a glass tube which has a tapered bore and thence via a flexible pipe to the

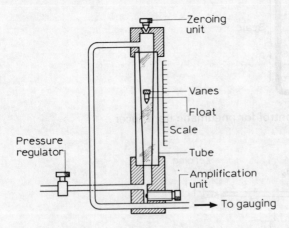

Fig. 4.39 Medium pressure control

measuring jet. The bore contains a light float equipped with small vanes causing it to rotate continuously in the air stream thus ensuring stability of the float at the centre of the tube (Fig. 4.39). When the measuring jet is unrestricted the float rises to the top of the tube but partial restriction at the jet reduces the flow velocity and the float then falls to a lower position in the tube. The position of the float against a scale beside the glass tube indicates the surface displacement at the measuring jet. The magnification of the instrument is largely determined by the tapered bore of the tube and a range of tubes allow magnification from ×1000 to ×40 000. For some applications an operating pressure of $140\,kN/m^2$ is used, e.g. for ball-jet gauges.

This sensitive and reliable system can be used for a wide variety of pneumatic gauging applications, e.g. snap gauges, plug gauges, etc., and banks of instruments can indicate a number of dimensions simultaneously. Because increased jet constriction causes the float to fall, careful note must be taken of the sense of the float movement when changing from external to internal measurement.

Measuring heads

Originally pneumatic gauging was developed in France to check the diameters of carburettor jets. Air at constant pressure was allowed to flow through the control jet and thence through the carburettor jet placed at the end of the second chamber. The 'back' pressure measured on a manometer gave an accurate indication of jet area. This constriction technique has fairly limited application and the two types of measuring heads now in common use are the direct head and the indirect or contact head (Fig. 4.40).

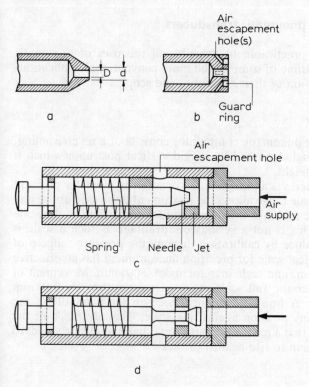

Fig. 4.40 Measuring heads

    (*a*), (*b*) Direct heads   (*c*) Forward head   (*d*) Reverse head

Direct heads
The jet shown in Fig. 4.40(*a*) has a tapered nose to ensure free escape of air as excessive land width would affect the characteristics of the system. The tapered nose also allows easier access for the jet in constricted measuring conditions. A satisfactory ratio between jet diameter D and land diameter d is $d = 2D$. The head shown in Fig. 4.40(*b*) allows considerable protection to be given to the nozzle by the provision of a guard ring and air escapement holes.

Indirect or contact heads

Air escapement from the measuring jet can be controlled by a flat plate or needle-type valve, and the jet is protected from accidental damage. Forward and reverse acting valve heads are shown in Figs. 4.40(c) and (d). The needle-type valve can be designed for short or long range measurement, slow taper needles providing ranges as long as 1·25 mm or more, which is not possible using direct heads. However, long range is only obtained by sacrifice of high magnification. It is interesting to note that a perfectly linear response can be obtained by the use of a parabolic needle.

4.15 Applications of pneumatic transducers

It is not possible or practicable to describe all the uses of pneumatic transducers, but an outline of some of the more conventional applications will provide an indication of their versatility and scope.

Pneumatic comparator

The well known Solex pneumatic comparator consists of a reverse acting, indirect measuring head, mounted to a rigid vertical post upon which it may be adjusted for height.

The head is connected via a pipe to an oil or water manometer pressure control system. The scale range allows the instrument to be used above and below the linear range and thus the upper and lower portions of the scale may be non-linear. This is not a serious disadvantage as such a scale is relatively easy to produce by calibration through the pressure range p of the instrument. A typical scale for precision measurement has an effective length of about 360 mm, and scale increments of 0·001 mm. Movement of the liquid column over the full scale represents approximately 0·03 mm surface displacement. A fine adjustment device on the head allows the column to be set at any position against the scale. The advantage of the reverse acting head is that a measured part larger than the setting standard causes the liquid column to rise against the scale.

Plug gauges

Pneumatic plug gauges are used for a wide variety of measurements. Some important examples are: single diameter, multi-diameter, average diameter, lobing, taper, straightness, squareness, ovality and centre distance.

Single diameter

The gauge incorporates two equal and opposite jets in parallel as shown in Fig. 4.41(a). The gauge can be made somewhat smaller than the bore so that it enters much more easily than the conventional plug gauge.

At first sight it might appear that the conventional plug gauge form is unnecessary and that a device simply consisting of two jets in parallel is all that is required [Fig. 4.41(b)]. Unfortunately the magnitude of the back pressure p is not entirely independent of the relative position of the workpiece to the jets and a displacement of the workpiece from the symmetrical position changes the scale reading by about one tenth of that displacement. The cylindrical plug gauge form eliminates this effect by providing sufficiently accurate location for the jets which ensures that the total air flow is virtually constant whatever the position of the gauge in the bore. Thus within the designed range of the gauge a reduction of flow through one jet causes an equal increase of flow through the other jet, i.e. the jets are self-compensating.

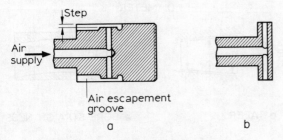

Fig. 4.41 Plug gauge: single diameter

One further aspect of pneumatic plug gauge design is of interest. In Fig. 4.41(a) jets are shown slightly stepped below the surface of the plug. This gives a measure of protection to the jets but, more importantly, if the jets are flush with the skirt when holes very close to the plug diameter are to be measured, the reading becomes unstable and self-compensation is lost. The step eliminates this effect and allows holes approaching the skirt diameter to be measured. The upper limit of the measuring range is defined by a hole larger than the plug at which the reading again becomes unstable.

Twin nozzles eliminate the need to spring load the plug against one side of the bore, thus simplifying gauge design, but the use of twin (or multiple) nozzles in parallel also has the effect of reducing magnification. From Eq. 4.1 (Section 4.14),

$$A_m = \pi DL$$

Let L_1 and L_2 be the surface displacements corresponding to two opposed nozzles in parallel; then

$$A_m = \pi D(L_1 + L_2)$$

When $L_1 = L_2$,

$$A_m = 2\pi DL \quad \text{and} \quad A_{mv} = 2\pi DL_v$$

Therefore

$$\frac{dG}{dL} = 0.4 \frac{R}{2L_v}$$

Thus to maintain magnification the average separation must be halved.

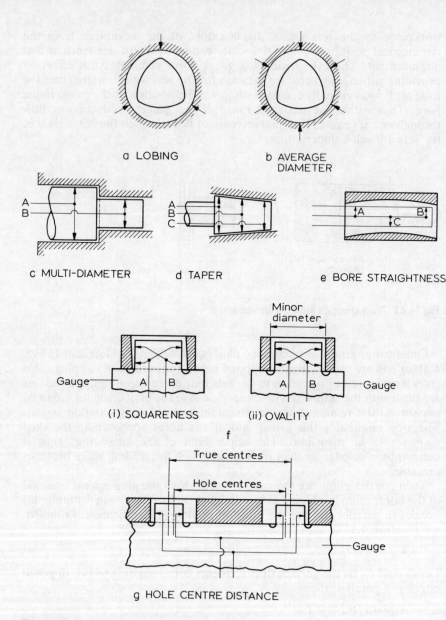

a LOBING

b AVERAGE DIAMETER

c MULTI-DIAMETER

d TAPER

e BORE STRAIGHTNESS

(i) SQUARENESS

(ii) OVALITY

f

g HOLE CENTRE DISTANCE

Fig. 4.42 Pneumatic gauging applications

A number of pneumatic gauging applications are shown in Figs. 4.42(*a*) to (*g*). For the sake of simplicity each jet is represented by an arrow.

Lobing
Relative rotation of plug and bore will cause high and low scale readings [Fig. 4.42(*a*)].

Average diameter
The introduction of a further three jets will provide a constant reading [Fig. 4.42(b)].

Multi-diameter
The progressive gauge shown in Fig. 4.42(c) provides simultaneous indication on separate manometers for a number of 'in-line' bores.

Taper
Three pairs of jets will check angle, straightness of taper and diameter simultaneously [Fig. 4.42(d)].

Bore straightness
Three jets in parallel are arranged as shown in Fig. 4.42(e). Jets A and B are equal and jet C has a flow equal to A + B. High and low readings will result from relative plug and bore rotation.

Hole squareness and ovality
The plug shown in Fig. 4.42(f) may be used to check either the squareness or the ovality of a hole. It consists of two separate circuits, A and B, each comprising two opposed jets in parallel and an indicator. The component position shown in (i) causes a high reading on circuit A and a low reading on circuit B. When the component is rotated through 180° the readings are reversed. The oval condition shown in (ii) produces two low readings and on rotation successive pairs of high and low readings. Thus the behaviour of the indicators clearly differentiates between lack of squareness and ovality.

Centre distance
Two plugs are mounted at the true hole centres. Two separate circuits are arranged in such a way that they sense variations in centre distance and yet remain insensitive to diameter variations, as a change of diameter of one or both holes affects both circuits equally [Fig. 4.42(g)].

Pneumatic gauging can be applied to external measurements in a wide variety of ways, such as ring gauges, snap gauges, height gauges, etc. Indirect heads are incorporated in large plug gauges for measuring cylinder bores and special direct heads are used for measuring the thickness of plastic sheet. The leaf-jet plug is an interesting application of the indirect or contact method which enables the diameter near the bottom of a semi-blind hole to be measured [Fig. 4.43(a)]. It also has the advantage that the diameter of very shallow holes (1·5 mm) can be measured.

The comparator plug gauge [Fig. 4.43(b)] is designed for use on the production line where absolutely clean conditions cannot be ensured.

Pneumatic transducers may be used to measure cutting tool deflections and thus cutting force, torque, etc. (see Chapter 8).

Two jets in parallel can be used for differential measurement.

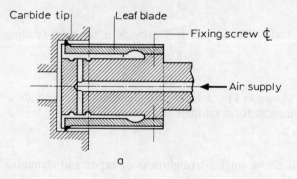

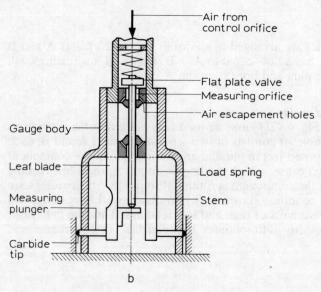

Fig. 4.43 Pneumatic gauging applications: internal measurements

Surface finish

Components measured with direct jets must have a smooth surface finish as any significant surface variation gives rise to error. The source of the error is shown in Fig. 4.44(a), where it is evident that the effective area of the jet depends upon its position relative to the grooves, the area increasing when the jet is directly above a groove and decreasing when it is above a crest. Rough surfaces require a contact head such as the ball-jet plug shown in Fig. 4.44(b) which measures the size over the crests, which is the size usually required.

Measurement of moving surfaces

In general, a jet calibrated to measure a smooth stationary surface will provide the same reading when the surface is in motion, at surface speeds

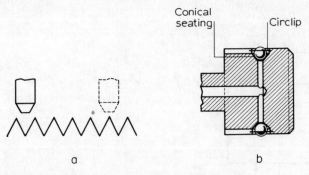

Fig. 4.44 Effect of surface finish on gauging

up to at least 30 m/s, e.g. in-process measurement during cylindrical grinding.

Calibration

When the usual slip gauge technique is not applicable, as in the case of plug gauges, standard ring gauges made to provide readings at the upper and lower end of the scale are normally adequate.

4.16 Electronic measurement

The great advances in reliability of electronic components and circuitry brought about by the Second World War laid the foundation for modern electronic measurement. The function of electronic transducers in metrology is to convert changes of length, or surface displacement, into proportional electrical changes which can be detected, amplified and recorded or displayed on a meter. To this end, the transducer is designed to provide a linear response over a range of ± 0.3 mm. While both resistance and capacitance transducers are used for displacement measurement the inductance transducer is most suited to accurate measurement of small displacements, because it suffers neither from the friction inherent in the resistance type, where physical contact between a slider and resistance is used, nor from the capacitance problem caused by the low sensitivity and unreliability introduced by the large extra capacitance of the transducer leads. Differential inductance transducers of two kinds are in use, one consisting of two internal coils connected to form an inductance bridge with two external coils, the other consisting of three internal coils. The latter configuration constitutes a transformer and is known as a linear variable differential transformer (LVDT) which does not require bridge connection. Neither type is superior to the other in operation.

The essential features of the construction of an LVDT are shown in Fig. 4.45(a). It consists of one primary and two secondary coils within which is mounted a ferromagnetic armature or iron core. The primary coil (C_p) is

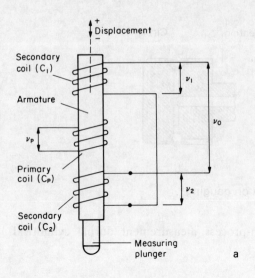

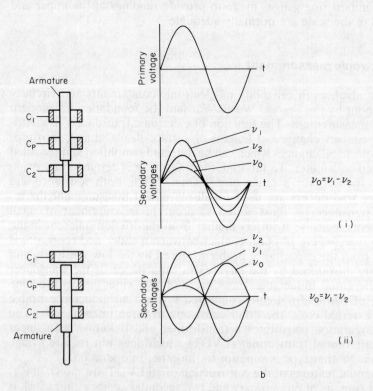

$v_0 = v_1 - v_2$

(i)

$v_0 = v_1 - v_2$

(ii)

b

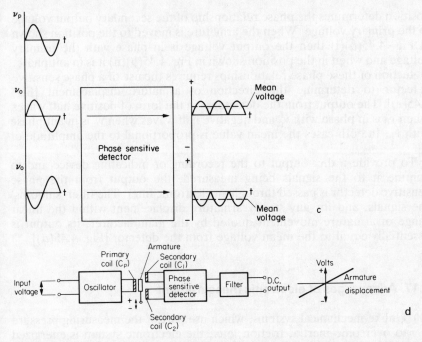

Fig. 4.45 (*a*) Linear variable differential transformer (*b*) Primary and secondary voltage phase relationships (*c*) Phase sensitive detector (*d*) LVDT-type transducer

energized by means of an alternating current of constant amplitude and frequency and may be mains or battery supplied. In both cases an electronic conversion circuit is incorporated to produce the necessary input characteristics to the primary coil. The effect of the alternating voltage of the primary coil is to induce alternating voltages in the secondary coils (C_1 and C_2) by electromagnetic coupling and the presence of the armature augments this effect, thereby increasing the voltages in the secondary coils.

The secondary coils are connected in series opposition so that when the core is centralized in the coils as shown in Fig. 4.45(*a*) the voltages induced in them are equal and the net output voltage is zero:

$$v_0 = v_1 - v_2 = 0$$

where v_0 is the secondary coils' output voltage and v_1 and v_2 are the induced secondary coil voltages.

When the armature is axially displaced from its central or null position the coupling between the primary and secondary coils changes; the difference between the secondary voltages is no longer zero, resulting in a net output voltage.

Within a limited range of armature displacement the amplitude of the voltage is proportional to the displacement.

The direction in which the armature moves from its centralized or null position determines the phase relationship of the secondary output voltage to the primary voltage. When the armature is moved to the position shown in Fig. 4.45(b)(i) then the output voltage is in phase with the primary voltage and when in the position shown in Fig. 4.45(b)(ii) it is in antiphase. Detection of these phase relationships requires the use of a phase sensitive detector to determine the direction of armature displacement [Fig. 4.45(c)]. The output from the detector is in the form of positive half waves when v_0 is in phase with v_p and negative half waves when v_0 is in antiphase with v_p. In both cases the mean value is proportional to the amplitude of v_0.

To provide a d.c. output to the recording or indicating device and to confine it to the signals being measured, the output from the phase sensitive detector is passed through an electronic filter. The filter 'smooths' the signals, and for any steady armature displacement within the linear range of armature movement quoted by the manufacturer, its output is essentially equal to the mean voltage from the detector [Fig. 4.45(d)].

4.17 Advantages of electronic measurement

(1) Unlike mechanical systems, which use part of the measuring pressure to overcome inertia, friction, etc., the electronic system is energized from an external source which allows for an extremely low measuring pressure resulting in negligible component distortion so that soft or thin walled components are easily measured.
(2) Friction is present at the transducer springs and at the meter springs and pivots but its magnitude is insignificant.
(3) Speed of response is of the order of 0·1 seconds.
(4) The magnification is changed electrically and a number of ranges are available on one instrument at the turn of a switch. A typical instrument provides five ranges in both English and metric systems over a scale length of about 100 mm.

| *English* (in) | ±0·0001 | ±0·0003 | ±0·001 | ±0·003 | ±0·010 |
| *Metric* (mm) | ±0·003 | ±0·010 | ±0·03 | ±0·10 | ±0·30 |

(5) A number of transducers can be connected to one instrument and readings taken in turn by switching.
(6) Pointer zero setting is electrical which eliminates the need for fine adjustment on the transducer position.
(7) Signals from any number of transducers can easily be added or subtracted in any desired proportion, e.g. change in taper angle measured by two transducers can be expressed as one reading on the meter.
(8) The signal output can be used to operate recorders, sorting gates, machine controls, light signals, etc.
(9) Remote reading at 30 m and more from the transducer does not present a problem.

4.18 Applications of electronic transducers

Mounted to a comparator stand an electronic transducer makes an excellent fine measurement comparator for standards room and interstage production measurement.

Block gauge comparator

The error reducing effect of differential measurement is used to advantage in the block gauge comparator. The differential signal from two opposed gauging heads of high sensitivity is displayed at the meter, thus avoiding the need for a gauge interferometer for routine gauge block calibration (see Section 3.8).

Horizontal internal comparator

This comparator is designed to gauge holes in the range 6 mm to 300 mm diameter by employing two internal probes. The measuring distance is initially set by means of slip gauges mounted in a special fixture and located on the instrument table to ensure parallelism of the setting faces. An interesting feature is the spring suspension of the measuring probes aimed at ensuring frictionless transfer of the probe movement to a cartridge-type transducer (Fig. 4.46). Comparators using one measuring probe are also available for checking holes in the range 0·5 mm to 6·0 mm.

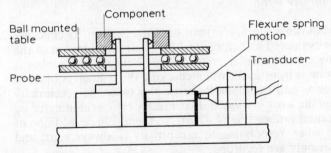

Fig. 4.46 Horizontal internal comparator with spring suspension

Differential gauging

An arrangement for taper measurement by electronic gauging is shown in Fig. 4.47(*a*). Both probes have initially been set to zero from a master taper. When the part to be measured is introduced individual changes in diameters A and B may be read in turn on the meter. An equal increase or decrease in the diameters produces equal displacements of meter reading from each probe thus indicating zero change of taper. If one of the diameters changes while the other remains unchanged, the algebraic difference between the two readings, when expressed in terms of the probe separation x, represents both the change in taper and its sense, i.e. an increase or a decrease. This result holds true if both diameters change. The evaluation of the algebraic difference (or sum) of two separate probe readings is time consuming and open to error and it is much easier to perform these operations electronically, displaying the result as a single meter reading. Such gauges incorporate a switch position which allows single probe readings to be taken for initial setting purposes, etc., and a second switch position for differential gauging.

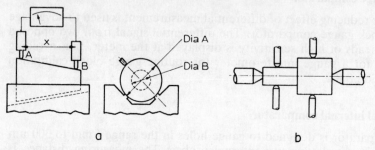

a   b

Fig. 4.47 Differential gauging

(a) *Taper measurement by electronic gauging*
Let master gauge reading for A and B equal zero, i.e. $A = B = 0$.
Increase in dia. $A = \delta_1$, increase in dia. $B = \delta_2$. Differential reading

$$(A + \delta_1) - (B - \delta_2) = \delta_1 + \delta_2$$

(b) *Eccentricity error*

The arrangement shown in Fig. 4.47(a) can, of course, be used for checking cylinders. Taper is evaluated as before, and by electronic addition of the probe readings, twice the diameter error midway between the probes is produced. One probe is insufficient when checking the diameters of work mounted on centres as half the diameter error plus twice the eccentricity error is sensed when the work is rotated. Eccentricity error is eliminated by the use of two opposed probes [Fig. 4.47(b)], as the algebraic addition of the probe outputs when responding to eccentricity is always zero, and changes in diameter only are recorded.

The applications of electronic transducers to fine measurement is by no means limited to the examples described above. They have been and are currently used for grading diameters, checking squareness of end face to axis, roundness measurement both internal and external, either by means of a static probe and rotating workpiece or by transferring signals from a rotating probe through a slip ring, contour tracing, and surface texture measurement. In some of these applications side acting transducers are used and the usual precautions against 'sine' and 'cosine' error must be observed.

4.19 Measurement of angle

Angle measurement has already been mentioned in the discussion on precision measurement applications of transducers. Such methods require the manufacture of an accurate master gauge or gauges from which the initial transducer settings are made and against which the setting may be checked from time to time. There are also many occasions when gauges are required for directly checking tapered holes and in addition components are manufactured incorporating tapered features. Accurate measuring devices and techniques have been developed for these purposes. A second aspect of angle measurement not so far touched upon is measurement of angular rotation and, again, accurate techniques and devices are available. Angular measurement may broadly be classified as follows:

(1) Measurement of angular features on components or gauges;
(2) Measurement of the angular rotation of a divided circle.

Measurement of angular features

Angles may be obtained from the combination of accurate lengths to form a triangle. The sine bar, along with its variants the sine table and the sine centres, is designed with this in mind. The bar is essentially a hardened steel beam mounted on two hardened cylinders and conforming to dimensional and geometrical tolerance requirements essential to the accurate establishment of a desired angle (see Table 4.3). The cylinder centre distance (L) provides the hypotenuse of the triangle, and block gauges the opposite side (H) [Fig. 4.48(a)].

Table 4.3 Sine bar tolerances

| Nominal cylinder | Tolerances (mm) | |
centre distance (mm)	100	200 and 250
Dimension		
Cylinder centre distance	±0·0025	±0·005
Cylinder diameter equality	0·0025	
Geometry		
Upper surface flatness	0·0013	0·0025
Upper surface parallel to datum surface	0·0013	0·0025
Cylinder axes parallel and coplanar	0·0025	

Source: BS 3064:1969, *Sine bars and sine tables* (*excluding compound tables*).

Sine bars are most frequently used as shown in Figs. 4.48(b) and (c), but for angles greater than 45° the bar should be set at the complement of the angle as shown in Fig. 4.48(d), as the effect of manufacturing errors in the bar and also those arising from probable accumulated error in the gauge blocks begin to increase rapidly beyond this point. Sine tables have one hinged cylinder and tee slots to facilitate work holding. Compound tables are also available with which the required compound angle is set in two stages. The sine centres shown in Fig. 4.48(e) facilitate measurement of taper on circular work manufactured on centres, or work which may be mounted to a mandrel. It is evident that when the bar and work angles are equal the work surface, or bar surface as the case may be, lies parallel to

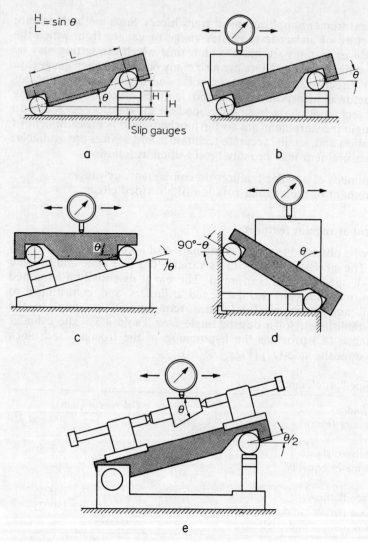

$$\frac{H}{L} = \sin \theta$$

a

b

c

d

e

Fig. 4.48 Measurement of angular features

the datum surface, with the exception of the sine centres when the bar angle must equal one half of the included angle of the work. This condition may be checked with a dial test indicator or other instrument of suitable sensitivity mounted on the datum surface and near to the bar.

Sources of error

Variations of dimension or geometry within the manufacturer's tolerances introduces small angle errors. Some of these are constant, e.g. a constant angle error is caused if the working surface and the cylinder axes are not parallel, while others, such as an error in cylinder centre distance, introduce a progressive increase of error with increase of angle. Block gauge tolerance accumulation is also a source of progressive error. The curve shown in Fig. 4.49 illustrates the possible effect of combined centre distance error and block gauge accumulated tolerance error.

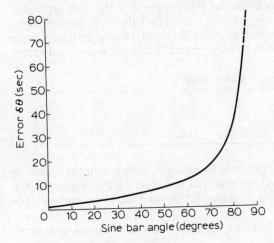

Fig. 4.49 Effect of combined centre distance error and block gauge accumulated tolerance error

100 mm bar
Block gauge accumulated tolerance: +0·0005 mm
Cylinder centre distance: −0·0025 mm

If H is the nominal height of the block gauge pile, L is the nominal cylinder centre distance and θ is the nominal angle required,

$$\sin \theta = H/L$$

and by partial differentiation,

$$\delta\theta \approx 1/L \, (\sec \theta \, \delta H - \tan \theta \, \delta L)$$

where $\delta\theta$ is the angle error, δH is the accumulated block gauge tolerance error and δL is the centre distance error.

Maximum error occurs when H and L are of opposite sign.

Block gauges can provide lengths only in small steps and it may not be possible to build a gauge pile to the exact length required for a given angle. The error introduced is small but its magnitude depends on the step change of the gauge set (0·0005, 0·001 or 0·005 mm). This and many other error sources are reduced by using a long rather than a short bar.

To ensure that compound angle error is not introduced the axis of the work must always be parallel to the axis of the bar.

4.20 Combination angle gauges

An angle gauge is a hardened steel block approximately 75 mm long and 16 mm wide which has two lapped flat working faces lying at a very precise angle to each other [Fig. 4.50(a)]. They are supplied in sets and can be wrung together to form angles up to 90° when used in conjunction with a precision square block. The angles of the gauges in a thirteen piece set, which also includes a square block, are shown in Table 4.4. This arrangement allows angles in 3 second steps to be obtained; thus no required angle expressed in whole seconds can be more than 1·5 seconds in nominal error.

Table 4.4 Nominal angles of combination angle gauges

Degrees	1	3	9	27	41
Minutes	1	3	9	27	
Fractions of minutes	0·05	0·1	0·3	0·5	

Each angle gauge is a wedge; thus two gauges wrung with their narrow ends together provide an angle which is the·sum of the angles of the individual gauges. Subtraction of angles is obtained when the narrow ends are opposed [Fig. 4.50(b)].

The following example illustrates how an angle is obtained systematically.

Required angle is 33°16′42″.

	Gauges required	
Degrees	27 + 9 − 3	33°
Minutes	27 − 9 − 3 + 1	16′
Fractions of minutes	0·5 + 0·3 − 0·1	42″

A total of 10 gauges

A manufacturer's calibration certificate is supplied with the gauges which enables the user to assess the effect of angle tolerance build-up. This is, of course, very small but precise angles in terms of seconds of arc must be treated with caution, as tolerance build-up can amount to a few seconds of arc. Because of their high accuracy, angle gauges find wide application in the comparative measurement of angles in conjunction with angle dekkors, autocollimators, etc.

Precision polygons

These are hardened and stabilized steel blocks having lapped working faces normal to equal divisions of a circle. Normally a polygon has twelve faces each at 30° interval, although others can be obtained, the largest having seventy-two faces at 5° intervals [Fig. 4.50(c)]. Precision polygons are used in the main for calibrating rotary tables and dividing heads in conjunction with autocollimators, although their use is not confined to these problems.

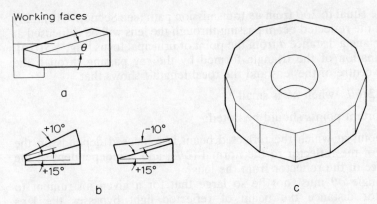

Working faces

θ

a

+10°
+15°

-10°
+15°

b

c

Fig. 4.50 Combination angle gauges and precision polygon

4.21 Angular measurement using optical instruments

Two important instruments used for angle measurement are the angle dekkor and the autocollimator. Both incorporate a collimating lens which

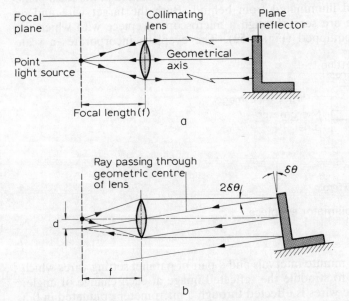

Focal plane

Collimating lens

Plane reflector

Point light source

Geometrical axis

Focal length (f)

a

Ray passing through geometric centre of lens

$2\delta\theta$

$\delta\theta$

d

f

b

Fig. 4.51 (a) Plane and (b) inclined reflectors

is designed to transmit a parallel beam of light radiating from a source at its principal focus. A plane reflector placed in the path of the beam and normal to the geometric axis of the lens will reflect the light along the transmission path to be refocused at the source [Fig. 4.51(a)]. If the reflector is inclined at a small angle $\delta\theta$ to the normal, the beam is reflected at an angle equal to $2\delta\theta$ from its transmission path (see Section 4.10). Any portion of the reflected beam passing through the lens will be refocused at the focal plane a distance d from the point of principal focus [Fig. 4.51(b)]. An examination of the triangle formed by the ray passing through the geometric centre of the lens and the focal length f shows that

$$d = 2f\delta\theta \quad \text{when } \delta\theta \text{ is small}$$

Four important points should be noted:

(1) The point at which the reflected beam is refocused depends on the angle of the reflector to the normal $(\delta\theta)$, and is independent of the distance of the reflector from the lens.
(2) The angle $\delta\theta$ must not be so large that for a given instrument to reflector distance the beam of reflected light bypasses the lens altogether.
(3) A long focal length is required for high magnification.
(4) Angular rotation of the reflector in the horizontal plane merely displaces the reflected image to the left or to the right of the source.

Autocollimator

In the microptic autocollimator, a target wire is mounted at the focal plane of the lens and illuminated from behind. Both the target wire and its reflected image are seen through a microscope eyepiece with which the instrument is equipped (Fig. 4.52). The eyepiece incorporates a scale

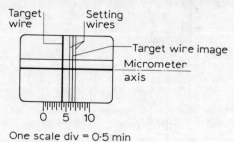

One scale div = 0·5 min

Fig. 4.52 Autocollimator eyepiece

graduated in 0·5 minute intervals and a pair of parallel setting wires which can be adjusted to straddle the reflected image at each change of angle. Movement of the wires is effected through a micrometer graduated in 0·5 second intervals, one rotation of the drum equalling one scale division movement of the wires, i.e. 0·5 minutes. The instrument is designed to be rotated through 90° about its longitudinal axes so that angles in both the horizontal and vertical planes can be measured. The instrument can be used at a considerable distance away from the reflector although the further the instrument is away the smaller the range of angle measurement. At a distance of 10 m, an angle range $\delta\theta$ is of the order of 10 minutes of arc.

4.22 Applications of autocollimators

Autocollimators are used to solve a wide variety of measuring problems, and the following applications are by no means exhaustive.

Slideway straightness

The instrument is used in conjunction with a reflector mounted to a base of such a length as to provide $0.5\,\mu m$ change of height for each 1 second of arc tilt. The slideway is divided along its length at intervals equal to the basic length and may be numbered as shown in Fig. 4.53(a). The reading

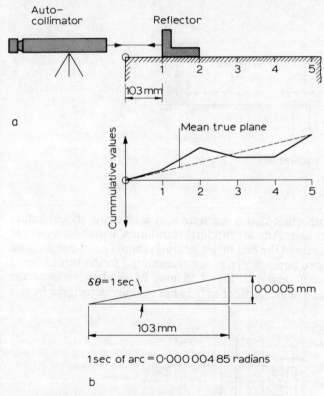

Fig. 4.53 Slideway straightness using autocollimator

In (b) linear rise or fall h (1 second of arc) is
$103 \times 0.000\,004\,85 = 0.0005\,mm$ $(0.5\,\mu m)$

obtained from the first position $(0, 1)$ of the reflector is taken to be zero and the reflector is moved to the second position $(1, 2)$. Any change of instrument reading at this position represents an incline or decline of the surface relative to point 1 on the slideway. At the third position $(2, 3)$ the incline or decline is relative to point 2 and so on. The change of angle at each position is easily converted to linear rise and fall and the cumulative values (from zero) are plotted to form a profile of the surface [Fig. 4.53(*b*)]. By joining the end points of the plotted profile the mean true plane of the surface is defined and deviations from this line represent the straightness errors of the slideway.

Slideway squareness

An optical square may be used in conjunction with an autocollimator to determine the squareness and straightness of machine slideways relative to each other (Fig. 4.54). The square is a prism designed to turn a beam of light through 90° irrespective of the angle of incidence.

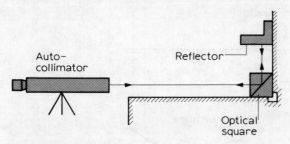

Fig. 4.54 Slideway squareness

Axial slip or float

It is particularly important that a machine tool lead screw should rotate accurately about its axis. Any longitudinal translation arising for example from lack of squareness of the end thrust bearings should be of insignificant proportions otherwise periodic errors are transmitted to the thread being cut. The arrangement shown in Fig. 4.55 may be used to measure the longitudinal float of a shaft. A float of 0.25μm is easily detectable by this method.

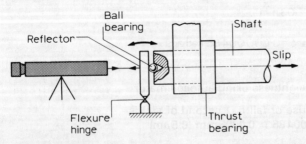

Fig. 4.55 Axial slip

Angular rotation

This is most easily done by mounting a precision polygon to the indexing device, e.g. a rotary table or dividing head. The autocollimator is aligned on a face of the polygon and a full check is made by rotating the device to ensure that a reading is obtainable from all faces. The table is set at 0° and the instrument reading at this position is taken to be zero. A second reading is taken by indexing through the nominal angle of the polygon and the difference between this and the first reading equals the error in indexing, assuming a perfect polygon. Successive readings are taken until the device has indexed through 360°. The last reading is, of course, a repeat of the first and should be zero. In a case when it is not zero the error represents the indexing error of the total angle turned through and equal proportions of the error are assigned to each of the individual angles measured. A typical arrangement is shown in Fig. 4.56(a). Three sources of error can be identified:

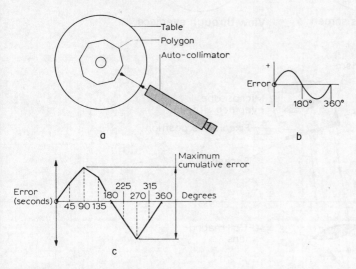

Fig. 4.56 Angular rotation

(1) Eccentricity of rotation which when considered separately is of sinusoidal form [Fig. 4.56(b)].
(2) Errors in the plane of rotation, i.e. wobble.
(3) Errors in the indexing mechanism, backlash, wear, etc. A typical error curve is shown in Fig. 4.56(c). No precision polygon is perfect and to establish a true rotational error curve the calibrated values of the polygon must be known and the instrument readings corrected accordingly.

4.23 Angle dekkor

The angle dekkor is an angle comparator designed for use in conjunction with a setting master which may be a sine bar or a combination of angle gauges. A microscope eyepiece, a ground glass screen and a collimating lens are mounted in a tube to form the instrument (Fig. 4.57). The screen, which lies at the focal plane of the lens, has two mutually perpendicular scales marked on it which are graduated in minutes of arc enabling estimations to about 0·2 minutes to be made. The essential function of the

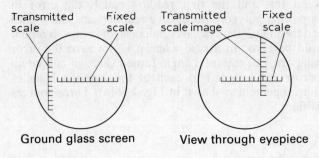

Ground glass screen   View through eyepiece

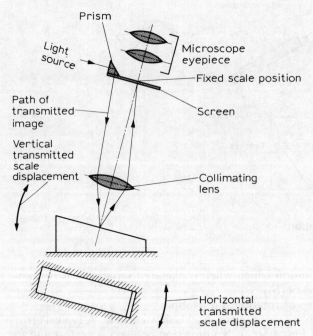

Fig. 4.57 Angle dekkor

instrument is to transmit an image of one of the scales to a reflecting surface which returns the image through the lens to be superimposed on to the other scale which is fixed. Both scales are then viewed simultaneously through the eyepiece. The effect of rotating the reflecting surface through an angle is to displace the transmitted scale image against the fixed scale horizontally or vertically.

The instrument is mounted by means of an adjustable arm to a small surface table. Both scales are seen when the optical axis of the instrument is normal to the reflecting surface within a small degree of error and the scale reading obtained thus represents a compound angle in terms of the instrument axis and the reflecting surface. Having adjusted the instrument and obtained a reading from the setting master on both scales, the master is replaced by the workpiece to be measured. The workpiece is rotated in the horizontal plane until the transmitted scale image crosses the fixed scale at the same position as before thus repeating the compounding effect in one plane. Vertical scale displacement now represents the difference in angle between the master and the workpiece.

4.24 Precision spirit level

A precision spirit level tube has an accurately ground bore, circular in cross-section and barrel-shaped along its longitudinal axis. When partly filled with liquid a bubble is formed which always lies at the highest position in the tube. When the tube is tilted the bubble is displaced along the tube to maintain its position at the highest point, the amount of movement depending on the angle of tilt and the radius of curvature of the tube bore. Precision levels made to British Standard Specification (BS 958:1968) have scale divisions 2·5 mm apart and for general precision work a level on which one scale division represents 10 seconds angle of tilt is usually used. The radius of curvature of the tube is given by

$$R = l/\delta\theta$$

where l is the length of one scale division, $\delta\theta$ is the angle of tilt (radians) and R is the radius of curvature of the tube:

$$R = \frac{2·5}{10^3 \times 0·000\,048\,5} = 51·5460 \text{ m}$$

The ultimate sensitivity of the level depends upon the length of base to which the tube is mounted. The standard base length to which the sensitivity of precision levels is related provides that a 0·0012 mm tilt over 250 mm base length shall produce an angle of tilt equal to 1 second of arc. Thus a 10 second bubble on a 250 mm base requires a tilt equal to 10 × 0·0012 mm for one scale division of bubble movement. The sensitivity of a level increases in inverse proportion to its base length, e.g. a 10 second bubble mounted to a 125 mm base requires only (125/250) × 0·012 mm tilt per division; thus its sensitivity has doubled. One type of block level has a lapped flat base which allows slip gauges to be wrung to the surface so that sensitivity may be varied when required.

When the base of the level lies exactly in the horizontal plane the bubble should lie at the centre of the scale markings and this condition should be repeated when the level is rotated end for end in the same position. However, to eliminate the small error in vial setting relative to the base which must be assumed to exist, two readings are taken at any one position by reversing the level, the mean value indicating the true error in level of the surface.

Levels are used in the main for checking the straightness or flatness of surfaces but one special application is the level comparator (see Section 4.13).

A level can also be used as an angle comparator in conjunction with a sine bar or master setting gauge as shown in Fig. 4.58. The wedge provides

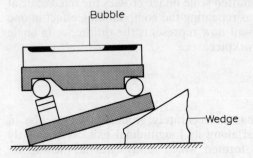

Fig. 4.58 Use of spirit level as an angle comparator

stepless adjustment of the surface table so that the bubble can be set approximately at the centre of the level scale; this reading then represents the angle of the sine bar. If the component is placed on the table parallel to the sine bar with the level mounted to it, any difference of reading represents the difference in angle between the bar and the component.

Study problems

4.1 (a) List the degrees of freedom of the following articles:

    (1) A ball on a flat surface
    (2) A ball in a vee groove
    (3) A ball in a conical hole
    (4) Two balls connected by a bar and resting on a flat surface
    (5) Two connected balls in a vee block
    (6) Two connected balls constrained by a conical hole and a flat surface
    (7) Two connected balls constrained by a vee block and a flat surface
    (8) A cylinder resting on a flat surface
    (9) A cylinder resting in a vee block
    (10) An engine piston in its cylinder
    (11) A micrometer screw
    (12) A vernier height gauge scriber.

(b) Explain why it is that cones, cylinders and balls cannot be completely located by the application of simple kinematic or semi-kinematic fixtures.

Answers: (1) 3R, 2T (2) 3R, 1T (3) 3R, 0T (4) 2R, 2T (5) 1R, 1T (6) 2R, 0T (7) 2R, 1T (8) 2R, 2T (9) 1R, 1T (10) 0R, 1T (11) 1R, 1T (12) 1R, 3T

4.2 (a) The terms 'degrees of freedom', 'constraint' and 'semi-kinematic' are terms used in reference to instrument design. Explain what is meant by these expressions.

(b) If the slide system of an instrument is required to allow motion in one plane, show by means of diagrams how this can be achieved by the application of kinematic design.

4.3 (a) Explain why it is important to maintain the principle of alignment in linear measurement.

(b) What is meant by the term 'cosine error'? Give three examples where its effect is significant.

4.4 List the values of sin θ, tan θ and θ radians in one degree steps up to five degrees and comment on the results in relation to sources of error in precision measurement of length and angle.

4.5 From an M88/2 metric gauge block set build two piles for each of the following lengths, 16·07 mm and 54·786 mm, using the minimum number of gauges. State the number of gauges in each pile.

Answers: 3 and 4; 6 and 6

4.6 Explain in detail how you would find the size of the gap in a caliper-type gauge by means of gauge blocks.

A 200 mm sine bar is to be set up to an angle of 32° 50′ 6″. Find the length of the block gauges required using an M88/2 set.

Answer: 108·444 mm

4.7 (a) A conical taper gauge is to be measured by the technique illustrated in Fig. 4.48(e). If the included angle of taper is intended to be 10° and the length of the gauge is 100 mm, calculate the length of block gauges required to set up the 250 mm sine centres.

(b) On testing along the gauge with a dial test indicator it is found that there is a fall in reading from left to right of 0·5 mm indicating that the gauge angle is different from its expected value. Calculate by what amount the gauge pile must be changed and state the included angle of the gauge.

Answers
(a) 21·789 mm
(b) +1·25 mm; 10° 34′ 31″

4.8 Explain the difference between a uniform cross-section beam simply supported at its Airey points and one supported at its points of minimum deflection.

4.9 (a) Show by means of a diagram how a plane reflector can be used as a means of magnification in measuring instruments.

(b) Determine the standard angle gauge build-up for the angle 75° 42′ 11″. State the nominal error in the gauge build-up and the minimum number of tapered gauges required.

Answers: 1 second of arc; 7

4.10   Using Sections 4.21 and 4.22, find the maximum straightness error for the
        first five stations along a straight edge given the following autocollimator
        readings. Draw a graph to illustrate the result.

Position	Autocollimator readings (seconds of arc)
0	−
0–1	+5
1–2	−8
2–3	−12
3–4	+10
4–5	+10

Answer: 11 μm = 0·0011 mm.

5 Assessment of surface finish

The earliest method used to assess the smoothness or otherwise of metal surfaces was by sight and touch, and in general a surface which was highly reflective was considered to have a good (smooth) finish. Under these conditions surface quality depended on a personal and thus a subjective assessment. By the 1930s such methods were no longer adequate to fulfil many design requirements and particular attention began to be focused on methods whereby a quantitative, i.e. numerical, assessment of surface texture could be made which would be independent of personal opinion. Subsequent experience has shown that no single parameter, e.g. average peak to valley height, is capable of providing a fully adequate description of surface texture characteristics. Present practice is to specify one parameter. This, together with the production process to be used and the direction in which the measurement is to be made, is considered sufficient to control the surface finish required for many purposes although it must be understood that this by no means provides all the information about a surface.

Before any attempt can be made to provide a measure of the characteristics of a surface it is necessary to define what is generally meant by the terms 'surface finish' or 'surface texture', as developed by machining processes and finishing techniques, such as grinding, lapping, turning, milling, die casting, forging, etc.

5.1 Surface texture

Those regular or irregular surface spacings which tend to form a pattern on the surface. The general aspect of the surface produced by the manufacturing process.

The component parts of the surface texture may be defined as follows:

Roughness

The short wavelength irregularities arising from the production process which comprise individual scratch or tool marks such as that produced by a single traverse of a planing tool across the surface. Such marks contain within them further small irregularities which are also included in the definition.

The lay

The tool or scratch marks taken collectively which characterize the particular process. Where these show definite directional characteristics as, for example, in planing, then this is called the 'lay' of the surface. Surface finish measurements are usually, but not always, taken across the lay as the surface is at its roughest in this direction. The effect of inclining the direction of measurement from the direction normal to the lay is to cause an apparent increase in the wavelength of the lay grooves, thus giving a false impression of the shape of the surface (Fig. 5.1).

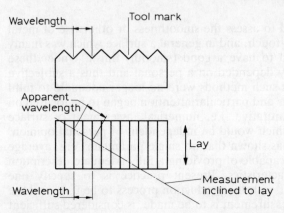

Fig. 5.1 Error from measuring at an angle to the lay

Waviness

The longer wavelength irregularities upon which roughness is superimposed. Waviness may be induced by vibration, hard spots, imperfect truing of a grinding wheel, chatter, heat treatment, etc.

General errors of form

These may arise from general kinematic faults in machine tools, such as slideway wear, or from induced kinematic errors such as tool above or below centre when taper turning. Again, there may be general flexure of the workpiece during machining giving rise to errors of form. Such errors are not generally included in surface finish measurement because of their long wavelength.

The diagrams shown in Fig. 5.2 illustrate schematically the ways in which a surface may deviate from perfect smoothness and geometrical form. From Fig. 5.2 it is clear that the characteristics of a surface are closely associated with the wavelength and amplitude of the surface irregularities and, in particular, wavelengths from different sources may be superimposed one upon another to form a complex wave pattern. The signals from a modern electronic stylus instrument may be used to form a graphical record of a portion of the profile of the surface under investigation or to provide a numerical parameter. When a parametric assessment of a surface is required the presence of long wavelengths will affect the value obtained usually by increasing it; thus the influence of longer wavelengths must be suppressed. The form that this suppression takes depends on the basic design of the stylus instrument.

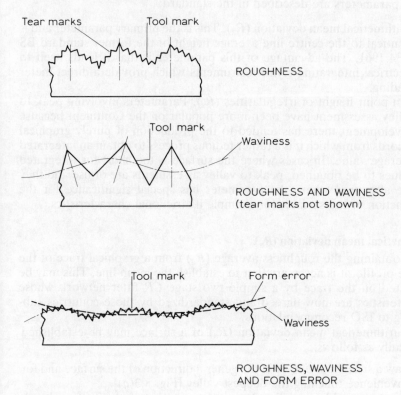

Fig. 5.2 Errors of form

5.2 Parameters used in surface finish measurement

A number of parameters have been specified and used in various countries throughout the world and the following names and their abbreviations are probably the most well known:

Centre line average (c.l.a.): R_a, h_{cla}, R_u, a.a.
Root mean square: r.m.s., R_g
Maximum peak to valley height in the sample: R_t, R_{max}
The average of the R_t values found in five consecutive samples: R_{tm}
The average of the five highest peaks and five deepest valleys in the sample: R_z
The average or levelling depth of the profile: R_p.

The parameter which has become the most widely accepted over the years is the centre line average height h_{cla} which is a mean line or M-parameter.

Arising from the change to SI units, international agreement has been reached on the terminology, standards for instruments and roughness comparison specimens, see BS1134:1972.

Two parameters are described in the standard:

(a) Arithmetical mean deviation (R_a). This is the primary parameter and is identical to the centre line average height of the former standard BS 1134:1961. The advantage of this parameter is that it lends itself to electrical integrating stylus instruments which provide a direct meter reading.

(b) Ten point height of irregularities (R_z). Parameters involving peak to valley assessment have been more popular on the Continent because development there has tended to the production of purely graphical records from which it is a rather tedious process to obtain an integrated average value. In cases where the surface is too short for integrated values to be obtained, peak to valley assessments are of use and they are also used where the parameter has special significance for the function of the surface, for example its frictional characteristics.

Arithmetical mean deviation (R_a)

When obtaining the roughness average (R_a) from a graphical trace of the surface profile, it is necessary first to establish the mean line. This may be generated on the trace by a simple two stage CR filter network whose characteristics are now agreed and standardized by those countries subscribing to ISO recommendations.

The arithmetical mean deviation (R_a) of a surface may be established graphically as follows:

(1) Draw a straight line X–X in the general direction of the surface and for convenience touching the deepest valley [Fig. 5.3(a)].
(2) Select a suitable sampling length L such that if the surface has a distinguishable waveform a whole number of waveforms are enclosed.
(3) Find the area A under the curve using a planimeter or ordinate method. The height of the centre line C–C may be found from

$$H_m = A/L$$

where H_m is the perpendicular height from X–X to C–C.
(4) The trace is now divided into two halves so that the sum of the enclosed areas above the line $(P_1 + P_2 + \text{etc.})$ equates the sum of the enclosed areas below the line $(Q_1 + Q_2 + \text{etc.})$ [see Fig. 5.3(b)]. R_a may now be determined:

$$R_a = \frac{\text{areas } P + \text{areas } Q}{L} \times \frac{1000}{V_v} \quad \mu m$$

where V_v is the vertical magnification and the areas P and Q are expressed in square millimetres and the length L in millimetres.

The average of a number of samples is taken as the R_a for the measuring traversing length.

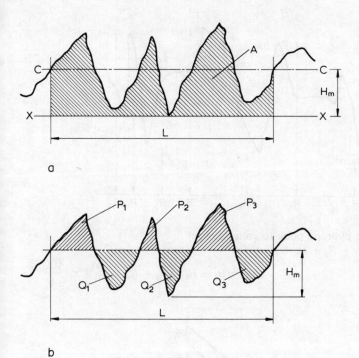

Fig. 5.3 Obtaining the roughness average

N.B. The horizontal magnification appears in both the areas and the sampling length and thus does not appear explicitly in the equation.

For most practical purposes the result obtained from an electrical mean line or a drawn mean line differs only by about 5% and is considered to be negligible.

It is of interest to note that the well known M-parameter, the root mean square or r.m.s. value, although officially abandoned in the USA in 1959 in favour of h_{cla}, now R_a, is still specified on drawings from some countries.

Average peak to valley height (R_z)

This parameter is much easier to obtain from a profile graph than R_a. A line is drawn parallel to the general direction of the profile from which the five highest peaks and five deepest valleys are measured and the average value computed (Fig. 5.4).

The graph shown at Fig. 5.5 allows a comparison to be made between some of the parameters in use and their expected average equivalent in R_a, but it must be emphasized that such correlations are only approximate and are by no means comparable with the agreement of repeated length measurement using different comparators.

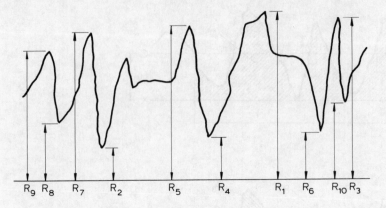

Fig. 5.4 Obtaining average peak to valley height

$$R_z = \tfrac{1}{5}\left[(R_1 + R_3 + R_5 + R_7 + R_9) - \right.$$

$$\left. (R_2 + R_4 + R_6 + R_8 + R_{10})\right] \times \frac{1000}{V_v}$$

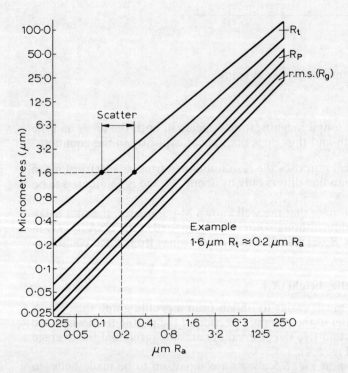

Fig. 5.5 Comparison between parameters and average equivalent

5.3 Tolerances for R_a values

It is neither desirable nor economic to produce a closer tolerance than is required for the function of a component. In the case of precision dimensions in engineering the tolerance in 95% of all cases is less than 1% of the nominal dimension, but in the case of surface finish a parameter tolerance of this order would be absurd owing to the much less precise nature of the assessment. To limit the variety of R_a values appearing on drawings, a preferred range of values following a simple geometrical series is recommended in which each step is twice the value of the previous step. Each step is assigned the letter N, i.e. N_1, N_2, N_3, etc., which avoids the need to quote μm R_a when prescribing a roughness value, and has the advantage that the system contains a built-in tolerance of -25% to $+50\%$, which is well suited to the specifications of surface roughness values (see Table 5.1).

Table 5.1 Steps for R_a values

Central values c.l.a. (μm)	R_a (μm)	N	$N^{+50\%}_{-25\%}$ (μm)
0·5	0·125	—	— —
1	0·025	N_1	0·02 to 0·04
2	0·05	N_2	0·04 to 0·08
4	0·1	N_3	0·08 to 0·15
8	0·2	N_4	0·15 to 0·3
16	0·4	N_5	0·3 to 0·6
32	0·8	N_6	0·6 to 1·2
63	1·6	N_7	1·2 to 2·4
125	3·2	N_8	2·4 to 4·8
250	6·3	N_9	4·8 to 9·6
500	12·5	N_{10}	9·6 to 18·75
1000	25·0	N_{11}	18·75 to 37·5
2000	50·0	N_{12}	37·5 to 75·0

A guide to probable ranges of values obtained in some common production processes is shown in Table 5.2, and a number of traces with their corresponding average R_a values taken on a Talysurf instrument are shown in Fig. 5.6.

The use of unequal magnifications to produce a graphical trace is generally unavoidable because the variations in height of the surface irregularities are much smaller than their wavelength. The resulting distortion gives a false impression of the shape of the surface profile and it is important to remember that they are in fact much smoother than traces of this type would suggest.

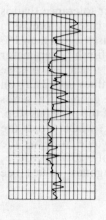

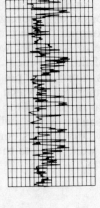

(c) (i) *Face milled surface*
Feed 0·3 mm per tooth; depth of cut 0·2 mm
Talysurf settings: $V/H = 2000/100$
meter cut-off = 0·8 mm

Results: R_a of graphical sample = 2·22 μm R_a

(c) (ii) *Face milled surface* As (c) (i), $V/H = 2000/20$

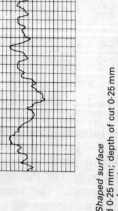

(a) *Shaped surface*
Feed 0·25 mm; depth of cut 0·25 mm
Talysurf settings: mag. ratio $V/H = 1000/100$
meter cut-off = 0·8 mm

Results: Average of 10 measuring traversing lengths = 3·52 μm R_a
Maximum = 4·5 μm R_a Minimum = 3·0 μm R_a
R_a of graphical sample = 3·75 μm R_a

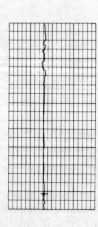

(b) *Lapped gauge block*
Talysurf settings: $V/H = 50\ 000/100$
meter cut-off = 0·8 mm

Results: Average of 5 measuring traversing lengths = 0·008 μm R_a
Maximum = 0·01 μm R_a Minimum = 0·006 μm R_a
R_a of graphical sample = 0·0075 μm R_a

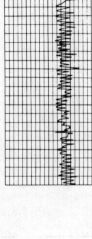

(d) (i) Ground surface (horizontal)
Talysurf settings: V/H = 20 000/20
meter cut-off = 0·8 mm

Results: R_a of graphical sample = 3·8 μm R_a

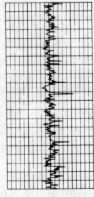

(d) (ii) Ground surface (horizontal)
As (d) (i), V/H = 20 000/100

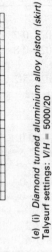

(e) (i) Diamond turned aluminium alloy piston (skirt)
Talysurf settings: V/H = 5000/20
meter cut-off = 0·8 mm

Results: Average of 5 measuring traversing lengths = 0·51 μm R_a
Maximum = 0·55 μm R_a Minimum = 0·48 μm R_a
R_a of graphical sample = 0·5 μm R_a

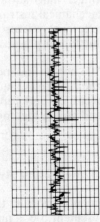

(e) (ii) Diamond turned aluminium alloy piston (skirt)
As (e) (i), V/H = 5000/100

Fig. 5.6 Portions of traces taken on a Talysurf instrument, showing average R_a values

Table 5.2 Ranges for roughness values in common production processes

Process	Range (N)	Central values (R_a)
Flat and cylindrical lapping, superfinishing	N_1-N_4	0·025–0·2
Diamond turning	N_1-N_6	0·025–0·8
Flat and cylindrical grinding	N_1-N_8	0·025–3·2
Finishing	N_4-N_8	0·1–3·2
Face and cylindrical turning, and milling, reaming	N_5-N_{12}	0·4–50·0
Drilling	N_7-N_{10}	1·6–12·5
Shaping, planing, horizontal milling	N_6-N_{12}	0·8–50·0
Sand casting and forging	$N_{10}-N_{11}$	12·5–25·0
Extruding, cold rolling, drawing	N_6-N_8	0·8–3·2
Die casting	N_6-N_7	0·8–1·6

5.4 Instruments and techniques

A number of instruments and techniques are in use for the purpose of surface finish assessment but the following are probably the most important from the point of view of the engineer:

(1) Electrical integrating stylus instruments.
(2) Tactile (finger nail) surface assessment and its development in the form of mechanical instruments.
(3) Light interference microscopes of various types.
(4) The production of plastic replicas of the surface.

Although (4) is not an independent method it is useful, for instance, in cases where the surface is inaccessible to instruments.

Light interference and replica methods are area sampling methods, while stylus and tactile methods sample a number of profiles or points on the surface.

5.5 Electrical integrating stylus instruments

These instruments provide the fundamental information required for surface measurement, i.e. a numerical assessment displayed on a meter or a graphical trace. Other methods of assessment can be and are referred to the results obtained by these instruments when required. The overall calibration of electrical stylus instruments is made against standard etched or electroformed surfaces having, for example, a uniform zig-zag profile of

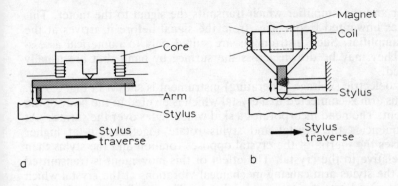

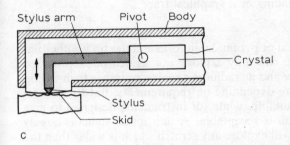

Fig. 5.7 Principal features of electronic stylus instruments

known dimensions. To check the minimum surface variation obtainable by the instrument a scratch-free optical flat may be used as a test piece.

Electrical integrating instruments employ an arm on which a diamond stylus is mounted. The stylus is drawn across the sample surface and its vertical movement transduced to electrical signals. The principal features of electronic stylus instruments are shown in Fig. 5.7.

In Fig. 5.7(*a*) the movement of the arm which constitutes an armature varies the air gap at the outer limbs of the E-shaped core; the coil wound limbs form two branches of a bridge circuit. A carrier wave is supplied to the bridge and the effect of varying the air gaps is to modulate or vary the amplitude of the waveform. The modulated wave is then amplified, demodulated (or smoothed) and either filtered to provide a meter readout or in the unfiltered condition made to operate a rectilinear recorder thus providing a graphical trace.

A moving coil type instrument is shown in Fig. 5.7(*b*). The coil is mounted above the stylus and moves with the stylus relative to a radial magnetic field provided by a magnet. The current generated by the vertical stylus movement is proportional to the amplitude and the wavelength or frequency of the stylus movement; the frequency depends on the spacing of the irregularities and the speed at which the stylus is traversed across the surface. Because the instrument must be insensitive to frequency within its working range, an *RC* correcting circuit is inserted between the receiving amplifier and the amplifier which transmits the signal to the meter. This eliminates unwanted frequencies from the signal before it arrives at the second amplifier. Such instruments are suited only to numerical assessments. They may be drawn across the surface by hand, but are usually motorized.

A piezoelectric (voltage generating) instrument is shown in Fig. 5.7(c). The stylus arm is connected to a crystal which is pivoted to the body of the instrument. The head incorporates a skid which slides over the surface. At low frequencies the crystal and stylus rotate together but at higher frequencies the inertia of the crystal opposes rotation and the stylus then moves relative to the crystal. The effect of this movement is transmitted through the stylus arm causing mechanical vibrations at the crystal which are transformed into proportional voltages. The amplified signal can be used to provide a meter reading or a graphical trace.

Stylus

Styluses are normally conical or pyramidal in form and the tip is either flat or radiused. A rounded tip will fully explore any scratch mark provided that it is sufficiently shallow and its radius is equal to or larger than the tip radius. Tip radii vary in size depending on requirements, but for general profile recording $2\,\mu$m is suitable, while for instruments designed to give only average readings $10\,\mu$m is acceptable. A flat tipped stylus is largely independent of depth and will explore any scratch which is wider than the flat if the slope of the sides of the scratch are not sheer. There may of course be deep narrow scratches which a tip cannot explore, but experience has shown that these are usually of little significance.

Datum

A datum is required in all instruments which mechanically explore surface irregularities and should conform to the nominal geometry of the surface. Both straight and curved datums for instance can be developed by incorporating a flexure spring linkage arrangement within the instrument on which the pick-up body is suspended. A rounded foot mounted on the pick-up body which slides along an optical flat, or, for rougher surfaces, a slideway which guides the pick-up body, provides suitable straight line datums. All these methods require accurate levelling and great rigidity in the instrument framework and it is more usual to use a single rounded skid or a flat swivelling pad or shoe as approximate datum forming devices. Skids or shoes are mounted to the pick-up body, which is hinged to the driving mechanism of the instrument [Fig. 5.8(a)].

The datum formed by a skid is the locus of the centre of curvature of its radius which usually ranges from about 6 mm to 50 mm. The greater the spacing of the crests of the surface, the more the skid movement departs from a straight line [Fig. 5.8(b)]. This increases the relative movement between the skid and the stylus and introduces phase effects which may give a false impression of the surface. However, provided attempts are not made to measure surfaces beyond the scope of the instrument, e.g. rough milled surfaces, such phase effects do not seriously affect the results. The shoe-type pick-up is used when the surface crests are wide apart, i.e. up to half the length of the shoe. There is no relative position of the stylus to the skid or shoe where phase effects are eliminated.

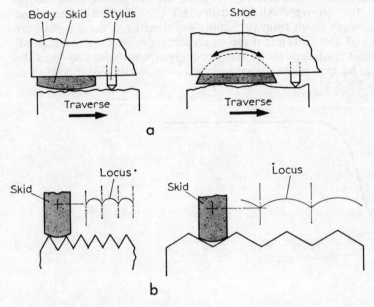

Fig. 5.8 Curved and straight datums

Measuring traversing length and sampling length

One complete traverse of the stylus of an electronic instrument is called the measuring traversing length and this is divided into from 3 to 10 sampling lengths. The sampling length chosen is determined by the type of surface under test and an increase in sampling length generally increases the amount of waviness accepted for the readout. The results of all the samples in the measuring traversing length are integrated by the instrument to provide a scale and pointer or digital readout which is the average of all the sampling lengths in one measuring traversing length.

Cut-off wavelength or meter cut-off
The frequency of the stylus movement as it rises up and down in the grooves is determined by the traversing speed.

If f is the frequency of the stylus movement, λ is the surface wavelength and v is the velocity of traverse, then

$$f = v/\lambda$$

Thus $f \propto 1/\lambda$ if v remains constant.

Both carrier modulated and current generating instruments require electronic filters to limit the wavelengths accepted for the meter reading, while it is a characteristic of the voltage generating type that it responds only within a given waveband.

At the short wavelength end of the spectrum the carrier modulated instrument responds only when the stylus tip begins to enter the grooves and the transmission characteristic is therefore attenuated until the tip bottoms in the grooves. An electronic filter is used to reject those frequencies which result from very short wavelengths as these signals are attenuated and also to reject those of greater wavelength than required; thus the meter reading is the product of a given waveband known as the pass band. The transmission characteristic is shown in Fig. 5.9(a). The

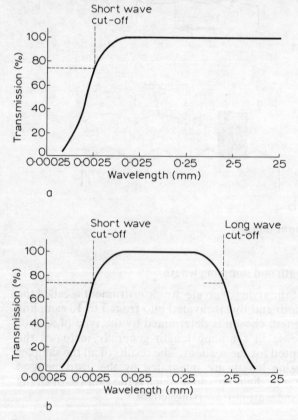

Fig. 5.9 Transmission characteristics for (a) carrier modulated instruments (b) current generating instruments

response of the current generating instrument is attenuated at high frequencies by the stylus effect, and because the magnitude of the current generated depends on the relative velocity of the coil to the magnet, it is also attenuated at low frequencies (long wavelength), as the output then tends to zero. The transmission characteristic is shown in Fig. 5.9(b). The upper and lower limits of wavelength cut-off are 75 ± 5% of the transmission characteristic. The wavelength or meter cut-off is made equal to the sampling length and can be varied by switching to suit the type of surface under test.

For surfaces produced by single point tools, a useful guide to determining meter cut-off is that the cut-off should exceed one feed spacing, but for many fine irregular surfaces a 0·8 mm cut-off is often used. The cut-offs usually available in electronic instruments are as follows:

Meter cut-off (mm)   0·08   0·25   0·8   2·5   8·0   25·0

The 0·08 mm cut-off is generally used for fine surfaces too short for longer cut-offs.

Finishing processes and suitable sampling lengths (meter cut-offs) are shown in Table 5.3.

Table 5.3 Cut-offs for finishing processes

Finishing processes	Meter cut-offs (mm)
Superfinishing, lapping, honing, diamond boring and turning, spark machining, polishing and buffing	0·25 and 0·8
Turning, reaming, broaching	0·8 and 2·5
Grinding	0·25, 0·8, 2·5
Boring, milling, shaping	0·8, 2·5, 8·0
Planing	2·5, 8·0, 25

5.6 Tactile surface assessment and mechanical roughness instruments

Tactile surface assessment

This essentially comparative test involves drawing a finger nail across the surface and by the same technique making a comparison with a range of electroformed test blocks made to conform in roughness with a suitable range in the N series and manufactured in such a manner as to take account of the actual production process involved. The assessment is complete when the two standard blocks in the set have been found which represent a 'rougher' and 'smoother' surface than the one under test. The 'rougher' test block is taken to be the grade of roughness of the surface under test (BS 2634:1974). This form of test is, of course, subjective but has nevertheless been found to give sufficiently consistent results in many instances. Tactile testing is based on the frictional properties of the specimen while electronic stylus instruments explore the geometry. When surface irregularities are random, as in the case of grinding, the parameters obtained from stylus instruments are also a good indication of the frictional properties of the surface and both tactile and stylus methods are comparable. However, considerable differences arise when more regular, periodic surfaces, e.g. rough turned surfaces, are assessed by each method in turn. When such surfaces are to be assessed by tactile methods then an electronic stylus instrument must be used to evaluate R_a as a check.

Mechanical roughness instrument (Mecrin)

A development from the tactile method which provides R_a values is the mechanical roughness indicator or Mecrin gauge. This gauge is suited only to non-regular surfaces where the frictional properties measured compare with those provided by electronic stylus instruments, such as ground, honed, lapped, hand filed and emery clothed surfaces, etc., to approximately $4 \cdot 5\,\mu m$ R_a (grades N_8 to N_9) and on the finer grades of turning and milling to $0 \cdot 8\,\mu m$ R_a (grade N_6). On regular surfaces of rougher values the instrument can be used as a comparator against surface roughness blocks but the readings then bear no relation to R_a values.

Principle of the Mecrin instrument

The Mecrin instrument assesses the surface through its frictional properties and the average slope of the irregularities.

A thin metallic blade when pushed against a surface at a certain angle will either slide or buckle depending on two factors:

(a) The surface roughness
(b) The angle of attack, i.e. the angle of the blade to the surface.

The essential behaviour of the blade is shown in Fig. 5.10. At angles below the critical angle the blade tip will simply slide along the surface [Fig. 5.10(a)], but if the angle is successively increased the angle will be

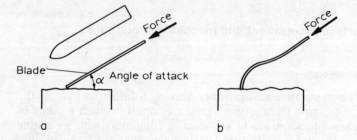

Fig. 5.10 Behaviour of the blade in the Mecrin instrument, showing (a) sliding blade (b) buckling blade

found at which the blade just begins to buckle [Fig. 5.10(b)]. This angle is the critical angle of attack. The smoother the surface the greater the critical angle and thus this angle is a function of the degree of roughness encountered. The essential form of the instrument is shown in Fig. 5.11 and the angle of attack is measured with a gravity dial indicator which incorporates a pendulum and gear mechanism and the buckling blade is observed through the transparent cover. The dial is calibrated in terms of the N grades and the corresponding central R_a values.

Calibration of the instrument is against hardened carbon steel specimens having nominal values of $0 \cdot 1$ and $0 \cdot 4\,\mu m$ R_a which are accurate to within $\pm 12\%$.

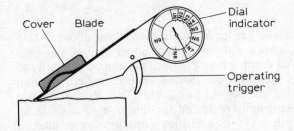

Cover Blade

Dial indicator

Operating trigger

Fig. 5.11 Basic form of the Mecrin instrument

Uncertainty of assessment
It is good practice to take the average of at least five readings when using an electronic stylus instrument, because the R_a value of each measuring traversing length on machined surfaces scatters by anything from 10% to 100% depending on the machining method. Each measuring traversing length, however, consists of from three to ten sampling lengths; thus the scatter from one sampling length to another may be greater than 100%. Because the Mecrin is a purely mechanical instrument it evaluates each individual sampling length and thus its scatter of results is generally larger than those obtained from electrical stylus instruments. However, the manufacturers claim that for general workshop purposes three to five readings on different parts of the surface produce a good enough average value for most purposes.

Range of application
The Mecrin instrument can be used for the following purposes:

(*a*) To provide μm R_a values for relatively smooth irregular surfaces.
(*b*) As a comparator for two surfaces to decide which is the rougher.
(*c*) As a limit gauge for roughness, i.e. GO and NOT GO.
(*d*) To establish the direction of the lay of a surface.
(*e*) In the case of a surface having a definite lay, to determine the direction of maximum roughness, e.g. a saw tooth profile of unequal angle. Electronic stylus instrument meter readings do not differentiate this condition.
(*f*) To establish a numerical scale of the frictional qualities of rough, regular surfaces. No correlation exists between such values and μm R_a.
(*g*) For use in conjunction with electrical stylus instruments to establish whether R_a values are also descriptive of frictional qualities.
(*h*) To measure short lengths down to 1 mm which may be inaccessible to stylus instruments.
(*i*) As a comparator for non-metallic surfaces, e.g. paper, plastics, wood, painted surfaces, etc.

Dial depth gauge

It is useful to define the coarser grades of roughness as those above $5.0\,\mu m$ R_a and most stylus instruments are almost at their upper limit of measurement at this value. The dial depth gauge has been developed primarily to measure rougher surfaces such as rough turned, shaped, milled, grit and shot blasted, spark eroded or cast surfaces, etc. The R_z and similar parameters are those most usually preferred for this type of work as an assessment of the total depth of the irregularities is usually of more interest than the R_a parameter. An advantage of the instrument is that a quick measurement can be made without the need for producing a graphical trace.

The gauge is essentially a dial test indicator in which the plunger has been replaced by a hardened steel or diamond stylus and to which two point or three point datum attachments can be fitted depending on whether the surface tested is flat or cylindrical (Fig. 5.12). The gauge is first set to

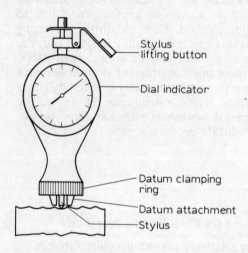

Stylus
lifting button

Dial indicator

Datum clamping
ring

Datum attachment

Stylus

Fig. 5.12 Dial depth gauge

zero on a setting standard and the surface measured by pressing the gauge on to it ensuring that the stylus engages a groove in the surface. The feet of the datum attachment are then pressed against the surface and a reading taken. This procedure is repeated at at least four other points on the surface and the average of the readings almost exactly equals the R_z value; the highest reading is the R_t value or maximum depth. When for any reason the R_a value is required an almost exact conversion can be made by dividing the R_z value by four, as for most coarser roughness grades $R_z = 4R_a$ to a tolerance of $\pm 15\%$. It must be emphasized, however, that excessive reliance should not be placed on such empirical relationships, as under other circumstances R_z may be as much as seven times R_a.

5.7 Light interference microscopes

The technique used to develop interference fringes on nominally flat or curved surfaces is explained in Chapter 3, and the basic optical system used in a suitably modified form can be applied to microscopes for surface finish examination.

The advantage of the interference microscope is that it allows an *area* of the surface to be examined and the more expensive versions provide a range of magnifications and provision for a camera, so that a permanent record of the fringe pattern may be obtained if desired. Very high resolution is possible with these instruments and scratch spacings $0.5\,\mu m$ wide are fairly easily seen. This order of resolution compares favourably with the normal electronic stylus instrument where response begins to fall off at scratch widths below $2.5\,\mu m$. High resolution of scratch depth can also be obtained and scratches as shallow as $0.05\,\mu m$ or even less can be resolved under good conditions. Multiple beam interference microscopes in which the interfering light beams are made to traverse the interference space several times permit scratch depth measurement of the order of $0.002\,\mu m$. Comparison microscopes allow the fringes appearing on a master simultaneously to be compared with the fringes on the component. The surface finish and sphericity of ball bearings are checked by this method.

Because of their high resolving power micro-interferometers are limited to the examination of smoother surfaces (peak to valley heights of less than $2\,\mu m$) and by virtue of their construction can only be used for direct observation of external surfaces on components within the size capacity of the instrument. Assessment of surface faults cannot directly be related to the R_a parameter but a good correlation with peak to valley parameters is possible. The main advantages are as follows:

(*a*) The area sample obtained allows surface details to be seen as a composite in the field of view, whereas stylus exploration is very selective.

(*b*) The fringes can be thought of as a series of cross-sectional planes and their direction can be adjusted to provide the most informative pattern.

(*c*) The method is non-destructive as there is no contact with the surface. The surfaces of soft or thin materials which normally could not effectively be explored with a stylus can be examined.

(*d*) No instrument recalibration is required.

5.8 Surface replicas

A simple but effective method of surface texture measurement where a surface is inaccessible to instruments or where the part is too large to mount or bring to an instrument is the preparation of a cast replica of the surface.

Essentially, the technique involves either pressing a piece of softened plastic on to the surface or placing a plasticine wall or metal ring round the specimen area and pouring in a plastic fluid. In either case, after a suitable setting time the replica may be removed and an instrument reading taken using a lightly loaded stylus.

Very high fidelity approaching 100% is obtainable using the fluid method and softened plastic sheet offers about 80% fidelity. Special kits with full instructions for use are available from manufacturers.

Where circumstances permit, the fidelity of the replica may be checked by comparing the profile graph of the sample with that of the replica. To ensure that both readings are taken along the same path, a 45° cross may be scribed on the sample and stylus readings taken through the intersection. If the stylus passes to one side of the cross two disruptions will appear on the trace indicating that the setting must be corrected.

Study problems

5.1 Define the following with reference to surface finish assessment and electronic stylus instruments:

(i) Roughness
(ii) Waviness
(iii) Lay
(iv) Sampling length
(v) Meter cut-off
(vi) Arithmetic mean deviation
(vii) Ten point height of irregularities
(viii) Measuring traversing length.

5.2 (a) As an aid to the assessment of surface finish profiles, profile traces are often reproduced by means of a rectilinear recorder. Explain the effects of horizontal magnification, vertical magnification and stylus radius as factors in the interpretation of such a trace.

(b) 'Many electronic stylus instruments incorporate a skid as a means of datum formation.' Discuss this statement and show by means of a diagram the limitations of this method of datum formation.

(c) The most widely used meter cut-off value used in surface finish assessment is 0·8 mm. Explain the reasons for this and give practical examples where the use of larger and smaller meter cut-off would be appropriate.

(d) Tactile methods have found increasing application in surface finish assessment. Outline the technique and indicate its major advantages and limitations.

5.3 (a) The following techniques may be used for surface finish assessment:

(i) Tactile
(ii) Electronic stylus instrument
(iii) Interferometry.

Briefly describe each technique and give a clearly defined application in each case.

(*b*) A rectilinear pen recording of a diamond turned surface is shown in Fig. 5.13. The sampling length (*L*) used was 0·8 mm and the *V*/*H* magnification ratio was 5000/100.

Calculate the British Standard parameter R_a if the areas (in square millimetres) above and below the mean line are as follows:

A B C D E F
60 115 96 92 109 70
Answer: 1·36 μm

(*c*) Define the term 'ten point height of irregularities (R_z)', and use a profile sketch to illustrate your answer.

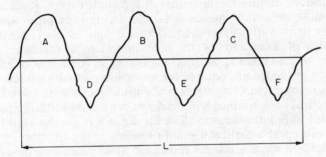

Fig. 5.13 Pen recording for Problem 5.3

5.4 (*a*) A series of waves takes the form of equilateral triangles of length of side 40 mm. Taking five waves as representing a sampling length, determine the 'R_a' value when the vertical magnification is ×5000.

(*b*) Show that the R_z value of the waveform lies between four and seven times the R_a value.

Answers
(*a*) $R_a = 1·732$ μm
(*b*) Ratio $R_z/R_a = 4$

5.5 (*a*) Explain what is meant by the term 'lay' when applied to a machined surface and illustrate by means of sketches how the amplitude and wavelength of a surface finish assessment may be affected by the direction of measurement across that surface.

(*b*) Make a schematic diagram of a surface profile containing both roughness and waviness characteristics and explain how choice of sampling length can affect the value of a surface finish parameter. How is the meter cut-off of an electronic surface finish assessment instrument related to a chosen sampling length?

6 Strain measurement

Until recent times one of the most difficult problems facing engineers had been to find the stresses acting upon a body by the direct application of measuring devices. Before the invention of the electrical resistance strain gauge the most important means available for this purpose was the extensometer in its various forms (mechanical, optical, etc.), but these have a number of disadvantages, the most important of which are their relative bulk, which makes application impossible in conditions of limited space, and the gauge length required for application, usually not less than 12 mm. Thus many engineering stress problems formerly were solved on a purely theoretical basis coupled with trial and error tests and large factors of safety which were introduced to allow for the lack of precise knowledge of stress conditions at a particular point or points in the structure.

The principle on which electrical resistance strain gauges are based was established by Lord Kelvin in 1856 when he showed that a stress applied to a metal wire, besides changing its length and diameter, also changed its electrical resistance. In the 1930s this effect was used by American workers to develop independently the bonded wire electrical resistance strain gauge which is attached by means of a suitable cement to the surface under test and subjected to the same strain. Since this type of gauge was developed a number of gauges have become available based on effects other than change of electrical resistance but the resistance gauge is still by far the most widely used. The most important gauges used for strain determination are given in Table 6.1.

Table 6.1 Types of gauge for strain determination

Gauge types	Effect of strain
Bonded wire ⎫ Bonded foil ⎬	Change of electrical resistance
Semiconductor ⎭	
Photoelastic	Fringe displacement
Extensometers	These include a variety of methods for measuring extension, i.e. mechanical, optical, pneumatic, inductance, capacitance and acoustic responses

6.1 Strain

A body subjected to external forces is in a condition of both stress and strain. The effects of stress, i.e. change of shape of the body, involve change in the fundamental quantity, length, which can be measured; thus, provided there is a known relationship between stress and strain, the stresses occurring in a body can be computed if sufficient strain information is available.

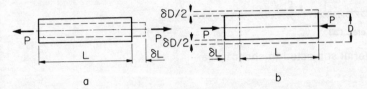

Fig. 6.1 Uniform bar loaded (*a*) in tension (*b*) in compression

Consider the simple case of a uniform bar loaded first in tension and then in compression (Fig. 6.1). It is seen that strain appears along the axis of the applied load and, in all directions normal to that axis, the bar grows longer and thinner (tension) or shorter and thicker (compression).

The change in length in the direction of the direct stress caused by the load P is the linear extension δL, but for a given load this extension is dependent upon the length of the bar: the greater the length the greater the extension. Strain may be defined as extension per unit length irrespective of whether the bar is lengthened or shortened; thus in each case direct or longitudinal strain is $\delta L/L$, where L is the length prior to the application of the load.

Lateral or transverse strain

Lateral strain arises from the increase or decrease in the dimension normal to the applied load, and is computed in the same way as direct strain. The ratio of lateral strain to direct strain is called Poisson's ratio, i.e.

$$\text{Poisson's ratio} = \frac{\text{lateral strain}}{\text{direct strain}} = \frac{\delta D/D}{\delta L/L}$$

and is taken to be positive.

This ratio is particular to any given metal or alloy; it is as low as 0·21 for zinc and as high as 0·35 for brass. The value for steel is 0·29.

The constant connecting stress and strain in elastic materials under direct stresses is the modulus of elasticity E, which is the slope of the stress/strain curve, thus

$$E = \frac{\text{stress}}{\text{strain}} \quad \text{and} \quad \text{stress} = E \times \text{strain}$$

Shear stress and strain

Shear stress occurs along a plane parallel to the applied force and Fig. 6.2 shows a block of material before and after the application of a shear force.

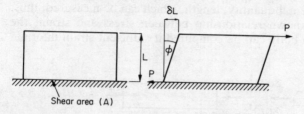

Fig. 6.2 Material subjected to shear force

Shear stress is determined by the ratio of the applied load to the area over which it acts. Hence

$$\tau = \frac{P}{A}$$

where τ is the shear stress, P is the shear force and A is the shear area.

Shear strain is the ratio of extension to original length and is defined as $\delta L/L$ (Fig. 6.2). Where δL is small compared with L then ϕ radians is a good approximation to $\delta L/L$.

$$\gamma = \frac{\delta L}{L}$$

where γ is the shear strain, δL is the extension and L is the original length.

The constant connecting shear stress and shear strain is the modulus of rigidity G; thus

$$G = \frac{\text{shear stress}}{\text{shear strain}}$$

and

$$\text{shear stress} = G \times \text{shear strain}$$

Static, transient and dynamic strain

Static and transient strain

Strain which remains at a constant value for an appreciable length of time is called static strain and can occur in stationary or moving structures. A rotating engine shaft under constant torque is subject to steady or only slightly varying strain, a condition equivalent to static strain. Likewise a cantilever under a constant bending load or a rod or spring under a constant tensile or compressive stress are in a state of static strain [Figs. 6.3(a) to (d)].

A strain/time relationship is shown graphically in Fig. 6.3(e). Notice that the curve is divided into separate parts, transient and static. The transient portions indicate an increase or decrease in strain with time as load is steadily increased or reduced to the required value, when it remains constant. Transient strain is a form of dynamic strain because it changes with time.

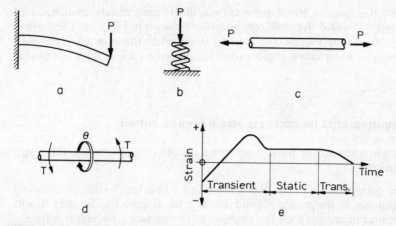

Fig. 6.3 States of static strain: (*a*) cantilever (*b*) spring (*c*) rod (*d*) rotating shaft under constant torque. Part (*e*) shows a strain/time relationship

Dynamic strain
Strain which is changing with time is dynamic strain and the problems associated with recording such a strain depend on the rate at which it is changing, as there is obviously a limit to the ability of an observer to follow

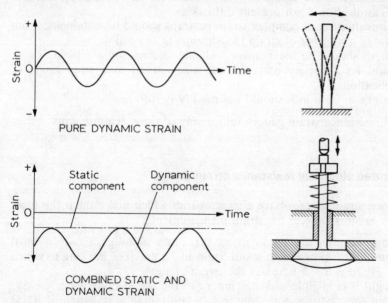

Fig. 6.4 Strain/time curves

and plot, on a time base, strain variations indicated by a scale pointer or even from an instrument displaying a digital readout. Furthermore, an element may simultaneously be subjected to both static and dynamic strain components. Simple strain/time curves illustrating purely dynamic and combined static and dynamic conditions are shown in Fig. 6.4. The engine valve spring is under static compressive strain when the engine is stationary and is subject to dynamic compressive strain as the engine valve opens and closes.

6.2 Requirements for accurate strain measurement

Ideally gauges used for measuring strain should conform to the following requirements:

(a) The gauge should be small in size and easy to attach to the specimen or component; its profile should be as low as possible so that it will respond in unison with the changes in the surface to which it is fixed.
(b) The gauge should be highly sensitive in the direction of the measured strain but of low sensitivity in the transverse plane (cross-sensitivity). The strain/resistance characteristics should be linear.
(c) Stiffness in all directions should not be such that the stiffness of the tested surface is modified.
(d) Calibration should be easy and, once made, should remain stable with time, dynamic loading, changes of temperature, pressure or humidity.
(e) Speed of response should be high so that time lag is negligible. Remote indication should not present difficulties.
(f) The evaluation of complex strain patterns should be obtainable from as small a number of strain measurements as possible.
(g) Gauges should be inexpensive, reliable and readily available. There should be a variety of types and sizes suited to a wide range of applications.
(h) Immersion in liquids should not modify performance.

Bonded resistance strain gauges fulfil many of these requirements.

6.3 Bonded electrical resistance strain gauge

Resistance strain gauges have characteristics which make them the most versatile existing devices for strain measurement:

(a) Gauge lengths are as small as 0.127 mm although those in most common use range from about 5 mm to 12 mm. The backing to which the gauge is fixed increases the overall length.
(b) Weight is negligible and attachment to the tested body is fairly easy.
(c) Strain sensitivity is quite low, e.g. a constantan wire gauge of 100Ω resistance would show an increase of approximately 0.25Ω on low carbon steel strained to the elastic limit.
(d) Temperature, pressure and humidity, behaviour in liquid environments, etc., all affect performance but protection or compensation can usually be provided.

(*e*) Strain gauges can indicate static, transient and dynamic strain (50 000 Hz) or more, and remote indication and recording presents little difficulty.

Metal resistance strain gauges are made in two basic forms, wire and foil. The foil types, which are pressed from thin sheet foil, have the advantage that the gauge can take almost any shape that can be drawn; they also have a lower profile, very good linear cross-sensitivity, and, because the grid is rectangular in form and very thin, heat is dissipated more readily than from wire gauges. Because of their generally superior qualities foil gauges have largely superseded wire gauges except for post-yield applications and where grids in excess of 150 mm long are required (Fig. 6.5).

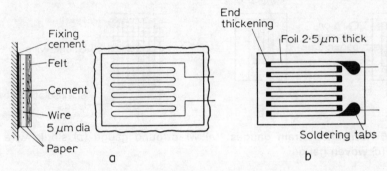

Fig. 6.5 Metal resistance strain gauges: (*a*) flat grid wire gauge (*b*) etched foil gauge

The resistance R of a metal depends on its electrical resistivity ρ, its area a and its length L according to the equation

$$R = \rho L / a$$

Thus, to obtain a high resistance gauge occupying a small area, the metal chosen has a high resistivity, a large number of grid loops and a very small cross-sectional area. Wire gauges are embedded in plastic cements and sandwiched between thin paper or plastic insulators, and are sometimes encapsulated to give added protection. The cement holds the wire rigidly on to the backing so that it will not buckle under strain. Foil gauges are usually cemented on to a backing but may also, by means of a special process, be transferred directly to an insulated surface which eliminates the operating temperature limitations of paper or plastic backings. Two important features of foil gauges not present in wire gauges are the thickenings at the end of each loop which, by introducing a low transverse electrical resistance, reduce cross-sensitivity to almost negligible proportions, and the provision of relatively large tabs tapered into the grid provides easy soldering or welding of the leads and reduces the danger of fatigue failure.

Besides the conventional wire and foil gauges there are a number of other types much less widely used (Fig. 6.6).

***Wrap-round gauges* [Fig. 6.6(a)]**
The advantage of this type of gauge is that it can be made in short gauge lengths, typically 2 to 6 mm, but gauges up to 12 mm are available. The transverse sensitivity is small as the end loops lie perpendicular to the surface.

***'Single' wire gauges* [Fig. 6.6(b)]**
Transverse sensitivity is kept to a minimum by joining the separate wires of the grid by means of thick copper bridge pieces having low electrical resistance.

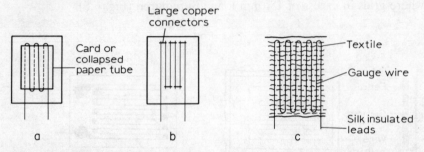

Fig. 6.6 Resistance strain gauges: (a) wrap-round gauge (b) single wire gauge (c) woven gauge

***Woven-type gauges* [Fig. 6.6(c)]**
These gauges are used to measure large strains in fabrics, etc.

It is highly desirable that the change of resistance $\delta R/R$ of a strain gauge should bear a linear relationship to the measured strain $\delta L/L$ and metallic strain gauges fulfil this requirement. This ratio is called the *gauge factor*, *K*.

6.4 Gauge factor or strain sensitivity

The electrical resistance of a metallic conductor varies directly as its resistivity and length and inversely as its cross-sectional area; this follows from $R = \rho L/a$. The metallic crystal lattice forms a regular atomic pattern and the particular form of bonding between the atoms—metallic bonding—involves mutual sharing of all the valency electrons by all the atoms in the metal. Thus current passes along a conductor in the form of directional motion of the electrons, called electron flow. The increased length and decreased area of a gauge under tensile strain accounts for part of the increase in resistance as the metallic lattice will suffer distortion but these changes alone do not fully account for the total resistance change; thus other changes in the metal lattice must also occur bringing about a change in the resistivity of the metal. This latter effect is an important consideration as it is well known that the resistivity of metals also changes with temperature.

The gauge factor K is the ratio of change of resistance $\delta R/R$ to the change of gauge length $\delta L/L$; thus

$$K = \frac{\delta R/R}{\delta L/L}.$$

where R is the nominal resistance of the gauge.

The gauge factor is supplied by the manufacturer and may range from 1·7 to 4 depending largely on the length of the gauge, although most wire and foil gauges have a gauge factor of about 2. Thus, provided that a means is available for measuring the change of resistance, strain can be determined and hence stress. The following example illustrates this point.

Example 6.1

A strain gauge (gauge factor 2) measures the strain on the surface of a shaft subjected to a tensile stress. The nominal resistance of the gauge R is $120\,\Omega$ and the change of resistance $\delta R = 0\cdot012\,\Omega$. Strain $\varepsilon = \delta L/L$ and from the above equation $\delta L/L = \delta R/RK = \varepsilon$. Therefore

$$\varepsilon = 0\cdot012/120 \times 2 = 0\cdot000\,05$$

E for steel is $206\,\mathrm{GN/m^2}$ and stress $= E \times$ strain. Therefore

$$\text{stress} = 206 \times 10^9 \times 0\cdot000\,05 = 10\cdot3\,\mathrm{MN/m^2}$$

The example illustrates that δR is very small and to measure this accurately a Wheatstone bridge circuit is used incorporating a sensitive galvanometer. A rough guide to the sensitivity of the gauge under discussion is that a change of stress intensity of $0\cdot5\,\mathrm{MN/m^2}$ will bring about a change in δR of approximately $0\cdot0006\,\Omega$. It follows that an increase in gauge factor increases sensitivity, but this is limited in metal gauges, largely because of the relatively low resistivity of metals, a limitation which is overcome in semiconductor strain gauges which have gauge factors of the order of ±100 or more.

6.5 Strain gauge alloys

The alloys most widely used for static strain measurement are the variously named 55% copper, 45% nickel alloys known as 'advance', 'copel' and 'constantan'. For dynamic strain measurement the 52% iron, 36% nickel, 8% chromium, 0·5% molybdenum alloy 'iso-elastic' is usually used. To avoid confusion the name 'advance' will be used to identify the copper/nickel alloys.

Advance has a gauge factor of about 2 which remains constant well into its plastic range and its temperature coefficient of resistance is $\pm2\,\mu\Omega\,^\circ\mathrm{C}/\Omega$ which is very low compared with say nickel (6000) or iron (5000). Corrosion resistance as would be expected of this type of alloy is also good, up to $400\,^\circ\mathrm{C}$. The resistance of a $100\,\mathrm{mm}$ length of $25\,\mu\mathrm{m}$ diameter wire is approximately $95\,\Omega$ compared with nickel and iron (approximately $23\,\Omega$). Iso-elastic alloy has the following characteristics: temperature coefficient of resistance $+175\,\mu\Omega\,^\circ\mathrm{C}/\Omega$, resistance approximately $232\,\Omega$, gauge factor

3·5. The higher temperature coefficient of resistance of iso-elastic is the limiting factor which makes it suitable only for dynamic strain measurement, as in these circumstances the strain is changing rapidly, the measurements are short term and the effect of temperature variation is usually insignificant.

6.6 Wheatstone bridge

The highly sensitive Wheatstone bridge is used to detect changes in strain gauge resistance. An outline of a simple direct current strain instrument and gauges is shown in Fig. 6.7. It consists of a galvanometer, four resistors

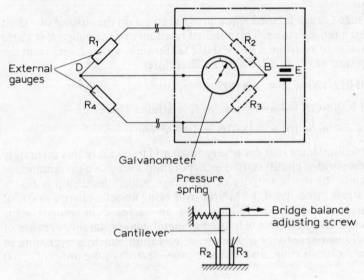

Fig. 6.7 Simple strain gauge instrument

(R_1, R_2, R_3, R_4) and a battery. Resistance R_1 is the gauge used for strain measurement. Resistance R_4 is a second strain gauge which for the present purpose is assumed to remain at constant resistance. Resistances R_2 and R_3 are variable resistors which by adjustment are used to balance and rebalance the bridge, i.e. to reduce the current across the galvanometer arm to zero. When the bridge is balanced the ratio of the gauges and variable resistances are equal; thus

$$\frac{R_1}{R_4} = \frac{R_2}{R_3} \quad \text{i.e.} \quad R_1 = R_4 \times \frac{R_2}{R_3}$$

An important characteristic of the Wheatstone bridge is that its output voltage is a non-linear function of resistance change in the bridge; thus the above ratio is strictly true only when the bridge is balanced, i.e. when the voltages at D and B are equal and the current through the galvanometer arm is zero. However, provided that the resistance change in the bridge is small the change in bridge output voltage is virtually linear, e.g. for a resistance change of 1% the departure from linearity will be of the order of 0·005% of this change.

Two methods are available for static strain measurement: continuous reading from one change of strain to another without rebalancing, which is convenient but less accurate as the bridge output tends to non-linearity if the strain is successively increasing or decreasing; or the null balance method, in which, after each successive change in strain, the bridge is rebalanced. As the strain indicator will be calibrated under null balance conditions this method offers the highest accuracy while also maintaining linear bridge output.

The strain indicator is calibrated for gauges of a given gauge factor; thus it provides accurate readings only when gauges having the same gauge factor are used. Most instruments incorporate a variable resistor which allows the strain indicator to be matched to gauges having somewhat different gauge factors; however, in the event that no such adjustment exists or that the gauge factor required is beyond the range of the adjustment, the strain can be computed if the indicated strain is multiplied by the ratio of the instrument gauge factor value to the gauge factor of the gauges in use. For example, if the instrument gauge factor value is 2 and the strain gauge factor is 3·5, then

$$\text{true strain} = \text{indicated strain} \times \frac{2}{3\cdot 5}$$

Overall measuring accuracy

Overall measuring accuracy must be apportioned between the strain gauges and the instrumentation. It will depend on the gauge factor tolerance, temperature coefficient of resistance, gauge resistance tolerance, bonding quality, number of gauges used and how well they are matched, etc. The total error (gauges plus instrumentation) should be within ±5% for static or very slowly changing strains.

6.7 Simple strain gauge applications

It is usual to incorporate more than one strain gauge in the bridge for the following reasons:

(a) To increase output for a given strain, thus increasing sensitivity;
(b) To provide temperature compensation;
(c) To eliminate unwanted effects, e.g. a rod subjected to a tensile force will almost certainly suffer some bending; thus if the strain due only to tension is required the gauges must be so arranged on the rod and in the bridge that the bridge output corresponds to strain produced by tension alone.

Wheatstone bridge rules

The following rules offer a useful guide to the effects of the positions of the gauges in the bridge arms:

(1) Bridge unbalance increases in proportion to the *algebraic difference* of changes of resistance in two adjacent arms.
(2) Bridge unbalance increases in proportion to the *algebraic sum* of changes of resistance in two opposite arms.

Fig. 6.8 illustrates that there are four pairs of adjacent arms (R_1, R_2; R_2, R_3; etc.) and two pairs of opposite arms.

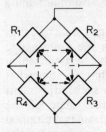

Fig. 6.8 Bridge arm relationships

Bridge rule 1
A simple cantilever beam is under pure bending stress and loaded, as shown in Fig. 6.9. Two active gauges, each of nominal resistance R ohms, are applied as near to the position of maximum bending moment as

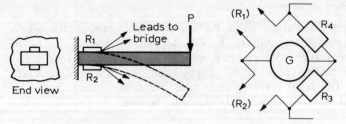

Fig. 6.9 Gauges applied to a simple cantilever

possible and with the gauge longitudinal axis parallel to that of the cantilever. The gauge on the upper surface of the beam is subjected to tensile strain, the lower gauge to an equal compressive strain; thus the resistance changes in each case (δR) are virtually equal, δR being positive in tension and negative in compression. Applying rule 1,

$$(\delta R_1) - (-\delta R_2) = 2\delta R \qquad (6.1)$$

where $\delta R_1 = \delta R_2$. Thus the bridge output is doubled. Further consideration indicates that temperature compensation is also achieved in this case.

The electrical resistivity of the gauge and the material to which the gauge is bonded changes with change of temperature. This effect is independent of any strain applied to the gauge and if left uncompensated will totally swamp mechanical strain readings. In addition, unless the coefficient of linear expansion of the gauge is the same as that of the material to which it is bonded, then temperature change during measurement will also be a source of false strain readings due to differential expansion. The temperature coefficient of resistance of advance alloy is much smaller than that of many other alloys (see Section 6.5), but for static strain measurement temperature compensation is always applied whenever possible as this improves accuracy. Gauges R_1 and R_2 (Fig. 6.9) are close together and any temperature change occurring should apply equally to both. This being the case, any change of resistance due to temperature change will be equal and of the same sign for both gauges. Applying rule 1,

$$(\delta R_1 \pm \delta R_t) - (-\delta R_2 \pm \delta R_t) = 2\delta R \pm \delta R_t \mp \delta R_t = 2\delta R + 0$$
$$(6.2)$$

where $\pm \delta R_t$ is the resistance change due to temperature. Thus temperature compensation is achieved. The above result can of course be obtained using the arms R_1, R_4; R_2, R_3; etc.

Bridge rule 2
A rod is subjected to a tensile load as shown in Fig. 6.10 but is also subject to some bending owing to difficulties in applying a purely tensile load.

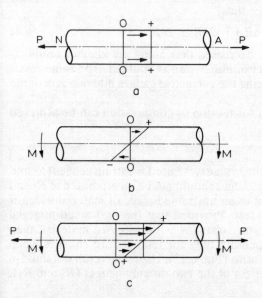

Fig. 6.10 (a) Strain distribution in pure tension
(b) Strain distribution in pure bending
(c) Strain distribution in combined tension and bending

Pure tensile strain is uniform across the rod cross-section as shown in Fig. 6.10(a), while the effect of bending is to produce maximum strains at the surfaces of the rod which are equal and opposite, i.e. tensile and compressive [Fig. 6.10(b)]. The combined effect [Fig. 6.10(c)] indicates an increase in tensile strain on the 'humped' or convex side of the rod and an equal and opposite decrease in tensile strain on the concave side. Two active gauges are bonded to the rod under tension as shown in Fig. 6.11.

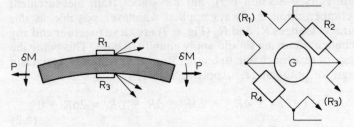

Fig. 6.11 Active gauges for simple direct stress

Applying rule 2,

$$(\delta R_1 + \delta R_B) + (\delta R_3 - \delta R_B) = 2\delta R + 0 \tag{6.3}$$

where $\delta R_1 = \delta R_3$ is the resistance change due to tensile strain and δR_B is the resistance change due to bending strain.

Consideration of temperature change reveals that there is no temperature compensation in this case; thus

$$(\delta R_1 \pm \delta R_t) + (\delta R_3 \pm \delta R_t) = 2\delta R \pm 2\delta R_t \tag{6.4}$$

Bridge output is increased or decreased depending on whether temperature rises or falls and its effect in either case is doubled. The same result would be obtained by introducing the two active gauges into one arm of the bridge.

Temperature compensation for tension or compression can be achieved by means of 'dummy' gauges.

Dummy gauges
In Fig. 6.11 only two arms of the bridge were used for strain gauges (R_1 and R_3) but there is no reason why gauges should not be incorporated at R_2 and R_4. Strain gauges are attached to an unstrained piece of material which is similar to the material under test. Provided that the unstrained material experiences the same temperature changes as the strained material, then the dummy gauges will compensate only for temperature changes when introduced to adjacent bridge arms (Fig. 6.12). Using the result obtained in Eq. 6.4 and subtracting the effect of the two dummy gauges (R_2 and R_4), by rule 1,

$$(2\delta R \pm 2\delta R_t) - (\pm\delta R_t \pm \delta R_t) = 2\delta R + 0$$

Thus temperature compensation is achieved.

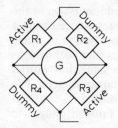

Fig. 6.12 Dummy gauges for temperature compensation

Poisson method

The dummy gauge is bonded at right angles to the active gauge on a member in simple tension (Fig. 6.13). Gauge R_2 is reduced in length

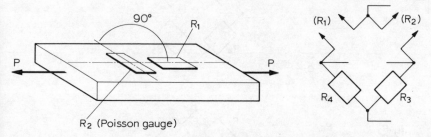

Fig. 6.13 Poisson method for temperature compensation

depending on Poisson's ratio for the material, approximately 0·3 for steel; thus

$$(\delta R_1 \pm \delta R_t \pm \delta R_B) - (-0.3\delta R_2 \pm \delta R_t) = 1.3\delta R \pm \delta R_B \qquad (6.5)$$

This arrangement provides increased sensitivity and full temperature compensation but no compensation for bending, and is used when it is not convenient or possible to apply gauges in corresponding positions to the underside of the member. It is also necessary to find the precise output ratio by applying known loads to the member. A further increase in sensitivity and compensation for both bending and temperature can be achieved by applying gauges to both sides of the member and in the same relative positions, R_3 becoming the active gauge on the underside.

Separate measurement of combined forces and bending moments

Further consideration of the simple cantilever suggests that gauges may be so arranged in the bridge that they provide an output from forces applied in one direction but not in another. The cantilever shown at Fig. 6.14(a) is subjected to both an axial and a bending load. With the bridge arrangement shown the gauges provide an output only from the axial load. Gauges R_1 and R_3 are in opposite bridge arms; thus any resistance changes are additive, but such changes, if they are of equal magnitude, must be of the same sign to provide an output. When P_B is applied the resistance changes are of equal but opposite sign; thus output from the bridge is zero. Consideration of the effect of the axial force P_A indicates that both gauges are subjected to equal resistance changes of the same sign; thus output from the bridge is proportional to the sum of these resistance changes. The same result is obtained for any combination of directions of P_A and P_B. Gauges R_2 and R_4 are mounted either as dummy or Poisson gauges to provide temperature compensation.

An arrangement which provides an output from P_B only is shown in Fig. 6.14(b). Gauges R_1 and R_3 are in opposite arms and are of the same sign,

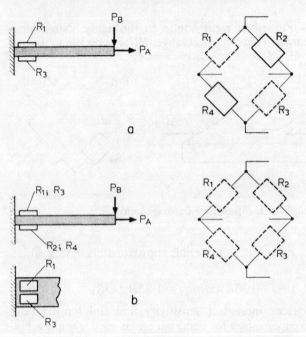

a

b

Fig. 6.14 Separate measurement of combined direct and bending strains

and likewise R_2 and R_4; thus their output is proportional to the sum of their resistances. When the axial force P_A is considered all gauge resistance changes are of the same sign and by their bridge positions mutually cancel each other. Temperature change has the same effect on the gauges as axial force; thus the system is fully temperature compensated.

Measurement of both bending and axial forces can be obtained through a combination of the systems previously described. Two separate bridges are required and gauges R_2 and R_4 are used as dummy or Poisson as before.

A further development of this approach is the use of a cantilever cylinder which senses bending strains in two mutually perpendicular directions (Fig. 6.15). If the effect of the horizontal applied force P_H is considered it is clear that gauges R_H will respond to bending in the horizontal plane, i.e., R_{1H} and R_{2H} are in adjacent arms and as their signs are opposite they are additive, and similarly so are R_{3H} and R_{4H}. Direct tensile or compressive effects P_A resulting from the applied force P_H are eliminated using this arrangement.

A consideration of the effect of the vertical applied force P_V produces a similar result, i.e. P_B. The system is also fully temperature compensated and output is augmented.

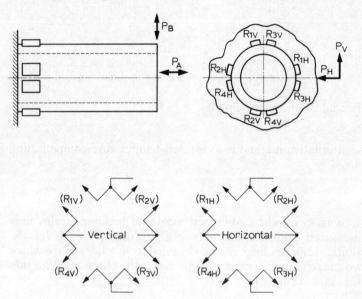

Fig. 6.15 Measurement of bending strains in two mutually perpendicular directions

An arrangement for measuring torsional strain using four gauges is shown in Fig. 6.16. The maximum tensile and compressive strains (the principal strains) occur at angles of 45° to the shaft axis, and to obtain maximum output from the gauges they should be applied at this angle. This arrangement provides four times the sensitivity of a single gauge with full temperature compensation and eliminates bending and axial tensile or compressive effects.

When the static or steady strain on a rotating body is non-torsional, then the problem of temperature compensation arises because of the difficulty in placing the temperature compensating gauge in a position where it will not be affected by centrifugal forces. If a dummy gauge is used then it is attached to a separate piece of metal and mounted in such a position as to be subject to zero centrifugal force, i.e. at the centre of rotation. When this is not possible then the effect of centrifugal force on the gauge must be evaluated. Using this technique the dummy gauge may be displaced at a distance from the active gauges and thus full temperature compensation is

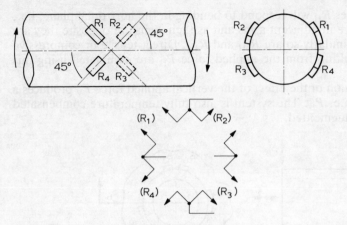

Fig. 6.16 Torsional strain measurement

unlikely. The alternative method is to use self-temperature-compensating strain gauges.

Flexagauges

There are circumstances when combined axial and bending strains may need to be measured from one side only, e.g. enclosed pressure vessels. Two proportional strain readings can be obtained from a flexagauge which consists of two gauge filaments mounted one above the other on either side of a plastic separator (Fig. 6.17).

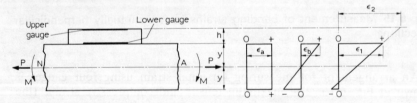

Fig. 6.17 Flexagauge for measurement of combined axial and bending strains

Evidently the upper gauge sustains greater strain than the lower gauge under bending and this strain is proportional to the height h of the gauge above the surface. Thus, by similar triangles,

$$\frac{\varepsilon_b}{h} = \frac{(\varepsilon_2 - \varepsilon_1)}{y}$$

Therefore

$$\varepsilon_b = \frac{h}{y}(\varepsilon_2 - \varepsilon_1) \quad \text{and} \quad \varepsilon_a = \varepsilon_1 - \varepsilon_b$$

Therefore

$$\varepsilon_a = \varepsilon_1 - \frac{h}{y}(\varepsilon_2 - \varepsilon_1)$$

where ε_a is the axial strain, ε_b the bending strain at the surface, ε_1 the indicated strain from the lower gauge, ε_2 the indicated strain from the upper gauge, y is half the material thickness and h is the thickness of the flexagauge.

6.8 Self-temperature-compensated strain gauges

A completely self-compensated gauge should exhibit zero change of resistance with change of temperature when bonded to a specified material. Consider a conventional advance gauge bonded to a steel base. The coefficient of linear expansion of this alloy is $15\,\mu\text{m}\,^\circ\text{C/m}$, while the

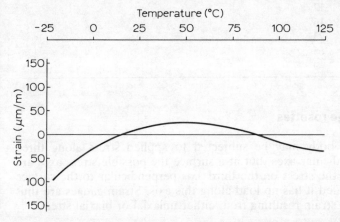

Fig. 6.18 Error curve for a temperature compensated strain gauge

coefficient of steel is $12\,\mu\text{m}\,^\circ\text{C/m}$; thus under rising temperature the free expansion of the gauge is prevented and as a result the gauge is in compression and $\delta R/R$ from this source is negative. Conversely, the thermal coefficient of resistance of the gauge itself is positive; thus $\delta R/R$ from this source is positive. If these resistance changes are equal and opposite then change of resistance due to temperature is zero from these sources. It is of interest to note that a similar gauge bonded to aluminium, coefficient $23\,\mu\text{m}\,^\circ\text{C/m}$, would be in tension. The most widely used self-compensated gauges are made from specially prepared 'selected melt' alloys for use on specified materials.

The temperature coefficient of resistance of the gauge is, by suitable heat treatment during manufacture, matched to the coefficient of linear expansion of the material on which it is to be used. For physical reasons such matching can only be ensured over a limited range of temperature and to overcome this limitation the manufacturers calibrate selected gauges from each batch produced and supply an apparent strain/temperature graph for use with the gauges.

For the error curve illustrated in Fig. 6.18, if strain measurement is carried out at 50 °C then the gauge error at that temperature is approximately $30\,\mu m/m$. If the apparent strain is $75\,\mu m/m$ then the actual strain is $75-30 = 45\,\mu m/m$.

Table 6.2 gives some of the materials for which self-temperature-compensated gauges may be purchased. Another type is made by connecting two different wires in series to form the grid, one having a positive and the other a negative gauge factor. Increase in resistance in one wire due to temperature is almost equally compensated by a similar decrease in the other. Such gauges must still be matched for use on specified materials.

Table 6.2 Materials used for self-compensated gauges

Material	Coefficient of linear expansion $(\mu m\,°C/m)$
Steel	12
Austenitic steel	16
Aluminium	23
Plastic	65
Titanium	9

6.9 Strain gauge rosettes

Any point in a body may be subjected to applied stress along three mutually perpendicular axes, but at a surface the possible stress axes are reduced to two, the stress on the third axis perpendicular to the surface being zero provided it has no load along this axis. Strain gauges are thus used to measure strain resulting from either uniaxial or biaxial stress.

Uniaxial stress

Hooke's Law is valid only along the line of action of a uniaxial applied stress and within the elastic limit. In all directions other than the line of action the law does not apply because of the Poisson effect. Induced stress is zero along planes perpendicular to the applied stress, although Poisson strain is present.

Biaxial stress

Hooke's Law is not valid in any direction on a surface subjected to biaxial stress because Poisson strain occurs in all directions. In such a system the maximum and minimum direct stress values are always mutually perpendicular to each other and are called the maximum and minimum *principal stresses*; the planes on which they act are called the principal planes, and the strains on the principal planes are called the *principal strains*. Shear stresses and strains on principal planes are zero. When biaxial stresses are present the direction of the principal stresses may be either known or unknown. To take the simplest case, where the principal stress and thus the principal strain directions are known the equations for stress along the mutually perpendicular axes x and y are

$$\sigma_x = \frac{E}{1 - v^2} (\varepsilon_x + v\varepsilon_y)$$

$$\sigma_y = \frac{E}{1 - v^2} (\varepsilon_y + v\varepsilon_x)$$

where σ_x and σ_y are the principal stresses, v is Poisson's ratio, E is Young's modulus and ε_x and ε_y are the principal strains. Clearly both principal strains must be known to determine either one or both of the principal stresses. The simplest rosette must thus consist of two mutually perpendicular gauges which must be accurately positioned in the principal stress directions. The direction of the principal stresses may be determined by the brittle lacquer of 'stress-coat' technique in which the surface under test is coated with a special lacquer which exhibits a large number of fine cracks when the body to which it is applied is subjected to a given level of stress. The crack pattern which emerges is analogous to the strain field at the surface and from examination the principal strain directions may be determined. A further refinement of the technique involving the use of a separate calibrating strip provides a rough approximation to within ±20% of the maximum principal stress value.

When the directions of the principal stresses are unknown or not known with sufficient certainty it is necessary to use three strain gauges, which will provide sufficient strain information for the principal strains and hence the principal stresses to be determined, or again to utilize the brittle lacquer technique. The gauges are arranged to form a convenient pattern and to confine the strain measurements to the smallest possible area, as ideally measurement at a point on the surface is required at which strain values are constant. Point measurement is impossible but a closer approximation is achieved by using short rather than long gauges where strain gradients in the plane of the gauges are likely to exist. Although any angles between the gauges may be used, in practice the simplest solutions and smallest errors are obtained by using the largest possible angles, and commercial gauges are manufactured with these factors in mind. The basic arrangements of the main types of commercial gauge are shown in Fig. 6.19.

An overlapped two gauge rosette suitable for applications where the principal strain directions are accurately known is shown in Fig. 6.19(a). Overlapping reduces the area covered by the gauges to a minimum. Gauges constructed in this manner are not suitable for use on members subject to severe bending or torsion and having a neutral axis close to the surface, e.g. thin sheet material, as the stress gradient from the neutral axis of the material to the surface is very high and thus the strain on the upper gauge is significantly greater than the strain on the lower gauge. Foil gauges, which are very much thinner than wire gauges, suffer less from this error source but single plane configurations offer the easiest solution.

Two rectangular rosettes are shown in Fig. 6.19(b) and a delta rosette is shown in Fig. 6.19(c). These are particularly useful when the directions of the principal stresses are in doubt. The tee–delta rosette shown in Fig. 6.19(d) incorporates one overlapping gauge which is used as a check on the results obtained from the other three gauges.

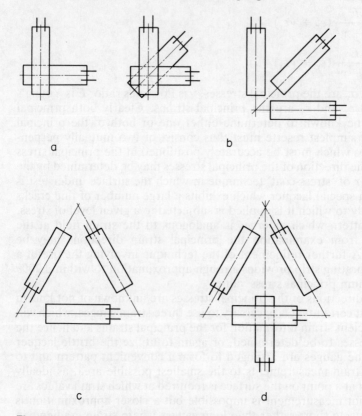

Fig. 6.19 Basic arrangements of the main types of gauge
(a) Two gauge rosette (90°) (b) Rectangular rosettes (45°)
(c) Delta rosette (d) Tee–delta rosette

6.10 Lead connections

The lead wires connecting the gauge to the bridge should have a low resistance compared with the gauge so that temperature variations cause only small resistance changes; they should be flexible and insulated to suit operating conditions. Plastic-coated wire is suitable for normal temperature operation but other insulators such as fibreglass, ceramics, etc., are used for higher temperatures. Leads from conventional gauges offer no temperature compensation problems provided that they are at the same temperature as each other. However, lead compensation is required when using a single self-compensated gauge and this may be achieved by the three lead system shown in Fig. 6.20. Temperature change in the battery lead L_3 does not affect bridge balance.

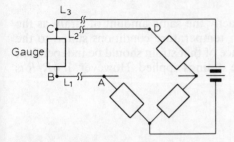

Fig. 6.20 Strain gauge lead wire compensation

Gauge leads L_1 (AB) and L_2 (CD) are in adjacent bridge arms by this arrangement and similar resistance changes in both leads will be cancelled. Normally, commercial instruments have at least two external bridge arms and to complete the bridge the second arm should incorporate a dummy gauge maintained at constant temperature so that only changes at the active gauge affect bridge output.

6.11 Sources of error in strain gauge installations

The following factors will affect the accuracy of strain observations.

Temperature change

Perfect temperature compensation is unlikely to be achieved for the following reasons. No two gauges have identical electrical resistances, coefficients of expansion or gauge factors, although selection from the same batch reduces the effect of these differences to very small proportions. Apart from these considerations the gauges should be protected from draughts and incidental temperature changes which might affect one gauge and not another. Quite small temperature gradients across the test body can cause significant false strain readings. The effect of a small temperature change is illustrated by the following example.

A 120Ω gauge, gauge factor 2 and temperature coefficient $12\,\mu\Omega\,°C/\Omega$ is subjected to a temperature rise of $5\,°C$.

$$\delta R = (120 \times 12 \times 10^{-6} \times 5)\ \Omega$$

The apparent strain is given by

$$\varepsilon_a = \frac{\delta R}{RK} = \frac{120 \times 12 \times 5}{120 \times 2 \times 10^6} = 30\,\mu\text{m/m or 30 microstrain}$$

A stress of approximately $6\,\text{MN/m}^2$ would produce this strain on steel.

The above remarks apply equally to the internal arms of the bridge, and also to the leads.

Hysteresis

The strain gauge should sustain exactly the same amount of strain as the surface to which it is bonded under temperature conditions suited to the bonding cement, and the maintenance of that strain should be independent of the length of time over which the strain is applied. However, if $\delta R/R$ is

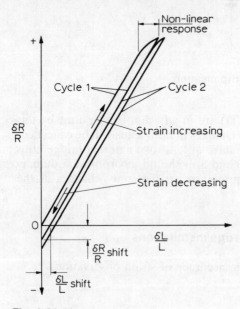

Fig. 6.21 Hysteresis loops

plotted against $\delta L/L$ to a high strain level a small measure of non-linearity may develop and on relieving strain to zero a hysteresis loop is formed. Normally, repeated cycles will form further, though rapidly narrowing loops (Fig. 6.21). It is usual to cycle the gauges a number of times before use to a higher strain level than actually required to eliminate this effect. Severe hysteresis arises from faulty bonding and will not be eliminated by cycling.

Creep

Both the backing cement in which the gauge filament is embedded and the bonding cement holding the gauge in position must be much stronger than the filament itself if strain is exactly to be transmitted to the gauge. If this is not the case then the gauge filament relaxes under strain and strain indication is less than true strain, becoming increasingly non-linear as strain increases. Creep arises from a number of sources:

(1) Faulty bonding either at the gauge–surface interface or within the gauge itself, i.e. the backing into which the filament is embedded.
(2) Operating temperature increase which softens the plastic bonds thus allowing the filament to relax. This effect largely provides the temperature limitation at which the gauge can satisfactorily operate. Paper-base cold setting cement gauges operate satisfactorily up to 50 °C and creep is of the order of 0·5% of the total strain in 24 hours. Thermosetting base gauges and cements exhibit little creep (0·05%) up to 50 °C and about 0·5% up to 100 °C. Operations above these temperatures are usually of short duration and require special precautions.
(3) Unlike hysteresis, creep is time dependent and sufficient time must be allowed for creep to become evident when the gauges are initially installed. Static strain tests are more likely to be affected by creep than dynamic tests which are usually of short duration.
(4) Smaller gauges more easily develop significant creep than large gauges because of their smaller bonding area; thus preference should be given to larger gauges wherever possible.

Fatigue

This usually occurs in dynamic strain installations resulting from stress reversals at the point where the connecting leads are attached to the gauge. In all cases leads should be well secured to prevent relative motion between the gauge and the leads. Fatigue can also cause decay in the gauge base or fixing cement leading to filament relaxation.

Humidity and moisture

Moisture absorption by the gauge backing or fixing cement causes volume changes which may extend or compress the grid. Thus gauges should be applied in dry conditions and any danger of moisture absorption due to changes of humidity should be guarded against by the application of moisture-resistant compounds such as silicone wax, bitumen or other compounds or by means of rubber covers, metal cans, etc. Precise details of waterproofing techniques for both gauges and lead connections are supplied by manufacturers. Another aspect of moisture absorption is that it can lead to a sharp fall in the impedance of the gauge to ground which should normally be at least $100\,M\Omega$ and preferably $1000\,M\Omega$. The reason for this is that the gauge is electrically in parallel with the backing and fixing cement and if these become conductors by developing low resistance then the effective gauge resistance is reduced.

6.12 Semiconductor or piezoresistive strain gauges

Semiconductor gauges are cut from single crystals of silicon or germanium in which are combined exact amounts of special impurities such as boron which impart certain desirable characteristics. Such crystals are known as 'doped' crystals.

The essential advantage of semiconductor gauges is their high strain sensitivity which allows very small strains to be measured accurately and, whereas wire and foil gauges have gauge factors of the order of 2, the gauge factors of most semiconductor gauges lie in the range 100 to 200. The change of electrical resistance of semiconductors may be either positive or negative, i.e. a gauge whose electrical resistance increases in response to tensile strain is known as a positive or p-type gauge and one whose resistance decreases in response to tensile strain is known as a negative or n-type gauge.

The gauge consists of a single rectangular filament about 0·05 mm thick by 0·25 mm wide and gauge lengths range from 1·5 to 12 mm. They are made as thin as possible as the breaking stress of the material rises as the cross-sectional area decreases and also the gauge can be bent to a much smaller radius of curvature without fracture. The element may be bonded to a plastic or stainless steel backing which can be welded in position or it may be unbonded in which case extra care must be taken in handling.

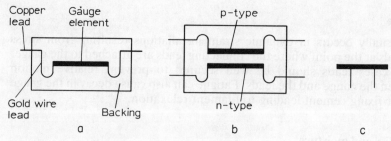

Fig. 6.22 Semiconductor strain gauges

In Fig. 6.22(a) a single filament gauge is shown with leads on either side. A number of lead configurations are available to suit requirements. In Fig. 6.22(b) a pair of filaments, one p and one n, is shown. This type provides temperature compensation because both have positive temperature coefficients of resistance. Backed gauges are bonded to surfaces by the same methods as wire and foil gauges with the precaution that because of the extreme brittleness of the filaments they should not be squeezed in any way. Unbacked gauges as shown in Fig. 6.22(c) are available but are not in wide use.

Lightly doped gauges have very high sensitivity, i.e. high gauge factors and also high electrical resistance of the order of 200 Ω, although gauges having resistances of 1000 Ω or even 10 000 Ω are available. Heavily doped gauges having lower electrical resistance also have lower gauge factors of the order of 50. At constant room temperature the change of resistance as a ratio of the unstrained resistance is very closely parabolic, i.e. the output is distinctly non-linear and a lightly doped p-type silicon gauge might have a relative resistance-change/strain curve as shown in Fig. 6.23(a).

The slope of the curve at any point is the gauge factor and it is evident that quite small strains, either tensile or compressive, bring about a change in gauge factor. It will be noticed that the two legs of the curve become more nearly linear as they increase in length and in fact heavily doped materials provide curves in which the gauge factor is virtually constant at constant temperature about the zero point [Fig. 6.23(b)].

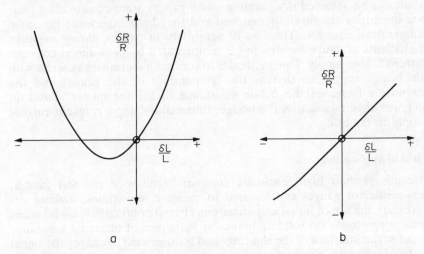

Fig. 6.23 Output characteristics of a p-type semiconductor strain gauge

Temperature changes cause considerable resistance and sensitivity changes in semiconductor gauges. Again, heavily doped gauges are much less affected in this respect; for example, a normal commercial p-type silicon gauge having a gauge factor of 120 could suffer a gauge factor variation of about −20 for a temperature rise of 100 °C, whereas a heavily doped p-type silicon gauge of 50 gauge factor would show virtually no change of factor for a similar rise in temperature.

Temperature compensation

If semiconductor gauges are to provide accurate results temperature compensation is essential. This can be achieved by the use of self-compensating gauges or by circuit arrangements which provide compensation in a similar manner to that used for wire and foil gauges, and in addition p and n combinations, thermistors, etc., may also be used.

The temperature coefficient of resistance of both n- and p-type gauges is positive but the gauge factor of n-type gauges is negative. Thus the positive temperature coefficient and the negative gauge factor can be balanced against each other, and these in turn against the non-linear characteristics of the Wheatstone bridge at high resistance variations, to provide temperature compensation within a limited temperature range. There are numerous circuit arrangements which can be used to provide near-linear outputs from semiconductor strain gauges. Where circumstances permit, similar gauges, one in compression and one in tension, can form two adjacent arms of the bridge; this is called 'push–pull' operation. In such circumstances the gauge non-linearities are in opposition and largely tend to cancel each other. Similarly, p- and n-type pairs such as those shown in Fig. 6.22(b) may be used, and in this case both gauges experience the same stress condition and are connected into adjacent bridge arms. A similar result can be obtained if separate p and n gauges are used providing their non-linearities are carefully matched and they both experience the same temperature changes. The loss of sensitivity in gauges having negative coefficients of gauge factor can be compensated by providing a constant current bridge supply. One method is to connect a thermistor in series with the bridge supply so that as the temperature of the gauges and the thermistor increases the fall in resistance of the thermistor allows an increase in voltage across the bridge, thus maintaining a constant current supply to the bridge.

Field of application

Because of their high sensitivity compared with wire and foil gauges, semiconductor gauges can be used to measure low strains, making unnecessary the use of signal amplification. They are particularly useful when measuring strains on rotating bodies as variations of electrical resistance occur at the interface of the slip rings and brushes used to convey the signal to the stationary strain measuring instruments. Such variations impose unwanted signals on the output which may be a considerable proportion of the total output when wire and foil gauges are used, thus making it difficult to identify the signal arising from strain.

6.13 Slip (collector) rings and conducting brushes

When strain gauges are attached to a moving body such as a rotating shaft or a turbine blade the gauge resistance changes must be conveyed to the stationary measuring system by an intermediate mechanism. This mechanism consists of rotating slip rings and stationary brushes. The leads from the gauges, which must be held in position very securely, are led to the centre of rotation and then soldered to rings incorporated in the rotating mechanism or to a separate shaft attached to the mechanism which carries the rings. A spring loaded stationary conducting brush or brushes in permanent contact with the rotating ring carries the current to the measuring system (Fig. 6.24).

The main problem to be overcome with this method is variation of electrical resistance at the interfaces of the rings and brushes. The change of resistance of an average strain gauge subjected to a strain equivalent of $7\,MN/m^2$ stress on steel is about $0 \cdot 01\,\Omega$ but the contact resistance variation or 'noise' may easily be equal to this amount on balance of all the rings and brushes in use, and if they were connected in series to the gauges the strain signal might be completely submerged in contact resistance variations. A combination of the following three methods is used largely to reduce if not completely to eliminate this effect.

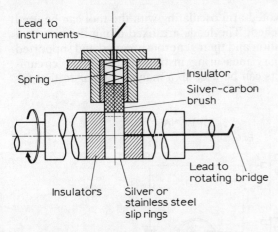

Lead to instruments

Spring

Insulator

Silver-carbon brush

Insulators

Silver or stainless steel slip rings

Lead to rotating bridge

Fig. 6.24 Slip ring and conducting brush

(*a*) The circuit is arranged so that the rings and brushes are connected in parallel with the gauge (Fig. 6.25).

(*b*) High resistance gauges are used to obtain a proportionately higher resistance change for a given strain (the qualities of semiconductor gauges are of value in this respect).

(*c*) Brush pressures and ring and brush materials are chosen to afford the best operating conditions. For general use silver, silver plated or stainless steel rings and silver–graphite brushes at pressures between 140 and 210 kN/m² are widely used.

The system shown in Fig. 6.25 can be used for null balance operation as a large balancing resistor R_B is incorporated in the circuit. Performance at high speed can be improved by incorporating two or more brushes in parallel on each ring, each having springs of a different spring rate so that the effect of resonances or other vibration sources will not cause all the brushes to lift from the ring at the same time. When not in use the brushes may be lifted from the rings.

Slip rings and strain gauge leads may also be brush painted on to surfaces using special silver paint. This is rather similar to the printed circuit technique and careful insulation with insulating paints is essential. This method may be useful when normal rings and brushes are difficult to apply. In all cases slip rings must have a very high quality surface finish and concentricity of rotation is essential, the latter being extremely important for high speed operation (10 000 to 20 000 r/min).

Circuits other than that illustrated in Fig. 6.25 are used when one or two strain gauges only can be applied to the moving part, but the method of signal transfer to the stationary measuring instrument remains the same.

An essential requirement when measuring strain on moving parts is to avoid fatigue conditions at the leads. Normally this presents little difficulty on rotating parts but when linear or oscillating motion is involved, as is often the case in machine tools, e.g. strain gauges attached to the tool on a shaping machine, then a pivoted arm oscillating with the tool can be used to which the leads are attached. The leads are fixed along the arm to a point near the centre of rotation and then generously coiled and supported before entering the stationary measuring instrument. In other circumstances linear sliding contacts can be used in a manner similar to that for rotational motion.

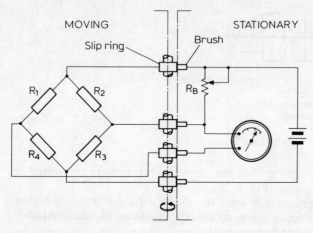

Fig. 6.25 Strain measurement on rotating elements

Frequency modulated telemetry

Suitable radio or television equipment is installed on the moving part and broadcasts the strain signals to a remote receiver. Each bridge voltage output modulates the frequency of a voltage controlled oscillator. The output signals from the oscillators are mixed for transmission and on reception are electronically filtered into their individual strain signals. This technique is becoming widely used.

6.14 Plastic strain

Most strain measurements are made within the elastic limit of metals but there are occasions when measurement well into the plastic range of a material, and even to rupture, is required. Resistance strain gauges, if they are of reasonable length, measure strain well beyond the elastic limit for all metals, recording strains up to $40\,000\,\mu\text{m/m}$ without serious error, but strains for very ductile metals can be as high as 25%, i.e. $250\,000\,\mu\text{m/m}$, and for such purposes special gauges may be used. Such post-yield gauges have the following characteristics and operating requirements:

(i) Highly ductile wire or foil
(ii) A plastic gauge factor equal to the elastic gauge factor
(iii) A fixing cement which prevents slip and is of sufficient ductility to resist cracking and rupture

(iv) A backing material, usually 0·025 mm thick nylon, which resists cracking or rupture at high strains.

Gauges fulfilling these requirements are commercially available to measure strains up to 150 000 μm/m.

The two following methods avoid the use of special gauges for measuring plastic strain by attenuating the strain on the gauge so that its output is less but proportional to the strain on the member.

The clip gauge
This consists of a spring steel bridge which is fixed to the body under test [Fig. 6.26(a)].

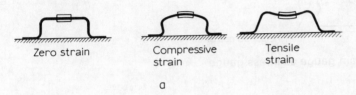

Zero strain   Compressive   Tensile
                strain   strain

a

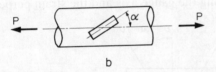

b

Fig. 6.26 Clip gauge, showing at (b) the method for attenuating gauge output

(a) Gauges are cemented to the upper and lower sides of the bridge and under strain the legs deflect much more than the bridge. Output from the gauges can be varied by varying the dimensions of the clip. Initial calibration is required.

(b) The second method is most easily appreciated by reference to a uniaxial stress field. In this case the maximum strain occurs along the axis of maximum stress; consequently, a gauge attached to the member at some convenient angle to the maximum strain axis will be subject to output attenuation proportional to the true strain [Fig. 6.26(b)]. A similar technique can be used on a biaxial stress field when the positions of the principal axes are known.

6.15 Miscellaneous applications

Stress measurement

The attenuation technique can be used to modify the output of a gauge so that it is proportional to stress rather than strain for the measurement of principal stresses.

Because both principal strains must be known to determine either one or both principal stresses the angle to the chosen principal plane to which the gauge is set must be such that the gauge is affected in correct proportion by both principal strains (Fig. 6.27). It can be shown that the angle required is dependent only on Poisson's ratio for the material, as in the case of principal stress shear stress is zero; thus

$$\tan \theta = \sqrt{v} \quad \text{or} \quad \theta = \tan^{-1}\sqrt{v}$$

where v is Poisson's ratio.

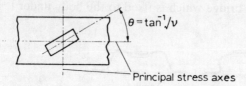

Fig. 6.27 Strain gauge as stress gauge

Stress gauges

These gauges also provide an output proportional to stress. Their grids are arranged so that they respond to the two orthogonal strains associated with the stress, i.e. the strain along the gauge axis and the strain perpendicular

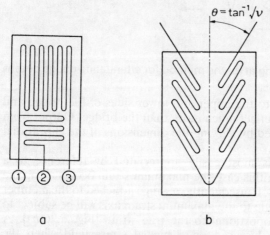

Fig. 6.28 Commercial stress gauges

to that axis. Two types are available, one having two mutually perpendicular grids whose lengths are proportional to Poisson's ratio [Fig. 6.28(a)], and are suited only to materials having the same ratio. These gauges can be used to measure stress along any axis including the principal stress axis by using leads (2) and (3) but in fact are unnecessary for that application as the attenuation technique applied to a normal gauge is completely satisfactory. The gauge becomes a normal strain gauge when leads (1) and (3) are used. The second type has a vee-shaped grid. Each arm of the vee is affected by shear strain, one arm being in compression and the other in tension due to shear; thus the effect of shear strain is eliminated. The angle θ of each arm of the gauge to the stress axis is equal to $\tan^{-1}\sqrt{\nu}$ as before [Fig. 6.28(b)].

Weldable gauges

These gauges are bonded on to a thin (0·125 mm) stainless steel shim which can then be welded in position. They are used for high temperature strain measurement where it is essential that the quality of the bond to the tested surface should be of the highest order. Such gauges may be used up to 400 °C. Gauges for dynamic measurement up to 800 °C are encapsulated in a stainless steel tube which is mounted on the shim.

Non-linear materials

Many alloys, e.g. cast iron, do not have linear stress–strain characteristics and it is necessary to investigate their properties in this regard by mechanical testing so as to determine the probable response of a gauge bonded to the surface. The necessary information must include a close approximation to the direct stress–strain relationship and also Poisson's ratio.

Gauges can be applied to non-metallic materials such as glass, plastics, ceramics, wood, concrete, etc., and in each case the behaviour of the material under stress must be investigated. Such considerations as surface finish and characteristics, e.g. porosity, must be assessed and environmental effects must also be investigated, e.g. moisture absorption by wood. A knowledge of the effect of adhesive cements must be obtained if gauges are to be applied to plastics as some of these may dissolve the surface.

6.16 Zero drift in strain instruments

Wheatstone bridge

Under d.c. operation bridge balance is virtually independent of the supply voltage but this condition is true only if the internal arms of the bridge are subjected to the same temperature conditions and have the same thermal coefficients as the gauges themselves.

Instrument instability

Some battery-operated instruments incorporate an audio frequency oscillator, a rectifier and an amplifier, and these provide a source for zero drift if the battery is allowed to decay as their performance depends on a stable battery voltage.

Zero drift increases in importance with time; thus short time readings will be little affected. Where the time between readings is long (weeks, months), then it is essential either to eliminate the effect of drift at each reading by returning the tested structure to zero strain and rebalancing the bridge if necessary, or, if this is not possible, to detect it and thence correct the apparent strain readings to obtain true strain values. A simple solution to the problem when a mains supply is available is to interpose a power regulator between the mains and the instrument, thus ensuring a constant voltage and current. Such regulators replace the battery and can provide alternating or direct current.

A separate dummy bridge may be used as a reference. Here gauges are attached to a piece of metal which remains unstrained. Suitably temperature compensated and balanced, such a bridge should remain at zero

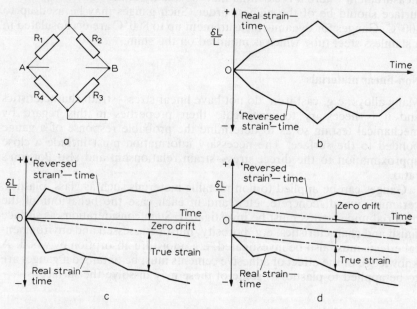

Fig. 6.29 Zero drift in instrumentation

strain; if it does not then the strain readings are taken to be zero drift and the active gauge readings adjusted accordingly.

The bridge galvanometer senses both the direction and magnitude of current flow when the bridge is unbalanced. If all the resistances in the bridge and the leads were initially equal, then reversing the position of the active and dummy gauges in the bridge should provide an equal and opposite reading on the galvanometer, e.g. if R_1 and R_4 were originally connected at A then the reverse would be shown when they were connected at B [Fig. 6.29(a)].

If zero drift does not occur, then a real strain–time and a 'reversed' strain–time curve plotted on the same axes should be mirror images of each other and the mean of both readings should be zero, the zero line produced representing the initial real strain reading [Fig. 6.29(b)]. If zero drift occurs, then the mean of the two readings will depart from the zero line and these departures when plotted provide the datum from which zero drift at any time may be derived [Fig. 6.29(c)].

It is unlikely that the resistances and bridge leads will be in perfect balance and in this case the two initial readings will be displaced from each other on the strain–time graph. The mean of the two readings then fixes the position of the zero line. The mean values of the readings are then plotted as before but because the real and 'reversed' strain curves are displaced the true zero strain line will be displaced by an amount equal to half the distance between the two initial readings [Fig. 6.29(d)].

It must be clearly understood that the methods outlined will detect zero drift only in the instrumentation and not in the gauges themselves. In practice, drift in the instrumentation is usually very small in comparison with gauge drift which is by far the most likely source of error.

6.17 Strain gauge calibration

The manufacturer tests samples from each batch of gauges to prove the accuracy and reliability of the gauges supplied. Average values of gauge factors, electrical resistances and sometimes temperature coefficients of resistance are provided with each batch purchased. Two gauges from a batch are tested on a symmetrically supported and loaded rectangular steel beam [Fig. 6.30(a)].

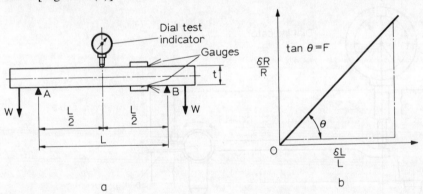

Fig. 6.30 Strain gauge calibration beam arrangement

The exact position of the gauges is unimportant provided that they lie within the vee or ball supports A and B with their axes parallel to the beam axis, as the bending moment to which the beam is subjected under load is constant within this length L and the tensile and compressive strains developed at the beam surfaces are equal but opposite in sign. A calibrated dial test indicator positioned at a point half way between A and B records the beam deflection at the centre of the span. Before loads are applied the dial indicator is set at zero and the bridge balanced. Equal loads are applied at W and values of resistance change $\delta R/R$, allowing for augmented output factors, and deflections y are recorded. Having rebalanced the bridge, further loads are applied until a suitable number of readings are obtained. It can be shown that the surface strain is given by

$$\varepsilon = 4ty/L^2$$

where t is the beam thickness, y is the beam deflection and L is the length of beam subjected to constant bending moment.

It can also be shown that the gauge factor $K = \delta R/R\varepsilon$.

From the values obtained a graph of $\delta R/R$ and ε can be plotted, the tangent of the resultant linear curve providing the gauge factor [Fig. 6.30(b)]. This may be compared with the manufacturer's value. An examination of the apparatus suggests that the value t should be taken to the centre lines of the gauges' grids but as this extra distance is negligible compared with the beam thickness it may be ignored in this case without detriment to the results. It should be noted that constant temperature conditions are essential during the test.

6.18 Extensometers

Prior to the invention and development of resistance strain gauges the main method used for determining strain was the extensometer. Extensometers are still used for certain purposes, e.g. on tensile test pieces and for

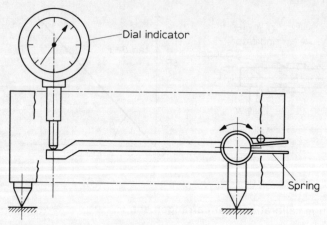

Fig. 6.31(a) Berry extensometer

structural applications in civil engineering where long gauge length and robust instruments are required. The main limitation of extensometers is their size which makes application difficult except in easily accessible positions; further, the elements to which they are attached must be geometrically simple such as rods of sufficient length and uniformity of cross-section to accommodate the instrument. Their use is limited largely to static strain measurement although dynamic measurement is possible with some types. Extensometers are sometimes referred to as strain gauges but in fact, as their name implies, they are extension measuring devices because the gauge length of the instrument must be known before strain can be computed.

Two similar methods, the knife edge and the conical penetrator, are used to ensure that the instrument responds in unison with the increase or decrease in length of the member to which it is attached. These are embedded into the surface of the member which consequently suffers minor damage, introducing a stress concentration and hence an error source. Three types are illustrated in Fig. 6.31, mechanical, optical and pneumatic.

Mechanical extensometers

The Berry extensometer shown in Fig. 6.31(a) is used for structural applications in civil engineering under approximately linear strain conditions over long gauge lengths up to 200 mm. An interesting feature of this gauge is the kinematically located spring loaded pivot spindle which eliminates bearing clearance.

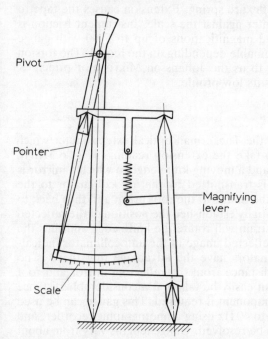

Fig. 6.31(b) Huggenberger extensometer

The Huggenberger [Fig. 6.31(b)] is another well known mechanical extensometer of which a number of models are obtainable, the most widely used being capable of gauge lengths of approximately 12 mm or 25 mm. This instrument depends entirely on very low friction knife edged pivots and may be reset to zero after each extension reading if desired. Magnifications up to 2000 can be obtained depending on the model.

The principle of the Johansson extensometer is shown in Fig. 6.31(c); here a twisted metal torsion tape is used to which a light pointer is attached at its centre. One end of the tape is attached to the fixed knife edge and the

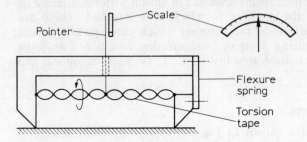

Fig. 6.31(c) Microkator extensometer

opposite end to the moving knife edge which is flexibly attached to the instrument body by a leaf or flexure spring. Extension causes the tape to unwind thus rotating the pointer against the scale. Instrument friction is reduced virtually to zero, and magnifications of up to 5000 with gauge lengths of 1 to 50 mm are obtainable depending on the model. The torsion tape device is often referred to as the Johansson Mikrokator principle. An advantage of this gauge is its low profile.

Optical extensometer

Another low profile gauge is the Tuckerman optical extensometer which requires an autocollimator to take the extension readings [Fig. 6.31(d)]. The gauge consists of a fixed and a moving knife edge to which a mirror is attached. A graticule image is transmitted by the autocollimator to the mirror which in turn reflects the image to the roof prism and thus back to the autocollimator. Having initially established the position of the reflected image at zero extension any strain will rotate the knife edge and thus the mirror, displacement of the reflected image in the autocollimator indicating the extension. Autocollimators have the advantage that there is no need to set them at a fixed distance from the reflecting mirror and roof prism; thus gauge readings can easily be taken at a considerable distance (metres) from the strained component if required. This gauge can be used for dynamic measurement up to 40 Hz using a photographic recorder, and strains as small as $2 \mu m/m$ can be resolved. Gauge lengths vary from about 6 mm to 250 mm depending on the model.

Pneumatic extensometer

A differential pressure extensometer is shown in Fig. 6.31(e). Here the moving knife edge operates as a flapper between two outlet jets, the effective area of each jet being equal to the area of the cylinder between

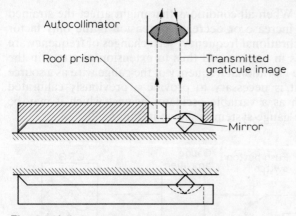

Fig. 6.31(d) Tuckerman optical extensometer

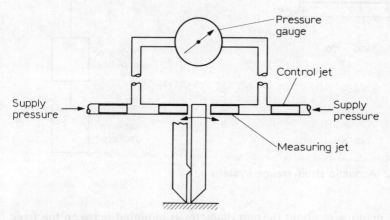

Fig. 6.31(e) Pneumatic extensometer

the jet and its corresponding flapper face. Both jets are supplied with a non-fluctuating and equal air flow at constant pressure. The effect of strain is to rotate the flapper and thus reduce the area of one jet while increasing the area of the other. Pressure on the constricted side rises towards the supply pressure and on the other towards atmosphere, the differential pressure being recorded on the pressure gauge. Provided that the gaps between the jets and the flapper are small, close linearity is obtained. Magnifications up to 100 000 and gauge lengths as small as 1 mm are obtainable. The pressure gauge can be sited at a distance from the sensing element.

Acoustic extensometer

A wire under tension vibrates at its natural frequency. The natural frequency changes if, for instance, the temperature or tension in the wire increases or decreases. When all conditions that might affect the strained wire remain steady an increase or decrease in tension is the only factor which will change the vibrational frequency; such changes of frequency are proportional to changes in tension and thus to extension or strain in the wire. In order to use the vibrational frequency of the gauge wire as a source of strain information it is necessary to provide a previously calibrated vibrational system such as a variable oscillator against which it may be compared. An acoustic gauge system is shown in Fig. 6.32.

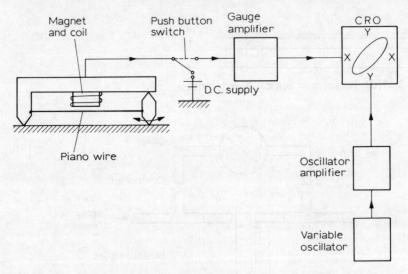

Fig. 6.32 Acoustic strain gauge system

Steel piano wire about 0·3 mm diameter is mounted between the fixed and moving knife edges of the gauge and mounted above the wire is a permanent magnet round which is wound a coil. The push button arrangement allows a pulse of direct current to flow to the coil which sets the wire vibrating at its natural frequency for a short period, transmitting a small alternating current to the gauge signal amplifier and thence to the X-plates of an oscilloscope. The Y-plates of the oscilloscope are supplied with a reference signal from the variable oscillator (range 200 to 2000 Hz) which is then adjusted until a circular or elliptical Lissajous figure appears on the screen when both the gauge and oscillator frequencies are matched and the vibrational frequency of the gauge wire is then known. The variable oscillator can be checked by replacing the gauge signal by the signal from a standard tuning fork.

The strain in a wire varies as the square of the frequency; thus

$$\frac{\delta L}{L} = \frac{4L^2\rho}{AE} \times f^2$$

where L is the wire length (m), A is the wire cross-sectional area (m^2), E is

Young's modulus of the wire (N/m^2), f is the vibrational frequency (Hz) and ρ is the density of the material (kg/m^2).

It is thus an easy matter to compute the strain caused by a change of frequency from the gauge but digital readout versions are now available.

Acoustic gauges are used mainly in civil engineering and have the advantages of robustness and long term reliability. High sensitivity of the order of $0.5 \mu m/m$ is readily obtainable and gauge lengths from 20 to 340 mm have been used. Because the system measures frequency, gauge lead and switch resistances do not affect the output. The gauges are easily covered for use externally on all types of structures and instead of knife edges studs may be fixed into the structure to support the wire, e.g. on steel girders. These gauges have operated successfully when mounted in a protective tube and immersed in concrete and, providing the covers are carefully sealed, operation under water offers few problems. A disadvantage is that quite considerable tension is required to provide a sufficiently taut wire; thus these gauges are not suitable for light structures.

Inductance extensometer

There are various ways in which linear movements can be transformed into inductance variations. A well tried method is the linear variable differential transformer (see Section 4.16 and Fig. 6.33).

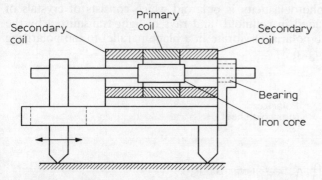

Fig. 6.33 LVDT-type extensometer

Commercial inductance transformers used for strain measurement have base lengths between 10 and 50 mm although base lengths as small as 0.5 mm are available for special purposes. The driving force required is less than 0.01 N and thus dynamic strain can be measured provided that the frequency of the primary coil voltage is at least 100 times the measured frequency.

6.19 Photoelasticity

Photoelasticity is a method of stress analysis which is extremely useful at the design stage. A study is made of the stress conditions in a scale model of the component made from a suitable transparent material such as Araldite, and from this the stresses in the original metal component can be deduced, both qualitative and quantitative results being obtained. When the model is stressed, placed in the path of a beam of polarized light and the light is arranged to fall on a screen, an interference pattern may be obtained. Inspection of the interference pattern indicates areas of high stress concentration and, equally important, areas of very low stress where the material is not being used to its best advantage. Full quantitative results of peak stresses at both the boundaries and interior of the model can easily be obtained and a simple process of scaling provides the actual stress likely to be present in the metal component.

Using this technique design faults can quickly and easily be located and suitable modifications made to the original design.

6.20 Polarized light

A beam of light is assumed to travel in wave formation in any number of directions transverse to the axis of propagation. If the waveform can be confined to one plane, then the light is said to be plane polarized. Certain crystals such as tourmaline and herapathite are said to have only one optic axis; that is, light can only pass through the crystal in one direction, and in the plane perpendicular to the optic axis light is absorbed. The polarizing medium used in photoelasticity is polaroid which consists of crystals of herapathite embedded in celluloid, and rays of light transmitted by the polaroid sheet (the polarizer) vibrate in a plane parallel to the polarizing axis as shown in Fig. 6.34.

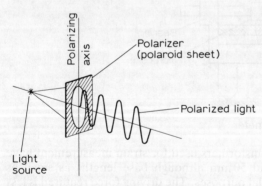

Fig. 6.34 Plane polarized light

Elliptically and circularly polarized light

If two plane polarized waves vibrating in planes at right angles have a phase difference of α wavelengths it can be shown that the resulting motion represents the equation of an ellipse and would represent elliptically polarized light. If the amplitude of the two waves are equal and the phase difference $\alpha = \pm\frac{1}{2}\pi$ radians then the resulting motion represents circularly polarized light.

A plane polariscope is shown in Fig. 6.35(a) where the axes of the polarizer and a second polaroid sheet, known as the analyzer, are crossed (perpendicular to each other). No light will be transmitted in this case as the emergent rays from the polarizer vibrate in a plane at 90° to the axis of the analyzer.

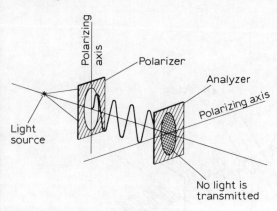

Fig. 6.35(a) Plane polariscope

6.21 Principles of photoelasticity

The technique of photoelasticity relies upon a property possessed by certain materials known as birefringence. These materials, when stressed, have the property of splitting a ray of plane polarized light (light vibrating in one plane only) at any point into two orthogonally polarized components, each parallel to a direction of principal stress at that point. The component waves propagate through the material at different velocities and the velocity of each of the components is proportional to the magnitude of the principal stress lying in its plane of vibration:

$$V_1 \propto \sigma_1 \quad \text{and} \quad V_2 \propto \sigma_2$$

where V_1 and V_2 are the velocities of the respective components and σ_1 and σ_2 are the principal stresses. The principal stresses are defined as the maximum σ_1 and minimum σ_2 values of direct stress than can be obtained at a point in a material. The principal stresses act along planes known as principal planes which are 90° apart. It may also be shown that the difference in the principal stresses at a point is equal to twice the maximum shear stress at that point:

$$\sigma_1 - \sigma_2 = 2\tau_m$$

where τ_m is the maximum shear stress at the point.

The emergent rays from the photoelastic model will have suffered a relative phase change or 'relative retardation' proportional to $(V_1 - V_2)$.

However, as $(V_1 - V_2)$ is in turn proportional to $(\sigma_1 - \sigma_2)$ the relative retardation of the emergent rays will be proportional to the difference in the principal stresses $(\sigma_1 - \sigma_2)$ at that point. The emergent rays can be recombined into a single plane by means of an analyzer, crossed with the polarizer (the planes of the respective polarizing axes are at 90°), such that only the components of the two rays parallel with the analyzer axis will pass through. This set-up is known as a plane polariscope and is shown in Fig. 6.35(*b*).

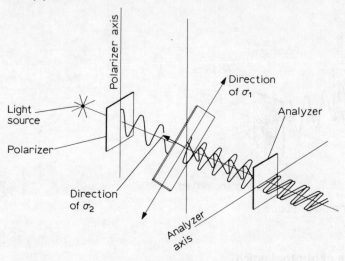

Fig. 6.35(*b*) Photoelastic specimen in the plane polariscope

The rays emerging from the analyzer will interfere optically, i.e. cancel each other in some places and reinforce in others. If the light is allowed to fall on a screen an interference pattern or 'fringe pattern' is obtained. The amount of interference at any point is proportional to the difference in the principal stress values at that point $(\sigma_1 - \sigma_2)$ and hence to the maximum shear stress:

$$\tau_m = \tfrac{1}{2}(\sigma_1 - \sigma_2)$$

If the original light source is monochromatic (e.g. mercury green) the fringes will appear as black lines on a green background, the black fringes corresponding to regions where the rays are 180° out of phase. These fringes are known as isochromatics and a typical fringe pattern for a disc subjected to a diametral load is shown in Fig. 6.36.

When the original light source is white and not monochromatic, each composite wavelength of the white light is cancelled in turn and the interference pattern becomes multi-coloured.

If plane polarized light is used a set of black lines known as isoclinics will be superimposed on the isochromatics. At all points in the model where a plane of principal stress is parallel to the optic axis of the polarizer, extinction will occur at the analyzer, and black bands will be formed on the fringe pattern. A detailed discussion of the use of isoclinics is beyond the

Fig. 6.36 Monochromatic fringe pattern of a disc subjected to diametral load (dark field)

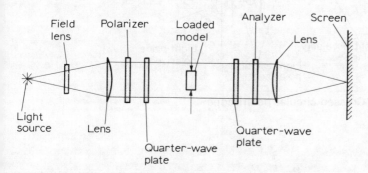

Fig. 6.37 Polariscope arrangement for circularly polarized light

scope of this chapter, but they may be used to determine the directions of the principal stresses within the model at any point. At this stage, however, to ensure that the isoclinics do not interfere with the analysis of the fringe pattern they are best removed. This may be achieved by inserting quarter wave plates in the polariscope field (Fig. 6.37) which produce circularly polarized light instead of plane polarized light. The isoclinics are thus removed while the remainder of the fringe pattern remains unchanged.

The quarter wave plates are normally made of mica and split a plane polarized ray of light into two orthogonally polarized components. The thickness of the plate is arranged so as to produce a phase difference, or relative retardation, of $\frac{1}{2}\pi$ radians, or one quarter of a wavelength, between the component rays. If the axes of the plate are arranged at 45° to an incoming plane polarized ray, then the amplitudes of the two component rays will be equal and circularly polarized light will result.

The quarter wave plates may be used in two ways, e.g. the plates can be adjusted to two relative positions in the instrument:

(a) 'Crossed', when the 'fast' plane (the component ray with the greater velocity is in this plane) is positioned opposite the 'slow' plane [Fig. 6.38(a)].

(b) 'Parallel', when the two 'fast' planes are arranged to coincide and the two 'slow' planes likewise [Fig. 6.38(b)].

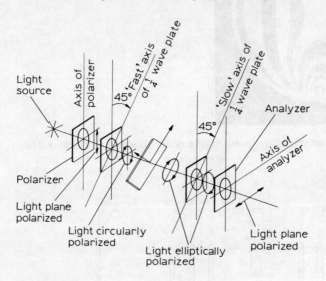

Fig. 6.38(a) Crossed circular polariscope

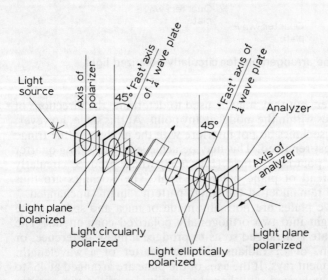

Fig. 6.38(b) Parallel circular polariscope

The crossed circular polariscope gives extinction of the light at the viewing screen when no photoelastic model is present (dark field) whereas the parallel condition produces an overall addition of half a wavelength and rotates the resultant plane of vibrations through 90° giving maximum brightness (light field).

A typical fringe pattern for a beam subjected to a central point load is shown in Fig. 6.39. Areas where there are a large number of fringes (A) represent areas of high shear stress as the interference is proportional to the maximum shear stress value at any point, whereas if the distance between fringes is large, or no fringes exist at all, the shear stress value is very low (B).

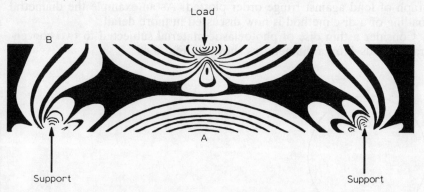

Fig. 6.39 Fringe pattern for simply supported beam loaded at the centre

6.22 Calibration of photoelastic materials

An essential requirement of photoelastic stress analysis is a calibration test to determine the sensitivity of photoelastic materials prior to model testing.

The fundamental equation of photoelasticity is

$$\sigma_1 - \sigma_2 = nf/t = nF \qquad (6.6)$$

where $\sigma_1 - \sigma_2$ is the principal stress difference at a point [= 2 × the maximum shear stress (N/m^2)], n is the fringe order at that point (new fringes appear at the point of observation as stress at that point is increased; the appearance of each new fringe increases the fringe order by one), t is the model thickness (m), F is the model fringe value or coefficient $(N/m^2$ fringe) and f is the material fringe value or coefficient $(N/m^2$ fringe/m or N/m fringe).

The material or model fringe coefficients are defined as the stress value required to produce one fringe order at any point in the material or model respectively.

Thus, if the material or model fringe value is known the principal stress difference, and hence the maximum shear stress at any point, can easily be calculated from the fringe pattern. At a boundary the principal stress normal to the boundary, σ_2, is equal to zero and thus fringe values at the boundary can be used to calculate the boundary stress σ_1.

The following calibration techniques are in general use:

(a) Diametral loading of a disc
(b) Simple tension
(c) Four point bending.

The three systems are used to determine the material or model fringe coefficients. Under a particular loading condition the value of fringe order is obtained at a point in the model where the stress difference $(\sigma_1 - \sigma_2)$ is known. This procedure is repeated for a series of different loads and a graph of load against fringe order plotted. As an example the diametral loading of a disc method is now discussed in more detail.

Consider a thin disc of photoelastic material subjected to two concentrated loads P on a diameter as shown in Fig. 6.40.

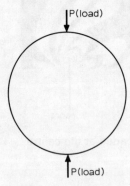

P(load)

P(load)

Fig. 6.40 Disc subjected to diametral load (compressive)

It can be shown that the principal stresses set up at the centre of the disc are given by

$$\sigma_1 = 2P/\pi tD \quad \text{and} \quad \sigma_2 = -6P/\pi tD$$

where t is the thickness of the disc and D is the diameter.

$$\sigma_1 - \sigma_2 = 8P/\pi tD \tag{6.7}$$

From Eqs. 6.6 and 6.7,

$$f(\text{the material fringe value}) = \frac{8}{\pi D}\frac{P}{n} \tag{6.8}$$

or

$$F(\text{the model fringe value}) = \frac{8}{\pi Dt}\frac{P}{n} \tag{6.9}$$

In practice the load on the disc is increased so as to produce successive fringe orders at the centre using the crossed circular polariscope set-up, thus producing a dark field or background. The ratio P/n in Eqs. 6.8 and

6.9 is given by the slope of the graph of load P against fringe order n which is a straight line through the origin (Fig. 6.41).

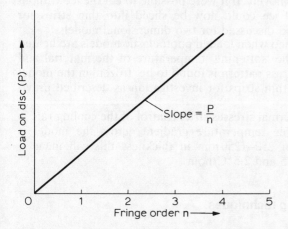

Fig. 6.41 Graph of load against fringe order for the diametral loading of a disc in compression

Further points may be determined for the graph without increasing the load range by using a light field background (polarizer and analyzer axes parallel) when the half order fringes are obtained. The points on the graph corresponding to the half order fringes will lie exactly between the points corresponding to the full order fringes (using the crossed circular polariscope set-up).

6.23 Three dimensional photoelasticity

The above discussion refers mainly to two dimensional models, i.e. thin models where the stresses do not vary considerably throughout the thickness. The method can be adapted, however, to deal with three-dimensional models using the 'frozen stress' technique (Fig. 6.42).

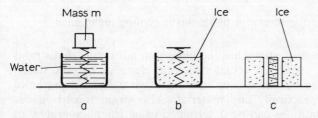

Fig. 6.42 'Frozen stress' principle
(a) Loaded spring   (b) Load removed   (c) Ice and spring sliced for examination

The figure shows a spring placed in a beaker of water and loaded with a mass m. The water may then be frozen such that the stress remains in the spring when the mass is removed. If it were possible to cut the ice without melting it the spring and ice could now be sliced into thin strips for examination by the method discussed for two dimensional models.

A similar effect is obtained when loaded photoelastic models are heated to a temperature above the 'softening' temperature of the material and then slowly cooled. The stress pattern is found to be 'frozen' in the model which may be sliced into thin strips for investigation as described previously.

In order to eliminate thermal stresses strict control of the cooling rate is essential and a one degree temperature gradient across the model is desirable. With models of 250–1250 mm in thickness this can mean a cooling rate of between 0·5 and 2·5 °C/hour.

6.24 Photoelastic coating techniques

Using these techniques strains are measured photoelastically by cementing transparent birefringent plastic material to the surface of a test piece. The technique is relatively new as it is only recently that materials have become available which show measurable optical effects at the order of strain to be expected in a metal within its elastic range.

A reflection polariscope is used to measure the fringe patterns produced and is arranged as shown in Fig. 6.43. It is now quite feasible to measure strain in this way although the sensitivity is not as high as in normal photoelasticity. Reflection of the light beam from the surface of the test piece is achieved either by polishing it or by using an adhesive containing aluminium.

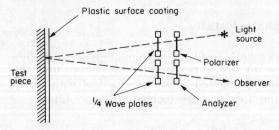

Fig. 6.43 Reflection polariscope for photoelastic coating techniques

This method of photoelasticity has the important advantage that strains and stresses on the surface of actual structural elements may be determined. Readings may be taken over surfaces of virtually any degree of complexity and of practically any material. Also strain records under dynamic loading conditions can be determined using cinephotography or stroboscopic techniques. The technique is highly suitable for use under field conditions and long term stability of the coating material is claimed.

The main limitation of the method is that the position at which the strain is to be measured must be accessible to a light beam, although observations can be taken at a considerable distance by telescope. Care is necessary to avoid errors resulting from alterations in the calibration constant of the material with temperature and resulting from differences in the coefficient of expansion of the test piece and the coating. Also the reinforcing effect of the plastic coating must be allowed for if strains in this section are being measured.

6.25 Photoelastic strain gauges

Transparent materials such as glass and plastic when strained are doubly refracting or birefringent. This effect when observed under polarized light reveals interference fringes in the material which are analogous to the strain induced. Relief of strain eliminates the fringes. Permanent fringes can be induced by heating the material while under stress and maintaining the stress until it has cooled. The 'frozen' fringe pattern so formed is

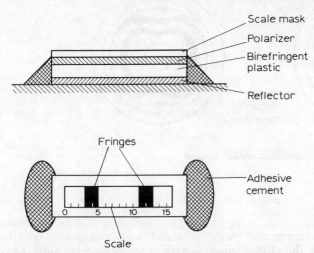

Fig. 6.44 Rectangular photoelastic strain gauge

permanent and change of stress simply causes fringe displacement. Rectangular and circular gauges based on this principle are commercially available. The gauges are of sandwich construction consisting of a piece of birefringent plastic approximately 2·5 mm thick on one side of which is a reflective coating and on the other a material which has the characteristics of a polariscope. Mounted above this is a calibrated and numbered strain scale (Fig. 6.44).

Gauges are mounted to surfaces with cements similar to those used for wire gauges although, because they are much less flexible, the surfaces to which they can be attached must be near to flatness. To eliminate the Poisson effect and thus ensure that strain along the gauge axis only is recorded, the gauges are cemented at their ends and not along their whole length. Two gauges can be used to determine principal strains in a biaxial stress field. Low tensile strain transmitted to the gauge displaces both fringes to the right and compressive strain causes displacement to the left. By noting the displacement of a particular fringe on the scale the strain magnitude can be determined. High strains cause fringes to pass off the scale but each time a fringe disappears it is replaced by a new fringe which appears at the opposite end of the gauge; thus careful note must be made of the fringe order. Bending or twisting of the surface, causing the fringes to rotate and become skewed, invalidates the strain measurement.

Gauges for measuring pure shear have fringes which are rotated to an angle of 45° to the gauge axis and these are used in the same manner as normal gauges except that they are cemented along their whole length.

Circular gauges used for principal strain measurement have circular fringes which become distorted under strain; they also move across the

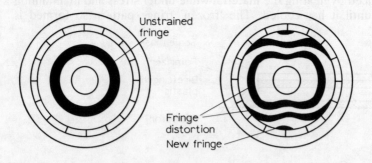

Fig. 6.45 Circular photoelastic strain gauge

gauge face, disappearing and being replaced with increase in strain magnitude, although the visible fringe pattern at any stage may appear to be extremely complex. It is essential to note the fringe order as in the case of rectangular gauges and this is done each time a new fringe begins to appear at the outside edge of the gauge (Fig. 6.45). This procedure is followed on both strain axes and, with the aid of a chart supplied by the manufacturer, the principal strains and thence the principal stresses may be determined. The main application for these gauges is as inserts in rock, concrete and similar materials.

Photoelastic strain gauges are direct reading devices and require no instrumentation. They are large, the minimum gauge length obtainable being about 20 mm, and the scale requirements limit their narrowness. They are inflexible and are thus suited only to flat or nearly flat surfaces. Their sensitivity is of the order of 40 to 75 μm/m and they have a maximum operating temperature of 50 °C.

Photoelastic stress gauges are also manufactured.

Study problems

6.1 (a) Define the terms:

   (i) Direct strain
   (ii) Lateral strain
   (iii) Poisson's ratio
   (iv) Modulus of elasticity.

(b) A steel tie bar 2 metres long and 50 millimetres diameter is subjected to a tensile load of 6 tonnes. Determine the tensile stress, the tensile strain and the lateral strain. The modulus of elasticity (E) is $200\,GN/m^2$ and Poisson's ratio (v) is 0·3. Express your answer in meganewtons per square metre and microstrain.

Answer: $30\,MN/m^2$; $+150$ microstrain; -45 microstrain

6.2 (a) Explain the meaning of the terms 'static', 'transient' and 'dynamic' strain, giving two practical examples of their occurrence in each case.

(b) Outline the advantages to be gained by the use of the electrical resistance strain gauge as a strain sensitive device in both static and dynamic conditions.

6.3 A strain gauge having an electrical resistance of $120\,\Omega$ and a gauge factor of 2·1 is used to test a steel specimen subjected to an axial tensile load. Calculate the induced strain if the increase in gauge resistance is shown to be $0·134\,\Omega$.

Answer: 532 microstrain

6.4 A strain gauge is attached to a 10 mm diameter spindle which is subjected to an axial load. Determine the magnitude of the load in kilonewtons given the following information: gauge resistance $350\,\Omega$; change in gauge resistance $0·15\,\Omega$; gauge factor 2·02; and modulus of elasticity $207\,GN/m^2$.

Answer: 3·45 kN

6.5 A component of 250 mm diameter was calibrated by means of the application of an axial load of 5 MN. A strain gauge mounted with its axis parallel to the direction of the calibration load yielded a reading of 558 microstrain. A consideration of the results strongly suggests that the gauge factor used (1·95) was incorrect. Calculate the correct strain reading and, assuming that the bridge is accurately indicating the value of $\delta R/R$, determine the correct value of the gauge factor. $E = 207\,GN/m^2$.

Answers: 492 microstrain; 2·21

6.6 (a) A transducer has a strain bridge consisting of four gauges two of which sense tensile strain and two compressive strain. Sketch a bridge arrangement in which the outputs from all four gauges complement each other and provide for full temperature compensation.

(b) The output of a Wheatstone bridge circuit is given by:

$$V_o = \frac{\varepsilon K V_s N}{4},$$

where ε is the strain, V_o is the bridge output (V), K is the gauge factor, V_s is the supply to bridge (V) and N is the effective number of active bridge arms.

Calculate the output voltage from the bridge if the supply is 15 V, the gauge factor 2·05, the gauge resistance 120 Ω and the maximum strain 500 microstrain.

Answer: 15·4 mV.

6.7 (*a*) Four strain gauges are used as a four arm bridge on a component subjected to tensile loading. The gauges are mounted in the Poisson configuration so as to provide compensation for both bending and temperature effects. Show on a diagram how the gauges would be mounted to the material and draw a sketch of the relationship of the gauges in the bridge circuit.

(*b*) The gauges are mounted to a component of rectangular cross-section 25 × 50 mm. Given that the gauge factor for each of the four gauges is 2·12, the maximum output signal from the bridge is limited to 10 mV and the supply voltage is 10 V, find the maximum allowable load on the component in kilonewtons. $E = 200 \, GN/m^2$; $v = 0·3$.

Answer: 181 kN

6.8 A cantilever has a cross-section 25 × 6 mm to which are mounted two electrical resistance strain gauges one above the 25 mm side and one below. Two identical resistors are used to complete the bridge and a bending load of 100 N is applied 200 mm from the centre line of the gauges. Utilizing the equation to bending

$$M/I = \sigma/y = E/R$$

and given that $I = 450 \, mm^4$ and $y = 3 \, mm$, calculate the maximum strain that may be applied to the gauges, if the maximum output from the bridge is limited to 6 mV, and hence select the most suitable input voltage from the list. $E = 200 \, GN/m^2$; $K = 2·15$.

Input voltages: 10; 7·5; 5; 2·5; 1.

Answers: 667 microstrain; 7·5 V

6.9 A torque transducer has four gauges set at 45° to form a full bridge. The transducer body is 15 mm diameter and the shear modulus for the material (G) is 75 GN/m². Calculate the output voltage when a torque equal to 53 Nm is applied and the input voltage is 2·5 V. Sketch the arrangement of the gauges in the Wheatstone bridge to provide maximum sensitivity.

Note: The direct strain (E) measured by each gauge is numerically equal to one half of the shear strain (γ) experienced by the component and each gauge of a pair yields readings of opposite sign.

The equation to torsion is:

$$\frac{T}{J} = \frac{\tau}{R}$$

where T is the applied torque, τ is the shear stress, R is the distance from the neutral axis to the plane of maximum shear stress and $J = \pi d^4/32$ is the polar second moment of area of the transducer body.

Answer: 2·92 mV

6.10   Figures 6.46(b) to (e) show arrangements of electrical resistance strain gauges. The gauges are connected into the bridge circuit shown in Fig. 6.46(a).

Comment briefly on each of the arrangements from the point of view of temperature compensation, etc.

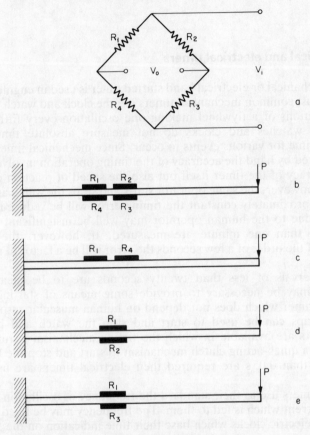

Fig. 6.46 Gauges for Problem 6.10

7 Measurement of time, speed, acceleration and frequency

7.1 Mechanical and electrical timers

Usually a mechanical or electrical hand started timer is used in engineering work. The most common mechanical timers are the clock and watch based on the oscillations of a flywheel making one oscillation every fifth of a second. Stop watches and clocks do not measure absolute time but measure the time for various events to occur. Since mechanical timers are normally started by hand the accuracy of the timing operation involves not only the accuracy of the timer itself but also the speed of reaction of the operator. If, however, the same operator starts and stops the watch and his time lag is approximately constant the timing error will be reduced. The timing error due to the human operator may well be insignificant when times greater than one minute are measured. If, however, the time measured is of the order of a few seconds the error will be a factor of major importance.

If time intervals of less than twenty seconds are to be measured accurately it may be necessary to provide some means of starting and stopping the timer which does not depend on human muscular response. Mechanical trips can be used to start and stop the watch and highly sensitive timers are available in which the timing mechanism is running steadily, with a quick-acting clutch mechanism to start and stop the hand. If errors less than 0·05 s are required then electrical timers are usually employed.

Electrical timers use as their standard the frequency of oscillation of an alternating current which is fed to them. The frequency may be fixed, as is the case with electric clocks which base their time indication on the 50 Hz mains frequency, or varied as the operator requires to suit the accuracy of the work. The higher the frequency fed to the timer and the more regular the oscillation the more accurate is the timing. Starting and stopping these devices is normally achieved by electric pulses. The number of cycles occurring between starting and stopping is recorded and displayed usually on a digital readout.

7.2 Electronic counter–timers

Electronic counter–timers are usually capable of measuring time and frequency in addition to counting applications. The majority employ large digital displays which can be easily read and they have a wide frequency range with a typical maximum counting frequency in excess of 100 kHz.

A block diagram of an electronic counter–timer system used for time measurement is shown in Fig. 7.1. The oscillator produces a stable high frequency signal which is fed to the divider. The divider may be set to select a suitable counting unit by switching the appropriate selector switch. For example, if the oscillator frequency is 100 kHz and the 'divide by 10^2' switch is selected a divider output of 1000 pulses per second is produced. If these pulses are now counted the final reading of the display will be in milliseconds.

The pulses are registered by the counter for a period determined by the 'start' and 'stop' pulses. The divider output pulses are connected to one input terminal of a logic AND gate which will pass pulses to the counter only

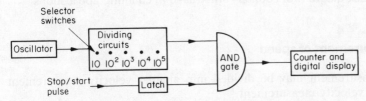

Fig. 7.1 Block diagram of counter–timer used for time measurement

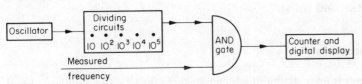

Fig. 7.2 Block diagram of counter–timer used for frequency measurement

when both its input signals are 'on'. The second input to the AND gate is derived from an electronic latch which may be 'set' (switched on) by applying the start pulse. The latch has the property that once 'set' its output will remain 'on' until a signal is applied to 'reset' it. The divider output pulses will therefore be passed to the counter when the latch is 'set'. If a 'stop' pulse is applied to the latch then the latch is 'reset' (switched off) and the passage of divider output pulses to the counter will be 'blocked'. The start and stop pulses can be initiated either manually or automatically according to the nature of the timing application.

The instrument may be used to measure frequency using the circuit arrangement shown in Fig. 7.2. It should be noted that the output from the oscillator and divider circuit is used as one input to the AND gate whereas the frequency to be measured is the second input. The 'gating' period or time for which the frequency pulses are to be counted is achieved from the oscillator and divider. For example, if the oscillator frequency is 100 kHz and the divider switch is in the 'divide by 10^2' position the 'gating' period is 0·001 seconds, and if 10 pulses are passed to the counter in this time this represents a frequency of 10 000 Hz or 10 kHz.

The third mode of operation of the device is for simple counting applications as shown in Fig. 7.3. In this case the oscillator circuit is not required and the pulses to be counted can be divided if necessary before passing through the AND gate to the counter. External start/stop signals can be supplied to the AND gate by using a start/stop pulse and a latch as before.

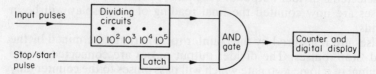

Fig. 7.3 Block diagram of counter–timer used in counting applications

7.3 Measurement of speed

Speed measurement may be divided into angular velocity measurement and linear velocity measurement.

The angular velocity of a rotating machine is usually expressed in radians per second (rad/s) or revolutions per minute (r/min).

Linear velocity is the distance moved per unit of time and is expressed as metres per second (m/s).

7.4 Tachometers

A tachometer is an instrument which measures directly the angular velocity of a rotating shaft. Tachometers may be broadly divided into mechanical and electrical instruments and are considered below.

7.5 Mechanical tachometers

Revolution counter and timer

The simplest method available in this category is to use a revolution counter and a stop watch. This method is quite satisfactory for measuring

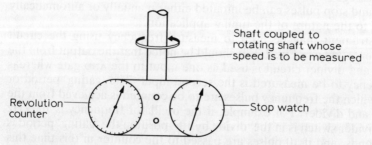

Fig. 7.4 Revolution counter with built-in timing device

low speeds and some instruments are commercially available which consist of a revolution counter with a built-in timing device (Fig. 7.4).

Slipping clutch type

This tachometer, shown in Fig. 7.5, consists of an indicator shaft driven by an input shaft through a slipping clutch. A pointer is attached to the indicator shaft which is rotated against the torque of a spiral spring. As the speed of the input shaft is increased, the greater is the torque applied to the indicator shaft which moves the pointer over a calibrated scale.

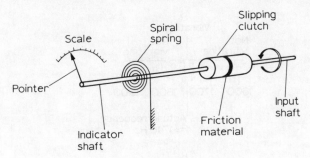

Fig. 7.5 Slipping clutch tachometer

Centrifugal force type

The centrifugal force type (Fig. 7.6) operates on the Watt governor principle. Two masses are mounted on leaf springs which are attached at one end to a driven shaft. The other ends of the springs are attached to a grooved collar which can slide on the shaft and move a pointer.

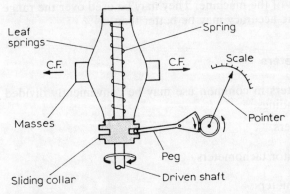

Fig. 7.6 Centrifugal force tachometer

As the speed increases the centrifugal force on the masses increases (i.e. centrifugal force $= mr\omega^2$, where m is the mass, r is the radius from centre of motion and ω is the angular velocity) thus causing the masses to move outwards and the sliding collar to move up the shaft. The movement of the collar is transmitted through a quadrant and pinion to a pointer. This instrument may be used to measure rotational speeds up to 40 000 r/min with a maximum accuracy of ±1%.

Resonance or vibrating reed tachometer

The vibrating reed tachometer consists of a set of thin cantilever members, each member having a different natural frequency of vibration [Fig. 7.7(a)]. The reeds are lined up in order of their natural frequency of

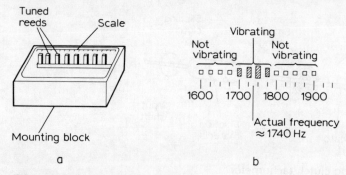

Fig. 7.7 Vibrating reed tachometer

vibration and when the frame of the tachometer is placed in mechanical contact with the frame of a rotating machine the reed with natural frequency closest to the frequency of the machine vibration will respond the most readily. The reed vibration is indicated against a calibrated scale [Fig. 7.7(b)].

An advantage of this instrument is that the meter need only be in contact with a non-moving part of the machine. They may be used over the range 600–10 000 r/min and the accuracy may be better than ±½%.

7.6 Electrical tachometers

The electrical tachometers in common use may be conveniently divided under the following headings:

(1) Inductive tachometers
(2) Tachogenerators
(3) Commutated capacitor tachometers
(4) Digital counters
(5) Stroboscopic tachometers.

Inductive tachometers

Eddy current or magnetic drag type
This instrument, shown in Fig. 7.8, has a rotating permanent magnet which

is driven by the machine shaft. Eddy currents are induced in the aluminium drag cup and produce a torque which rotates the cup against the torque produced by a spiral spring. The pointer attached to the cup indicates rotational speed on a calibrated scale.

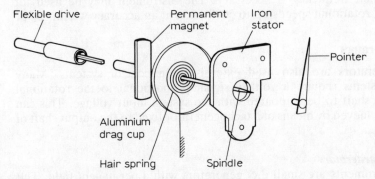

Fig. 7.8 Eddy current or magnetic drag tachometer (exploded view)

This instrument is normally used in automobiles when the scale is calibrated in linear velocity (miles per hour or kilometres per hour). When used for speed measurement in aircraft the flexible mechanical drive can be replaced by an electrical drive in the form of a small three phase a.c. generator coupled to the machine shaft and connected to a three phase synchronous motor which in turn drives the tachometer magnet.

The eddy current tachometer is normally used for measuring rotational speeds up to 12 000 r/min at an accuracy rather less than ±3%.

A.C. drag-cup generator type
This instrument has an aluminium cup which is rotated in a laminated iron magnet system. The stator core carries two windings which have their axes at right angles as shown in Fig. 7.9.

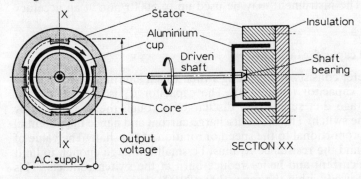

Fig. 7.9 A.C. drag-cup generator tachometer

When an alternating current is applied to one of the windings, eddy currents are induced in the aluminium cup. When the cup is rotated a cross-magnetizing flux is set up which induces an e.m.f. proportional to the speed of rotation at the output coils. This output voltage may be measured using a voltmeter calibrated in revolutions per minute. This type of tachometer is widely used in control systems where a linear output voltage at a constant frequency is necessary. The instrument may be used for measuring rotational speeds up to 5000 r/min at an accuracy within $\pm\frac{1}{2}\%$.

Tachogenerators

Tachogenerators are also used extensively in control systems. Many control systems require a voltage signal proportional to the rotational speed of a shaft to be compared with the system input voltage. This can easily be achieved by means of a tachogenerator fixed to the output shaft of the system.

D.C. tachogenerators

These instruments are small d.c. generators with a permanent field. The instrument may be fixed to the rotating shaft, and the output voltage from the tachogenerator is proportional to the rotational speed. The output voltage may be measured using a moving coil instrument calibrated in revolutions per minute.

The d.c. tachogenerator may be used for measurements up to 5000 r/min at an accuracy within $\pm2\%$ or in the case of the more expensive models $\pm0\cdot1\%$.

A.C. tachogenerators

A.C. tachogenerators are small brushless alternators having a rotating multi-polar permanent magnet. The alternator is driven by the rotating shaft and the output voltage is measured by a voltmeter calibrated in revolutions per minute.

As in the d.c. tachometer the output voltage is proportional to speed, but the frequency also varies with speed and affects the accuracy of the instrument. The instrument may be used up to 5000 r/min at an accuracy within $\pm2\%$.

Commutated capacitor tachometers

The tachometer consists of a rotating switch which alternately charges and discharges a capacitor (Fig. 7.10). The capacitor C_1 is charged from a constant voltage d.c. supply and discharged through the resistor R_2 by rotation of the switch. The mean discharge current and hence the potential across R_2 is proportional to the speed of rotation of the shaft. The value of $C_2 = 100\,C_1$ and the resistance R_1 must be small but large enough to limit the charging current and hence reduce burn at the switch contacts. This instrument is used within the range 200–100 000 r/min.

Digital signal pick-up tachometers

The electrical tachometers discussed so far give an analogue indication of

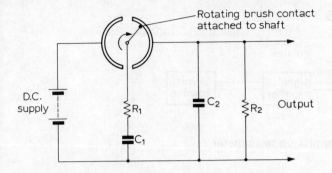

Fig. 7.10 Commutated capacitor tachometer

speed whereas these instruments give a pulsed or digital output signal. The digital output can be used for direct indication of speed, to transmit measurements for computation or for applications in a control system. As there is no physical connection between the transducer and the shaft little or no load is applied to the machine shaft which is a distinct advantage of this type of instrument. Various forms of digital pick-up may be used and three of the most popular are discussed below.

Inductive pick-ups
A typical system using an inductive pick-up is shown in Fig. 7.11. Each tooth on the wheel changes the reluctance of the magnetic circuit as it passes thus producing an e.m.f. change in the form of a pulse. The pulses are fed into a digital counter which counts the number of pulses for some preset time interval. The function of the signal modifier is to shape the digital signal to give a distinct series of pulses of usable amplitude.

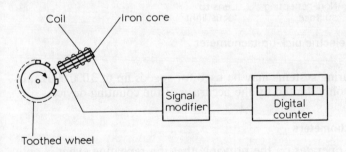

Fig. 7.11 Inductive pick-up tachometer

Capacitive-type pick-ups
Capacitive pick-ups have a vane attached to the machine shaft. As the vane rotates between the fixed capacitor plates a change in the capacitance to earth ratio is produced. The output is fed into a pulse shaper and a digital counter as shown in Fig. 7.12.

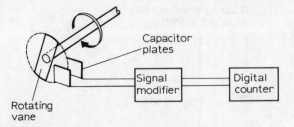

Fig. 7.12 Capacitive pick-up tachometer

Photoelectric pick-ups

This instrument consists of a photoelectric cell which is activated by light pulses deflected from a rotating machine shaft. The shaft has an intermittent reflecting surface and when a beam of light is focused on to the shaft a number of pulses of light are obtained. The frequency of the light pulses is proportional to the speed of the shaft and hence the frequency of the electrical output pulses from the photoelectric cell will also be proportional to the shaft speed. Again the pulses are shaped to provide a suitable input for a digital counter (Fig. 7.13).

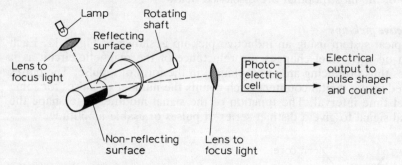

Fig. 7.13 Photoelectric pick-up tachometer

Digital measuring systems may be used for speeds up to 3 000 000 r/min and accuracy is only limited by the accuracy of the counting device.

Stroboscopic tachometers

The instrument operates on the principle that if a repeating event is only viewed when at one particular point in its cycle it appears to be stationary.

If a mark is made on a shaft and the shaft is slowly rotated under a steady light, the angular velocity may be found by watching the mark and counting the number of revolutions during a definite time interval. As the rotational speed increases, however, it becomes difficult to see the revolutions of the mark.

If a flashing light is substituted for the steady light and the frequency and duration of flashing is adjusted so that there is one very short flash per revolution then the observer will see the mark on the shaft apparently standing still. This is shown in Fig. 7.14, where the rotating disc is illuminated at one point during each revolution.

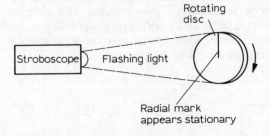

Fig. 7.14 Stroboscopic tachometer

Commercially available stroboscopes usually incorporate a neon tube which flashes at a rate set on a calibrated control switch, to read angular velocities between 600 and 20 000 r/min. It is possible to obtain the speed of a rotating shaft without making contact with it and the stroboscope is therefore particularly useful for measuring the speed of low powered machinery as no additional power is used to drive the measuring instrument.

A rotating shaft will also appear to be stationary if the flash frequency is any multiple of the shaft speed. A single mark on a shaft which is rotating at 1000 r/min will make two revolutions between flashes if the flashes are at the rate of 500 r/min. The shaft may make any number of complete revolutions between flashes and still appear to be stationary and therefore the above shaft will appear stationary at 1000 flashes per minute, and also at 500, $333\frac{1}{3}$, 250, etc. It is therefore desirable to have an approximate knowledge of the range within which the shaft speed may lie.

If the frequency of the flashing light is twice the shaft speed, a single mark on the rotating shaft will appear to be two standing marks 180° apart. A suitable technique for determining the shaft speed when the general speed range is unknown is as follows. Gradually increase the frequency of flashing from a low value until the rotating member appears to be stationary and note the frequency. The flash frequency is then doubled and if there is still only one apparent stationary image the frequency is again doubled. This procedure is continued until two images appear 180° apart. When these two images first appear the flash frequency is twice the speed of rotation.

7.7 Measurement of acceleration and vibration amplitude

Principles of the seismic instrument

The basic functional form of the seismic instrument is as shown in Fig. 7.15. The base is connected to the vibration source whose characteristics are to be measured. The mass tends to remain fixed in its equilibrium position so that the vibration motion is registered as a relative displacement between the mass and the base. This displacement is then sensed and measured by an appropriate transducer.

The seismic instrument may be used for either displacement or acceleration measurements by proper selection of mass, spring and damper combinations. In general, a large mass and a soft spring are desirable for vibration displacement measurements, while a relatively small mass and a stiff spring are used for the measurement of acceleration.

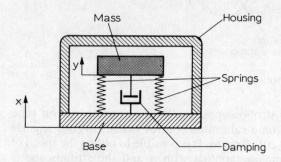

Fig. 7.15 Basic seismic mass instrument
Relative movement between the mass and the base $z = y - x$

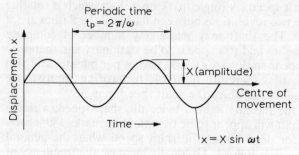

Fig. 7.16 Harmonic input applied to base of seismic instrument

If a harmonic input is applied to the base the movement is given by the expression

$$x = X \sin \omega t$$

where x is the displacement at time t from the centre of the movement, X is the maximum displacement or amplitude and ω is the frequency of the harmonic input.

A typical harmonic input is shown in Fig. 7.16. This is simple harmonic motion of amplitude X and frequency $\omega/2\pi$ Hz. It should also be noted that the acceleration of the base is given by $\omega^2 x$ and thus the maximum acceleration is $\omega^2 X$.

It can be shown that the relative movement between the mass and the base is given by

$$Z = \frac{\omega^2 X}{\omega_n^2 \{[1 - (\omega/\omega_n)^2]^2 + [2\zeta\omega/\omega_n]^2\}^{1/2}} \tag{7.1}$$

where ω_n is the natural frequency of the spring–mass system in radians per second and ζ is the damping ratio, i.e. the ratio between the actual damping present and the amount required for critical damping (no overshoots) (see Fig. 7.17).

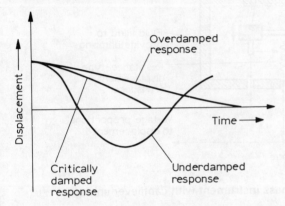

Fig. 7.17 Typical damped harmonic response curves

Measurement of displacement

If the frequency applied to the base of the seismic instrument, ω, is much higher than ω_n then the term $[2\zeta\omega/\omega_n]^2$ in Eq. 7.1 may be ignored compared with $[(\omega/\omega_n)^2]^2$ and an approximate expression for Z becomes

$$Z = \frac{\omega^2 X}{\omega_n^2 \{[(\omega/\omega_n)^2]^2\}^{1/2}} = \frac{\omega^2 X}{\omega_n^2 (\omega/\omega_n)^2} = X$$

Thus the relative movement between the mass and the base is approximately equal to the movement of the base. At frequencies higher than $2\omega_n$ this system can be used to measure the amplitude of vibration by means of a small displacement transducer between the mass and the base. A typical instrument is shown in Fig. 7.18.

Measurement of acceleration

If the input frequency ω is much smaller than the natural frequency ω_n then the expression for Z becomes

$$Z = \frac{\omega^2 X}{\omega_n^2 \sqrt{1}}$$

and this assumption remains valid for $\omega \leqslant 0.3\omega_n$.

However, $\omega^2 X$ is the maximum acceleration of the base and therefore

$$Z = \frac{1}{\omega_n^2} \times \text{maximum acceleration}$$

Thus the instrument shown in Fig. 7.18 could be used to measure the maximum acceleration of a vibrating part for values of ω up to about $0 \cdot 3\omega_n$.

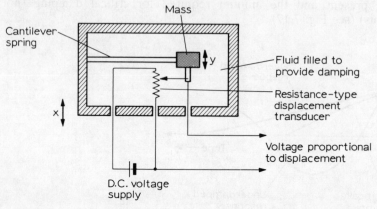

Fig. 7.18 Typical seismic mass instrument with cantilever spring

Strain gauge accelerometer

The electrical resistance strain gauge may also be used for a displacement-sensing device in a seismic instrument as shown in Fig. 7.19.

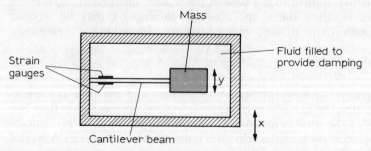

Fig. 7.19 Strain gauge accelerometer

The seismic mass is mounted on a cantilever beam and a resistance strain gauge is mounted on each side of the beam to sense the strain in the beam resulting from the vibrational displacement of the mass. Damping for the system is provided by the viscous liquid which fills the housing. The outputs from the strain gauges are connected to an appropriate bridge circuit which is used to indicate the relative displacement between the mass and the housing frame.

Piezoelectric accelerometers

The seismic instruments discussed so far have rather low natural frequencies within the range 2–1000 Hz. These instruments are therefore restricted to applications with fairly low frequency response requirements.

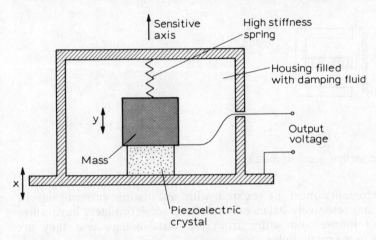

Fig. 7.20 Piezoelectric crystal accelerometer

The seismic instrument frequently employs a piezoelectric transducer for high frequency measurements. The basic element in a piezoelectric transducer is a block of crystalline material capable of generating an electrical potential when subjected to mechanical strain along a preferred axis. Examples of common materials possessing this effect are quartz and Rochelle salt (potassium sodium tartarate) and ammonium dihydrogen phosphate. These materials have a fairly high mechanical strength and are relatively cheap and easy to obtain. In order to increase sensitivity various polycrystalline ceramic materials have been produced such as barium titanate and lead zirconate titanate.

Piezoelectric accelerometers incorporate a mass attached to the mechanical axis of the piezoelectric crystal and held within the transducer body by a high stiffness spring (Fig. 7.20).

Because of the high stiffness of the crystal the natural frequency of such an instrument may be as high as 100 kHz, and the entire instrument may be quite small and light in weight. Piezoelectric accelerometers may be used to measure shock loading as they can withstand very high accelerations of up to 20 000 g. One disadvantage is that electrical impedance matching between the transducer and readout circuitry is usually a critical matter requiring careful design considerations (see Chapter 1).

Inductive accelerometers

Inductive accelerometers employ a pair of coils and a magnetically coupled mass (Fig. 7.21). When an acceleration is applied the mass is displaced and alters the magnetic coupling path which changes the inductive ratio of the coils. Inductive accelerometers offer a high electrical output for essentially continuous resolution and are used to measure static or dynamic accelerations.

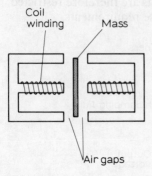

Fig. 7.21 Inductive accelerometer

These instruments must be excited with alternating current and be reactively and resistively balanced. Inductive accelerometers have a low frequency response and suffer from the disadvantage that they are susceptible to magnetic fields.

7.8 Effect of temperature on seismic instruments

Seismic vibration instruments may be influenced by temperature effects. Devices which employ a variable resistance transducer to sense the relative displacement between the mass and the instrument housing will require a correction to account for resistance changes due to temperature.

Also most seismic instruments are filled with a viscous fluid, e.g. silicone oil, to provide damping. Obviously the viscosity of the damping fluid will vary with temperature and a fluid with a small change in viscosity with temperature would be desirable. However, most fluids which fall into this latter category, e.g. gases, have low viscosities as well and are therefore unsuitable for use as damping fluids. One way of eliminating this problem is to introduce an electrical resistance heater into the fluid to maintain the temperature at a constant value regardless of the surrounding temperature.

Study problems

7.1 Explain how a stroboscope may be used to measure the rotational speed of a motor shaft.

7.2 Describe briefly the basic concept of the seismic instrument and discuss with the aid of appropriate diagrams three practical arrangements of this device.

What physical variables can be measured using the seismic instrument?

7.3 When would a piezoelectric transducer be used to advantage in a seismic instrument?

7.4 Explain the significance of the natural frequency of a simple mass–spring accelerometer. If the mass is halved and the strength of the spring is doubled calculate the resulting change in the natural frequency.

Answer: The frequency is doubled.

7.5 An inductive pick-up is used to measure the rotational speed of a motor shaft. The system used is shown in Fig. 7.11, the number of teeth on the wheel being sixty. The counter is set to read periodic time and a value of 1 ms is observed. Calculate the rotational speed of the shaft.

Answer: 16·67 r/s.

7.6 A stroboscope light is directed on to a rotating shaft which contains a single keyway. The keyway appears to be stationary when the flashing frequency of the lamp is 500 flashes per minute. The flashing frequency is then increased slowly and the keyway appears next to be stationary at a flashing frequency of 750 flashes per minute.

Estimate the rotational speed of the shaft and describe a checking procedure to verify the speed.

Answer: 1500 r/min.

8 Measurement of force, torque and power

The accurate measurement of power is of major importance in the engineering industry. Instruments used for power measurement are known as dynamometers and may be divided into two main groups:

(*a*) Absorption dynamometers
(*b*) Transmission dynamometers.

Absorption dynamometers absorb the power which is to be measured and dissipate the energy extracted in the form of heat or electrical energy. When the absorption dynamometer is used the engine under test is mechanically coupled directly to the dynamometer or brake, which applies a resisting torque to the common shaft. The magnitude of the resisting torque is measured using instruments connected to the dynamometer and hence the power output of the engine may be calculated.

A *transmission dynamometer* enables the torque on the engine shaft to be determined when it is driving a normal load, no power being absorbed by the dynamometer. Transmission dynamometers work on the principle that when a torque is applied to a shaft, and is resisted by an equal and opposite torque, the shaft twists through a small angle which is proportional to the applied torque (provided that the elastic limit of the shaft material is not exceeded). The applied torque may be calculated from a knowledge of the angle of twist for a given length of shaft and if the rotational speed of the shaft is known the power transmitted may be calculated.

Force measurement is closely associated with torque and power measurement since power is defined as the rate of doing work and work is defined as the product of force and distance. The accurate measurement of power therefore requires that force, distance and time may be similarly measured.

8.1 Force measurement

Force is defined as the product of mass and acceleration. The unit of force is the newton where 1 newton is the force required to give a mass of 1 kilogram an acceleration of 1 metre per second per second. That is,

$$1\,N = 1\,kg \times 1\,m/s^2$$

Instruments for force measurement are available over a very wide range and fall into three main groups:

(*a*) Mechanical methods
(*b*) Hydraulic and pneumatic methods
(*c*) Electrical methods.

In general, electrical methods are most useful when remote measurement of force is required. Electrical methods are highly sensitive and can detect very small forces but may be unreliable as they are influenced by stray magnetic fields and temperature changes. Hydraulic methods are used mainly to generate and measure large forces and apply the hydraulic ram principle. Referring to Fig. 8.1, a large force acting on the piston of area A_2 may be balanced by a much smaller force acting on the piston of area A_1, i.e.

$$F_1/A_1 = F_2/A_2 \quad \text{therefore} \quad F_1 = F_2 \frac{A_1}{A_2}$$

where $A_2 \gg A_1$.

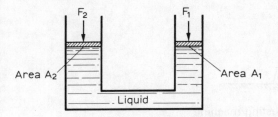

Fig. 8.1 Principle of the hydraulic ram

$$F_1 = F_2 A_1/A_2$$

8.2 Mechanical methods of force measurement

Simple lever

The simple lever provides a force measuring device by equating moments. An unknown force at one end of a pivoted lever may be balanced by applying a known force at the other end to provide equilibrium. When the lever is in equilibrium the moments of the two forces about the pivot point will be equal; thus the unknown force may easily be calculated from the lever ratio and the balancing force.

An example of a simple lever system where the lever arms are equal is the chemical balance. In order to reduce the number of masses required for balance an adjustable lever arm may be used with a rider mass which can be moved along one lever arm until balance is obtained (Fig. 8.2).

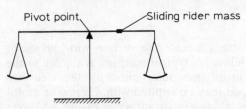

Fig. 8.2 Chemical balance

The simple lever principle may be applied to a tensile/compressive testing machine as shown in Fig. 8.3. The lower end of the vertically mounted test specimen is attached to some form of loading, either a screw jack or a hydraulic ram, whilst its upper end is gripped by a swivel and attached to a steelyard to measure load.

This type of machine would normally be used for testing materials such as low strength wire, plastic, fibre, etc.

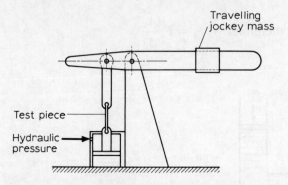

Fig. 8.3 Lever-type tensile testing machine

Compound lever

The simple lever may be compounded by introducing a series of pivot points and additional levers. A more compact machine is therefore capable of exerting greater loads and this principle is applied to a number of testing machines (Fig. 8.4).

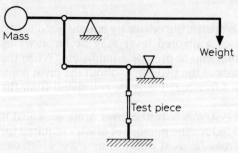

Fig. 8.4 Compound lever testing machine

Pendulum

Many machines for testing low strength materials such as wire, plastic or fibre incorporate a simple pendulum. A typical machine is similar to the steelyard testing machine discussed previously but with the steelyard replaced by a pendulum. The load may be applied with a screw or motor thus causing the pendulum to rise along a quadrant scale. Figure 8.5 shows a direct reading balance using the simple pendulum principle.

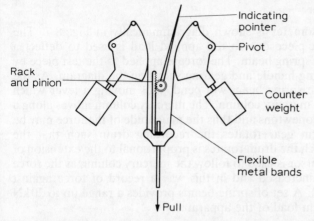

Fig. 8.5 Direct reading balance using the simple pendulum principle

Spring and proving ring

If a force is applied to an elastic member such as a spring or a steel bar, then the member will deform. Provided that the force is not excessive then the elastic deformation of the bar or spring may be measured, and this deformation is proportional to the applied force. For example, for a simple spring

$$F = kx$$

where F is the applied force, k is a constant and x is the spring displacement.

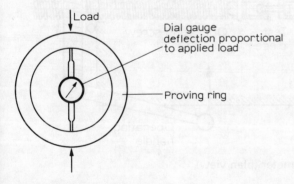

Fig. 8.6 Proving ring

The proving ring (Fig. 8.6) is a ring of known physical dimensions and mechanical properties. An external tensile or compressive force applied across the ring diameter causes distortion which is proportional to that force. The amount of distortion can be measured using a dial gauge, micrometer or strain gauges.

Hounsfield tensometer

The Hounsfield tensometer is shown diagrammatically in Fig. 8.7. The extension of the test piece due to the applied load is used to deflect a previously calibrated spring beam. The force is applied to the test piece by means of the operating handle and gearing shown in the diagram. As the force is increased the spring beam will bend, thus moving a lever which applies a force to the mercury column. The mercury column moves along a scale calibrated in kilonewtons and thus the magnitude of the force may be calculated. The worm gear rotates the recording drum such that the distance through which the drum rotates is proportional to the extension of the test piece. The cursor is used to follow the mercury column as the force on the test piece is increased and in this way a record of force against extension is obtained. A set of spring beams provides a range up to 20 kN which is the maximum load of the apparatus.

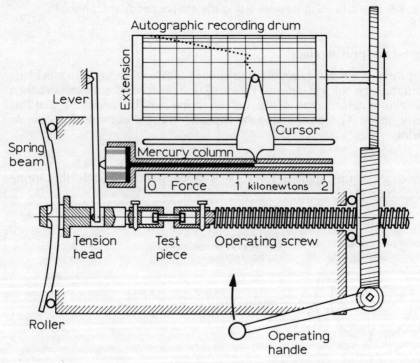

Fig. 8.7 Hounsfield tensometer (plan view)

8.3 Hydraulic and pneumatic methods of force measurement

Hydraulic pressure may be used to measure force as shown in Fig. 8.8. A chamber or capsule with a diaphragm and containing oil is connected to a Bourdon tube or some other suitable pressure measuring device. When a force is applied to the diaphragm a pressure is developed in the chamber equal to the applied force divided by the effective diaphragm area. This pressure is indicated by the Bourdon gauge which may be calibrated directly in force units. The apparatus is similar to the dead weight pressure tester discussed in Chapter 9.

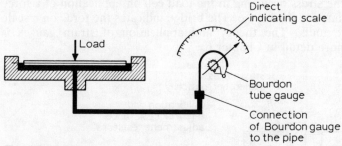

Fig. 8.8 Hydraulic load cell

A pneumatic load cell in which air pressure is used to measure force is shown in Fig. 8.9. This device is similar to the conventional pneumatic relay operating on the force balance principle and employing a nozzle and flapper unit. The weight of the force platform and fittings when no external force is applied is balanced by adjusting the pressure in the tare chamber.

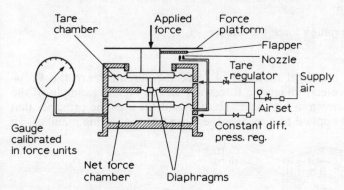

Fig. 8.9 Pneumatic load cell

When an external force is applied the flapper will move nearer to the nozzle thus restricting the passage of air from the nozzle to the atmosphere. The pressure in the net force chamber will thus increase as the external force is increased and this pressure is directly proportional to the applied force. The force may conveniently be measured using a Bourdon tube gauge calibrated in force units as shown in the diagram.

8.4 Electrical methods of force measurement

A typical strain gauge force transducer is shown in Fig. 8.10. In this system a column of steel suitably proportioned to provide the desired strain from a known load is either stretched or compressed by the load. Strain gauges are attached to the column, their electrical resistance being altered according to the load. The strain gauges are connected to the appropriate arms of a Wheatstone bridge. The bridge is balanced before a force is applied to the column, and the stress occurring in the load cell on application of a force upsets the balance of the bridge. The bridge indicates the force on a scale in appropriate units. The theory and application of strain gauges is discussed in more detail in Chapter 6.

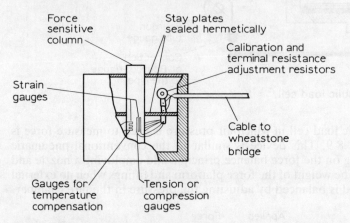

Fig. 8.10 Strain gauge force transducer

Two further electrical methods of force measurement are the Pressductor and the electromagnetic force balance. A typical example of the Pressductor is shown in Fig. 8.11. The Pressductor uses the principle that when a force is applied to a material, e.g. a steel supporting member, an

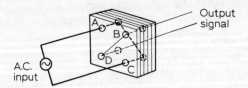

Fig. 8.11 Pressductor
Input is fed through A and back through C. Output lead is fed through B and D.

internal stress pattern is set up within the member. This stress will disturb the magnetic flux distribution within the member if a magnetic field is established. The Pressductor consists of a block of bonded laminations with four holes drilled through its thickness. A wire is fed through one hole diagonally across the back of the laminations and returns through another hole. This wire is fed with alternating current. A second wire is then fed through the other diagonal holes and connected to a suitably instrumented circuit.

Provided that no stress is applied to the block, a symmetrical pattern of magnetic flux is established within the block and no voltage is induced into the output wire. On application of stress the flux pattern is disturbed and a voltage is induced in the output wire, this voltage being proportional to the applied force on the block. This type of instrument may normally be used for measuring forces up to 220 N and above.

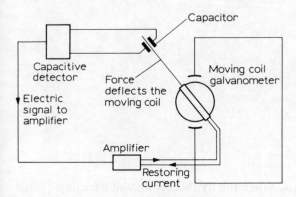

Fig. 8.12 Principle of electromagnetic force balance

When forces less than 10 N are to be measured the electromagnetic force balance principle can be used (Fig. 8.12). If a force is applied which deflects the moving coil from its zero position a signal is transmitted from the capacitive detector to the amplifier. The amplifier transmits a current proportional to this signal sufficient to produce a restoring force on the moving coil which is placed in a steady magnetic field. This restoring current is proportional to the deflecting force.

8.5 Power measurement

As stated in the introduction to this chapter, instruments used for power measurements are known as dynamometers and may be divided into absorption dynamometers and transmission dynamometers. Absorption dynamometers absorb the mechanical energy after measuring it whereas transmission dynamometers provide an indication of the force or torque which is passing through the dynamometer.

Absorption dynamometers may be divided into three major groups as follows:

(a) Mechanical methods
(b) Hydraulic methods
(c) Electrical methods.

8.6 Absorption dynamometers: mechanical methods

One of the most simple forms of measuring power is the rope brake shown in Fig. 8.13. A loop of rope is wrapped round the flywheel or brake drum, one end of the rope being connected to a spring balance while the other

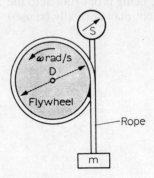

Fig. 8.13 Rope brake

end is connected to a mass. When the flywheel is rotated a frictional force is developed and the rope tightens, thus inducing a force on the spring balance. The torque on the flywheel is equal to the resultant force acting on the flywheel multiplied by the moment arm:

$$T = \tfrac{1}{2}D(mg - S)$$

where T is the torque (N m), D is the flywheel diameter (m), mg is the applied weight (N) and S is the force on the spring balance (N).

The power output from the driving engine can now be determined by multiplying the flywheel torque by its angular velocity in radians per second, i.e.

brake power $= T\omega$ watts

where ω is the angular velocity of the flywheel in radians per second.

The band brake shown in Fig. 8.14 operates on the same principle as the rope brake. A band of brake lining material (A) passes over the upper part of a flywheel F as shown. Attached to the ends of this band are two equally loaded mass carriers. At B a metal strap connects the band to a piece of belt which passes over and is attached at C to a small wheel D. The pointer E is fixed to the wheel D, and passes over the scale S. The power can be calculated from the following relationship:

brake power or the power output at engine shaft
$= \omega r \times$ scale reading in newtons

where ω is the angular velocity in radians per second and r is the flywheel radius.

Two further mechanical brakes commonly used are the Prony brake and the Appold brake. In the former the conversion of energy is by friction of a

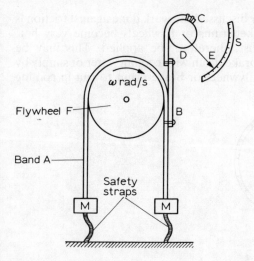

Fig. 8.14 Band brake

brake band or brake shoe on a brake drum. The braking action is due to friction between individual brake shoes or between a flexible brake band and the drum. Heat is dissipated by cooling the brake with water when in continuous use. The power output from the driving engine can be measured by determining the speed of rotation and the torque required to hold the brake arm still (Fig. 8.15).

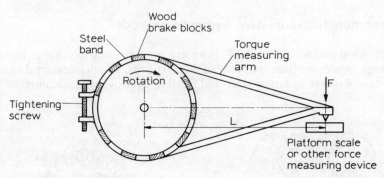

Fig. 8.15 Prony brake

A limitation of the Prony brake is the variation of the coefficient of friction between the brake blocks and the wheel. The Appold brake compensates for this by incorporating a lever which applies a known tension to the band of brake blocks (Fig. 8.16).

Any increase in friction drag causes the lever to move down and hit the lower stop. The stop causes the lever to pivot about C thus reducing the applied tension in the band. A reduction in friction drag will cause the lever to hit the upper stop and hence the applied tension in the band is increased.

In all the dynamometers so far discussed the work done against friction is dissipated as heat and the brake drums or flywheels become very hot. Efficient means of cooling must, therefore, be applied. This may be achieved by partially filling the brake drum with cooling water or simply by allowing the lower part of the flywheel or brake drum to run in cooling water.

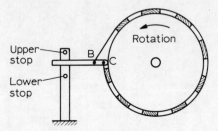

Fig. 8.16 Appold brake

A further mechanical method of power measurement is the measurement of indicated power or the power transferred to or from a piston as it reciprocates within a cylinder. A trace is taken of the variation of cylinder pressure with the cylinder volume during the operating cycle. The area of the indicator diagram produced is a measure of the work done per cycle and hence the indicated power. Engine indication is discussed in detail in Chapter 9.

8.7 Absorption dynamometers: hydraulic methods

The mechanical methods described above are not particularly suitable for testing high power engines running at high speeds. Mechanical brakes become cumbersome in larger sizes and flexible control is not obtained.

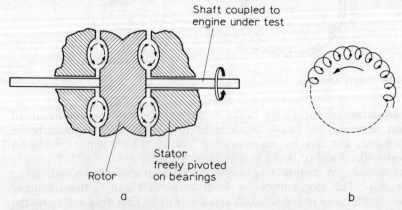

Fig. 8.17 Froude hydraulic dynamometer, showing (a) the principle (b) the helical path of the water

The hydraulic dynamometer consists essentially of a rotor mounted on the dynamometer shaft which is coupled to the shaft of the engine under test. The rotor is enclosed by a watertight stator casing mounted on trunnions and thus freely pivoted [Fig. 8.17(a)]. The stator casing is connected to the dynamometer arm and balance system and is in two halves, one of which is situated on either side of the rotor. The rotor and stator are fitted with a system of cup-shaped pockets, those on each half of the stator being of opposite pitch to those which they face on the rotor and thus forming spherical chambers when they match.

The stator and rotor pockets are so shaped that when the dynamometer is in action the path of the water is a helix as shown in Fig. 8.17(b). The vortex produced gives rise to a braking effect between rotor and stator, the stator tending to turn in the direction of rotation of the rotor.

The tendency of the stator to rotate is resisted by the dynamometer balancing system which is connected to the stator.

Control of load

The load applied to the engine is controlled by interposing sluice gates in the clearance space between the stator and rotor pockets. The gates may be moved using threaded rods which are operated by a hand wheel. The effect of blanking off part of the pocket area is to reduce the braking effect between rotor and stator and hence to reduce the load applied to the engine shaft. Smooth control of load over a wide range can be obtained using this method. Typical size range from a few kilowatts up to 35 MW.

Advantages of the hydraulic dynamometer over mechanical brakes

(1) The hydraulic dynamometer has a constant supply of water running through it so that the braking medium is also the coolant.
(2) The brake power of much larger, higher speed engines can be measured using a hydraulic dynamometer.
(3) Small braking loads such as friction forces acting at the shaft glands will cause an extra small torque to be applied to the stator. This torque, however, will be included in that measured on the balancing system.
(4) The hydraulic dynamometer may be protected from hunting effects by means of a dashpot damper.

Two further hydraulic dynamometers are the fan brake and the hydrostatic dynamometer. The former consists of a shaft having a series of radial arms fixed to it. The arms carry plates which are fixed normal to their direction of motion. On rotation of the brake a resisting torque is produced which can be shown to be proportional to the area of the blades, the speed squared, the density of the ambient air and the cube of the blade radius arm (Fig. 8.18).

In the hydrostatic dynamometer (Fig. 8.19) the engine input is connected to a hydraulic pump unit which is mounted on trunnions. The reaction to the applied torque is sensed by means of a transducer fitted on the pump unit base plate. The pump unit is mounted on an oil reservoir

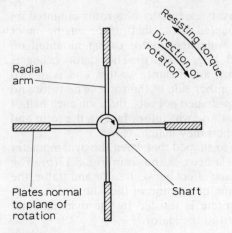

Fig. 8.18 Fan brake

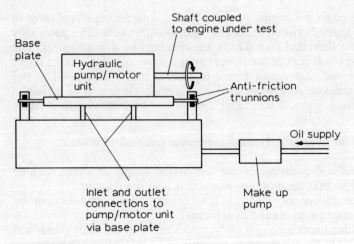

Fig. 8.19 Hydrostatic dynamometer

tank and a gear-type make-up pump is also fitted in the circuit. This device has the advantage that it may be used as a motor for engine starting and running in. In this case the engine on test may be rotated by supplying power from the make-up pump but if the dynamometer is designed purely for absorption then the make-up pump supplies only the system losses. Pressure and flow control valves may be incorporated in the hydraulic circuit so that the load characteristics of the dynamometer can be changed with suitable adjustment.

Apart from the start-up and motoring facility the hydrostatic dynamometer has the following additional desirable features:

(1) High torque at low engine speeds
(2) Accurate torque readings over the range of the machine

(3) Two directional operation
(4) The ability to be programmed on a computer.

8.8 Absorption dynamometers: electrical methods

If an engine is coupled to a dynamo and an electrical load is applied to the dynamo then the engine must produce power in order to drive the dynamo. The power output from the engine may be estimated if the load on the generator is known. Account must be taken of frictional effects, windage and electrical losses in the generator, and measurement accuracy may not be very good.

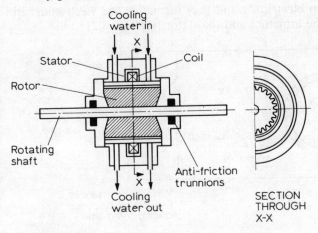

Fig. 8.20 Eddy current dynamometer

Two electrical dynamometers which operate on a similar principle to the Froude hydraulic dynamometer are the eddy current dynamometer and the all-electric dynamometer. The *eddy current dynamometer* consists of a toothed rotor coupled to the shaft of the engine under test and running inside the smooth bore of the stator, the clearance between stator bore and rotor teeth being very small. The stator carries circumferentially wound field windings and these, when excited by a small direct current, set up a magnetic flux which links the rotor and stator. The magnetic flux concentrates near the rotor teeth and, when the rotor rotates, eddy currents are induced in the stator shell near the surface. The eddy current fields react with the main field and set up a force on the rotor which tends to resist the torque applied by the engine. The stator is mounted in anti-friction trunnions and the torque measuring arm is fitted to the stator. A diagram of the eddy current dynamometer is shown in Fig. 8.20.

The power produced by the engine under test is dissipated as heat which is removed from the dynamometer by a flow of cooling water through the space between rotor and stator, the water being carried round and through the machine by the motion of the rotor teeth.

The following torques act on the stator casing and are all measured by the torque measuring device:

(1) The main torque due to the generation of eddy currents
(2) The torque due to slight hydraulic effects (cooling water)
(3) Friction torque of shaft bearings.

The *all-electric dynamometer* consists of an electric dynamo, the shaft of which is coupled to that of the engine under test and the stator of which is connected to a balancing system. The stator itself is mounted on anti-friction trunnions. The electromagnetic reaction between the rotating member (armature) and the stator causes a torque to be transmitted between the armature and stator. Control of the engine load is effected by loading the dynamo electrically and thus increasing the electromagnetic reaction between the armature and the stator (see Fig. 8.21).

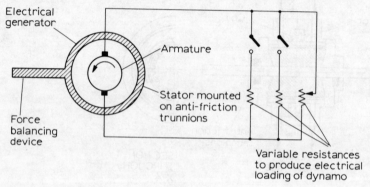

Fig. 8.21 All-electric dynamometer

On this type of dynamometer the resisting torque consists of the following:

(1) Friction torque
(2) Resistance torque due to windage
(3) Torque due to the electromagnetic reaction.

The sum of all these torques is measured by the balancing device which therefore gives an accurate determination of the torque applied to the engine.

An absorption dynamometer which is used to measure electrical power in an alternating current circuit is the wattmeter. The current is passed between two fixed coils in series while a moving coil acts as the wattmeter voltage coil and carries a current proportional to the voltage of the circuit across which it is connected. A high non-inductive resistance is connected in series with the voltage coil. The deflection of the moving coil depends on the currents flowing in the coils and the power factor.

In an alternating current circuit the instantaneous power is given by

$$p = ei$$

where p is the instantaneous power, e is the instantaneous voltage and i is the instantaneous current. Therefore if both the current and voltage waves are sinusoidal, and the current is lagging in phase by an angle ϕ, then

$$e = E_{max} \sin \omega t$$

and

$$i = I_{max} \sin (\omega t - \phi)$$

Therefore (substituting θ for ωt)

$$p = E_{max} I_{max} \sin \theta \sin (\theta - \phi)$$

The mean power is

$$p = \frac{1}{2\pi} \int_0^{2\pi} E_{max} I_{max} \sin \theta \sin (\theta - \phi) \, d\theta$$

$$= \frac{E_{max} I_{max}}{2\pi} \int_0^{2\pi} \tfrac{1}{2} \{\cos \phi - \cos (2\theta - \phi)\} \, d\theta$$

$$= \frac{E_{max} I_{max}}{4\pi} \left[\theta \cos \phi - \tfrac{1}{2} \sin (2\theta - \phi) \right]_0^{2\pi}$$

$$= \frac{E_{max} I_{max}}{2} \cos \phi$$

$$= EI \cos \phi$$

where E and I are the r.m.s. values of current and voltage, and $\cos \phi$ is known as the power factor.

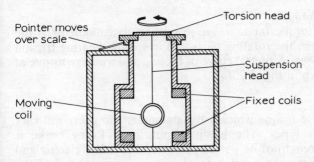

Fig. 8.22(a) Torsion head wattmeter

Wattmeters may be divided into two classes:

(1) Suspended coil, torsion instruments
(2) Pivoted coil, direct indicating instruments.

In the former class the moving, or voltage, coil is suspended from a torsion head by a metal suspension which serves as a lead to the coil. The moving coil is situated entirely inside the fixed current carrying coils. The torsion head carries a scale, and when in use the moving coil is brought back to the zero position by turning this head, the power being calculated by multiplying the number of divisions turned through by a constant for the instrument. A typical suspended coil wattmeter is shown in Fig. 8.22(a).

In the direct indicating instrument the moving coil is carried on a pivoted spindle and the movement is spring controlled. The moving system carries a pointer and a damping vane which moves in a sector-shaped box; Fig. 8.22(b) shows a typical instrument of this type.

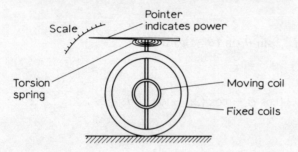

Fig. 8.22(b) Pivoted coil direct indicating wattmeter

8.9 Comparison of absorption dynamometers

Different dynamometers may easily be compared if the useful range of each is first determined. The useful range is limited by a number of factors which can be combined to form a dynamometer characteristics diagram. These factors are now considered in turn:

Friction and windage torque
The lowest possible torque input to an absorption dynamometer is the torque required to turn the rotating parts and overcome bearing friction and rotor windage losses. A typical curve of friction and windage torque at varying speed is shown in Fig. 8.23(a).

Loading limit torque
The maximum possible torque which a dynamometer can exert will vary widely with different types. The loading limit for a Prony brake is determined by the strength of its weakest structural part but electric and hydraulic dynamometers can exert zero torque at zero speed, and the maximum possible torque will increase with an increase in speed. This is shown in Fig. 8.23(b).

Mechanical limit torque and centrifugal limit
The maximum torque which a dynamometer may exert is limited by the mechanical strength of the dynamometer frame or by the range of the force

measuring device, whichever is the smaller. Therefore a top limiting mechanical torque independent of speed is introduced. Also a further strength limitation is introduced due to the maximum allowable safe operating speed which will limit the usable speed regardless of torque. These are indicated in Fig. 8.23(c).

Cooling limit
If a dynamometer is to absorb energy for an appreciable length of time there must be adequate cooling capacity to absorb this energy in the form of heat. The cooling limit is shown in Fig. 8.23(d) and will result in lower maximum allowable torque at higher speeds since power is torque times angular velocity.

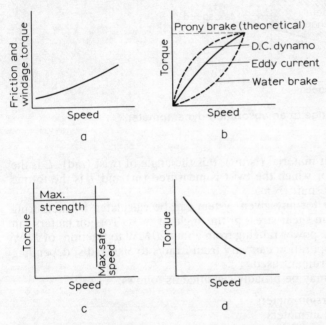

Fig. 8.23 (a) Friction torque   (b) Maximum torque
         (c) Mechanical limits (d) Limits of cooling

All the limiting conditions discussed above may be combined on one dynamometer characteristics diagram from which the useful range of the dynamometer may be determined (see Fig. 8.24).

8.10 Transmission dynamometers

If the torque transmitted by a shaft is measured the power can be calculated by multiplying the torque by the angular velocity of the shaft. It can be shown that

$$\frac{T}{J} = \frac{\tau}{r} = \frac{G\theta}{L}$$

where J is the polar second moment of area of the shaft section (m^4), τ is the maximum induced shear stress at the outside surface (N/m^2), r is the radius at which the maximum shear stress occurs (m), G is the modulus of

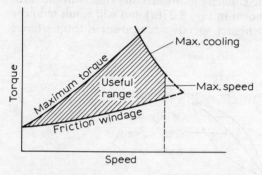

Fig. 8.24 Useful range of an absorption dynamometer

rigidity of the shaft material (N/m^2), θ is the angle of twist (rad), L is the length of shaft over which the twist is measured (m) and T is the torque transmitted by the shaft (N m).

Thus the torque for any given system can be calculated by measuring either the maximum shear stress or the angle of twist. Torsion meters can be used to measure power ranging from about 20 MW to fractions of 1 kW and the speed of operation can vary from 2 rad/s to 5000 rad/s, depending on the type of instrument used.

Torsion meters may be broadly classified as follows:

(a) Mechanical torsion meters
(b) Electrical torsion meters
(c) Optical torsion meters.

8.11 Mechanical torsion meters

The torque transmitted by a rotating shaft may be determined by measuring the angle of twist. The rotating indicator shown in Fig. 8.25 will give the angle of twist over a given length of bar. The angle of twist may be observed while the bar is rotating using a stroboscope and hence the torque calculated.

The power transmitted may now be calculated by multiplying the torque by the rotational speed of the bar, i.e.

$$P = T\omega \quad \text{watts}$$

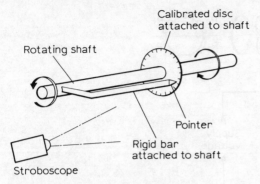

Fig. 8.25 Stroboscopic torque meter

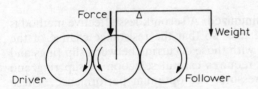

Fig. 8.26 Simple torque meter

where T is the torque (N m) and ω is the angular velocity (rad/s).

A simple torque meter suitable for applications where the driven shaft is near to and parallel with the drive shaft is shown in Fig. 8.26. The applied torque can be resolved as a force at the pitch circle diameter of the drive gear and for equilibrium this force is resisted by a force equal in magnitude but opposite in direction. The resisting force is applied through a lever system using weights.

8.12 Electrical torsion meters

Perhaps the most widely used electrical torsion meter is the strain gauge torque meter, the principle of which is shown in Fig. 8.27. The strain gauges are mounted mutually at 45° to the axis of the shaft. Under an applied torque the tensile and compressive principal strains can be measured and hence the applied torque may be calculated. The strain gauge output is brought out through slip rings and brushes to a strain bridge indicator. A major difficulty has been that the magnitude of the signal leaving the gauge is low and often the 'noise' level in variation of contact resistance is of the same order of magnitude as the signal itself.

Circuits and techniques have now been developed so that slip rings need not be a source of significant inaccuracy and three methods have been employed to overcome slip ring contact resistance variations. One method involves construction of an electrical circuit so that the slip ring contact resistance is not in series with the gauge itself but is placed at some point in

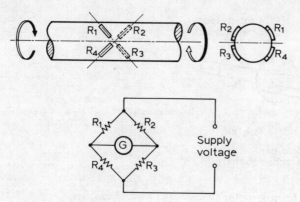

Supply
voltage

Fig. 8.27 Strain gauge torque meter

the circuit where its effect is minimized. A second, less effective method is to use high resistance strain gauges so that the resistance change of the gauges will be large compared with those occurring between slip rings and brushes. The third technique requires careful selection of slip ring and brush materials and brush pressures for optimum performance. These techniques are covered in more detail in Section 6.13.

If the applied torque can be used to vary the width of an air gap in a magnetic circuit then the resulting electrical output will be proportional to torque. Two castings, A and B, are fitted to the shaft at a known distance apart (Fig. 8.28). A is attached to B by thin steel strips which transmit

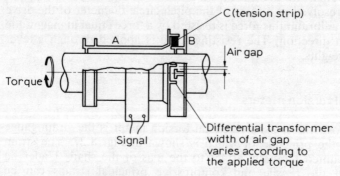

Fig. 8.28 Electrical torsion meter

tension but have little resistance to bending. A differential transformer is fitted between the two castings, one casting being attached to the two transformer coils while the second casting is attached to the iron core piece. A second differential transformer is included in the indicating circuit, the air gap being adjusted by hand using a micrometer screw.

The primary coils of the two transformers are connected in series and energized with alternating current while the two secondary coils are connected such that the induced e.m.f.s are opposed. A variation in air gap in either transformer will cause current to flow in the secondary circuit owing to the fact that the e.m.f. in one secondary coil is increased while that in the other secondary coil is reduced by an equal amount. The flow of current in the secondary circuit may be measured using a suitable instrument.

The air gap of the indicator unit may be adjusted using the micrometer screw until no current flows in the secondary circuit. The air gaps in the two transformers must now be equal. Hence the applied torque is directly proportional to the width of the air gap or the micrometer reading.

In practice the power is calculated by multiplying the micrometer reading by the shaft speed and a constant for the meter.

A meter similar to the above uses the principle of varying capacitance as a measure of shaft twist, and hence applied torque is available. The arrangement is similar to the above but in this instrument the plates of a condenser are connected to the castings clamped to the shaft. Any twist in the shaft will change the relative positions of the condenser plates and hence the output signal will vary. This output signal can then be used as a measure of applied torque. Hence

power transmitted = output signal × constant for meter.

8.13 Optical torsion meters

Using an apparatus similar to the electrical torsion meters described above, optical methods may be used to measure the angle of twist of a shaft. The apparatus shown in Fig. 8.29 is basically the same as that in Fig. 8.28 except

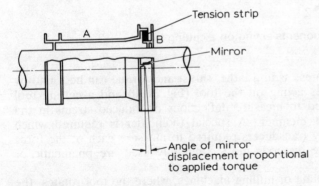

Fig. 8.29 Optical torsion meter

that in addition to the tension strips there are two links which have torque mirrors incorporated. Hence any relative movement of the two castings due to applied torque results in partial inclination of the two mirrors. If a beam of light from a source is reflected by the mirrors on to a graduated scale, a movement on the scale will represent a measure of applied torque.

If the mirrors are arranged back to back there will be a reflection from each mirror every half revolution which is quite sufficient if the torque remains constant during each revolution, e.g. a steam turbine. In applications where the torque varies during a revolution, e.g. a reciprocating engine, a second system of mirrors giving four readings per revolution would be desirable.

The deflection of the mirrors is directly proportional to the applied torque. Therefore

$$\text{power} = \frac{\text{scale reading (m)}}{\text{a constant}} \times \text{angular velocity (rad/s)}$$

where the value of the constant will be specific to the meter.

8.14 Power absorbed in machining operations

In most machining operations the motion of the cutting tool will be both angular and linear with respect to the work. The power absorbed in the cutting process can be divided into two sections:

(a) The power absorbed by the torque exerted on the rotating member;
(b) The power absorbed by the thrust needed to produce linear motion.

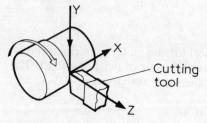

Fig. 8.30 Force components acting on a cutting tool

When the work rotates, as in a lathe, thrust and torque can be found by measuring the forces acting on the tool (Fig. 8.30) and a cutting tool dynamometer is used to measure deflections or induced strains in the cutting tool support member. A special toolholder is required which houses the necessary transducers required to measure each of the force components and the methods most commonly used are pneumatic or elastic deformation.

In the case of drilling or milling machines, where the tool rotates, the forces on the work are measured by means of a special workholder which houses both thrust and torque measuring systems. Torque measurement is achieved using a force transducer mounted at a known radius which detects the force produced at the end of an arm attached to the dynamometer body which is mounted in bearings. A typical pneumatic force transducer which produces a pressure signal proportional to applied force is shown in Fig. 8.31.

A force applied to the measuring head will deflect the measuring head thus closing the air gap and increasing the variable pressure signal which may be measured using a suitable pressure measuring device.

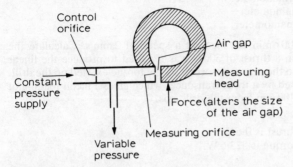

Fig. 8.31 Pneumatic force transducer

Study problems

8.1 A simple tensile testing machine is shown in Fig. 8.32. Calculate the force to be applied at A if the force on the specimen is to be 20 kN.

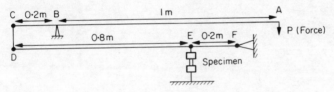

Fig. 8.32 Tensile testing machine for Problem 8.1

Answer: $F = 800 \, \text{N}$

8.2 A hydraulic load cell of the type shown in Fig. 8.8 is required to measure a maximum load of 500 kN. If the effective diameter of the diaphragm is 200 mm calculate the maximum pressure to be indicated on the Bourdon gauge. Assuming the scale is linear and operates over an arc of 270° calculate the sensitivity of the pressure gauge.

Answers: $15 \cdot 92 \, \text{MN/m}^2$; $16 \cdot 9° / \text{MN m}^{-2}$

8.3 A rope brake is used to measure the power of an engine under test. The diameter of the brake drum is 1 m and the spring balance records a load of $4 \cdot 57 \, \text{kg}$ when the applied load is 10 kg and the engine rotates at 3000 r/min. Calculate the power output from the engine under these conditions.

Answer: $8 \cdot 37 \, \text{kW}$

8.4 (*a*) Explain the meaning of the terms:

(i) Absorption dynamometer
(ii) Transmission dynamometer.

(*b*) Show with the aid of sketches how you would measure the power developed by an engine using each of the following:

  (i) A mechanical dynamometer
 (ii) A hydraulic dynamometer
(iii) An electrical dynamometer.

8.5 A drill running at 500 r/min advances at a speed of 2 mm/s. Calculate the power absorbed when a thrust of 300 N was required to produce the linear motion. Calculate also the power absorbed by the torque exerted on the drill. The torque is measured by a force transducer which gives a mean reading of 100 N at a radius of 100 mm from the drill axis.

Answers
Power absorbed by thrust is 0·6 W
Power absorbed by torque is 523·6 W

9 Measurement of pressure

Pressure measurement can be broadly divided into two groups as follows:

(a) The measurement of static pressure
(b) The measurement of fluctuating pressure.

The term 'static pressure' is widely used in the measurement of pressure, liquid level and rate of flow. When a fluid in a process is still or 'static', the static pressure at a point in the fluid is the pressure exerted by the height of fluid above that point. If a pipe full of a fluid in motion is considered, the static pressure at a tapping in the pipe wall may be found by connecting a suitable pressure measuring device to the tapping.

When it is required to measure a rapidly fluctuating pressure (e.g. the cylinder pressure in an internal combustion engine) the methods used for static pressure measurement are not suitable. In this case a pressure transducer, which converts the pressure into a signal which may be recorded, is used.

9.1 Static pressure measurement

Static pressure measurement may conveniently be considered under the following headings:

(a) Differential pressure measurement.
(b) Gauge pressure, which is the pressure measured above the local atmospheric pressure.
(c) Absolute pressure, which is the total pressure measured from zero pressure as the datum point. When the absolute pressure exceeds the local atmospheric pressure it may be considered to be the sum of the gauge pressure and local atmospheric pressure.
(d) Vacuum measurement. In this case the pressure to be measured is less than the local atmospheric pressure.

9.2 Differential pressure measurement

One of the most popular devices for measuring differential pressure is the U-tube manometer (Fig. 9.1). The glass U-shaped tube is filled about half full with liquid, usually either water or mercury. Generally speaking water is most commonly used as the measuring medium but if higher pressures or more compact gauges are required mercury is used. A scale is fixed between the limbs and the difference in level between the limbs A and B due to a pressure differential $(P_1 - P_2)$ may be measured. If the higher pressure P_1 is applied to A and the lower pressure P_2 to B, the liquid in A will be forced down, that in B will rise, and the action will continue until pressure P_1 is balanced by the sum of P_2 and the pressure due to the height of liquid column h between the two levels. Then

$$P_1 = P_2 + \rho g h$$

where P_1 and P_2 are absolute pressures (N/m^2), h is the difference in

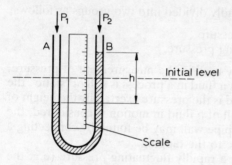

Fig. 9.1 U-tube manometer

levels (m), ρ is the density of manometer fluid (kg/m^3) and g is the acceleration due to gravity (m/s^2). Alternatively,

$$P_1 - P_2 = \rho g h$$

where $(P_1 - P_2)$ is the pressure difference applied across the manometer.

If limb B of the manometer is open to the atmosphere then in this case P_2 is the atmospheric pressure. Therefore the above equation becomes

$$P_1 - \text{atmospheric pressure} = \rho g h$$

Hence in this case the manometer is measuring the difference between the absolute pressure and the local atmospheric pressure. This is known as the *gauge pressure*.

Range of the simple U-tube manometer

The simple U-tube manometer is normally used up to 1·25 m mercury (0–162 kN/m²).

An industrial development of the simple U-tube manometer for measuring high pressures is shown in Fig. 9.2. Here one limb is of much larger diameter than the other. Also the limbs are often constructed of steel.

A differential pressure is applied to the manometer, the lower pressure P_2 to the wide limb and the higher pressure P_1 to the narrow limb. The liquid in the wide limb rises and that in the narrow limb falls until the following pressure balance is obtained:

$$P_1 = P_2 + \rho g H = P_2 + \rho g (h + d)$$

where H is the total difference in levels (m), h is the difference between the level in the small diameter limb and the zero level (m) and d is the difference between the level in the large diameter limb and the zero level (m).

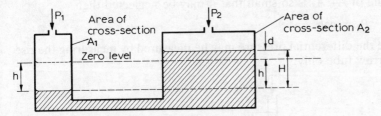

Fig. 9.2 Industrial U-tube manometer

Also the volume of liquid which has left limb A (the narrow limb) must be equal to that which has passed into limb B (the wide limb), i.e.

$$A_1 h = A_2 d \quad \text{hence} \quad h = A_2 d / A_1$$

where A_1 is the cross-sectional area of the small diameter limb (m²) and A_2 is the cross-sectional area of the large diameter limb (m²).

Substituting,

$$P_1 = P_2 + \rho g d \left(1 + \frac{A_2}{A_1} \right)$$

or

$$P_1 - P_2 = \rho g d \left(1 + \frac{A_2}{A_1} \right)$$

or

$$d = \frac{P_1 - P_2}{\rho g (1 + A_2 / A_1)}$$

The distance therefore that the liquid rises in the wide tube is proportional to the differential pressure $(P_1 - P_2)$. In many industrial manometers of this type a metal float is included in the wide chamber, the float being connected via a linking mechanism to a pointer or pen recorder. Therefore as the level of the liquid varies in response to changing pressure differentials so the float will ride on the surface of the liquid and record the change in level or differential pressure.

Cistern manometer

The working of the above instrument would not be affected if the narrow tube were inserted directly into the wide limb as shown in Fig. 9.3.

If a pressure differential $(P_1 - P_2)$ is applied to the manometer then

$$P_1 - P_2 = \rho g (h + d)$$

Also $A_1 d = A_2 h$, and therefore $d = (A_2/A_1)h$. Hence

$$P_1 - P_2 = \rho g h \left(1 + \frac{A_2}{A_1} \right)$$

If the value of A_2/A_1 is so small that it may be neglected then

$$P_1 - P_2 = \rho g h$$

Therefore the differential pressure may be measured by measuring the rise in the narrow tube only.

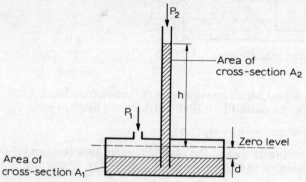

Fig. 9.3 Cistern manometer

In practice the cistern diameter (wide limb) is made so large compared with the narrow tube diameter that the drop in level, d, from the zero level in the cistern is negligible.

Inclined tube manometer

A special development of the U-tube manometer is the inclined tube manometer. The advantage of this device is that it gives an increased length of scale compared with the simple U-tube for the same differential pressure. One limb consists of a glass tube inclined at an angle to the horizontal or vertical, and the other of a wide chamber or cistern. The sloping tube carries a scale adjacent to it. A typical inclined tube device is shown in Fig. 9.4.

$$P_1 - P_2 = \rho g (h_1 + d \sin \alpha)$$

$$A_1 h_1 = A_2 d \quad \text{i.e.} \quad h_1 = \frac{A_2}{A_1} d$$

$$P_1 - P_2 = \rho g d \left(\frac{A_2}{A_1} + \sin \alpha \right)$$

and as in the previous example, if A_1 is large compared with A_2 the ratio A_2/A_1 may be neglected. Therefore

$$P_1 - P_2 = \rho g d \sin \alpha$$

$$d \sin \alpha = h$$

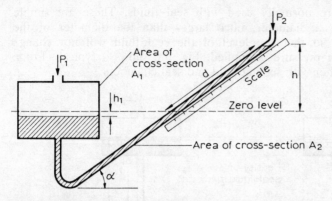

Fig. 9.4 Inclined U-tube manometer

where h is the height which would have been registered if an ordinary U-tube had been used.

If the tube is inclined at an angle of 30° to the horizontal, i.e. $\sin \alpha = \frac{1}{2}$, then

$$d \times \tfrac{1}{2} = h \qquad \text{or} \qquad d = 2h$$

Therefore a scale length of about double the normal value is obtained by inclining the tube at 30° to the horizontal.

Use of sealing fluids with manometers: the two liquid U-tube manometer

When the pressures of certain liquids are measured using a U-tube manometer it may be necessary to separate the liquid from the manometer liquid by using a sealing fluid. For example if the two liquids would

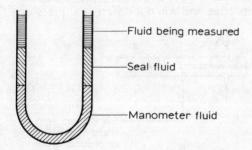

Fig. 9.5 U-tube manometer with seal fluid

undergo a chemical reaction when mixed, a seal fluid is required. Seal fluids must not mix with the manometer fluid or the fluid being measured and therefore they must be lighter than the manometer fluid but heavier than the measured fluid (see Fig. 9.5). Exactly the same amount of seal fluid is added to both columns of the manometer so that they cancel out.

Seal chambers are normally used with seal fluids. These are simple reservoirs having a diameter much larger than the diameter of the manometer tube so that the level of the seal fluid will not change significantly when pressure is applied. Fig. 9.6 shows a typical U-tube manometer together with sealing fluid and seal chambers.

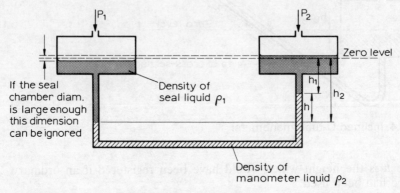

Fig. 9.6 U-tube manometer with sealing fluid and seal chambers

$$P_1 + \rho_1 g h_2 = P_2 + \rho_1 g h_1 + \rho_2 g h$$

Therefore

$$P_1 - P_2 = \rho_1 g (h_1 - h_2) + \rho_2 g h$$

$$= -\rho_1 g h + \rho_2 g h = (\rho_2 - \rho_1) g h$$

Diaphragms, diaphragm stacks and bellows gauges

The *single diaphragm* in its most simple form is a thin flat plate of circular shape. The plate is fixed round its edge and when a differential pressure

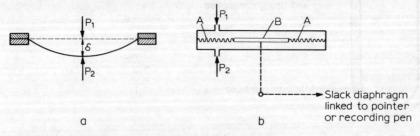

Fig. 9.7 (*a*) A simple diaphragm: differential pressure = $P_1 - P_2$
(*b*) The slack diaphragm differential pressure gauge

occurs across it the plate will deflect as shown in Fig. 9.7(*a*). Only for relatively small movements is there a linear connection between pressure and deflection and some modification of this simple case is desirable for practical instrumentation.

For the measurement of low pressures an extremely flexible diaphragm is required. The diaphragm assembly is made in the form of a ring of fabric with a disc of metal or other rigid material at the centre. The principle of a fabric or 'slack' diaphragm differential pressure gauge is shown in Fig. 9.7(b).

A is the fabric and B is the solid centre piece which is linked to a pointer or recording pen. With the slack diaphragm gauge it is unnecessary for the diaphragm assembly to be circular and quite often it may be elongated. A variety of materials have been used for the slack diaphragm, the most popular being leather, plastic, rubberized fabric, nylon and silk. Gauges working on this principle can be used up to 1 m of water or about $10 \, kN/m^2$.

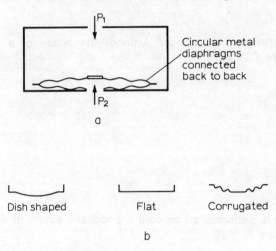

a

Dish shaped   Flat   Corrugated

b

Fig. 9.8 (*a*) Metallic capsule pressure gauge
(*b*) Typical diaphragm shapes

An alternative form of pressure measuring instrument is the *metallic capsule*. The instrument consists of a pair of circular metal diaphragms connected back to back to form an elastic capsule as shown in Fig. 9.8(*a*). One pressure is applied to the inside of the capsule which is surrounded on the outside by the other pressure. The deflection of the capsule is found to have a linear relationship with the pressure provided the movement is not excessive. The diaphragms used in a capsule gauge are generally dished, flat or corrugated in shape [Fig. 9.8(*b*)].

A deflection many times greater than that of a single capsule can be obtained when a series of corrugated metal diaphragms each containing a central hole are joined in a leak-proof manner at the inner or outer edges as shown in Fig. 9.9. If $P_1 > P_2$ the diaphragm stack is compressed. The number of diaphragms used may vary from two (the capsule) up to twenty or so.

The *metallic bellows* is similar in shape to the diaphragm stack but its method of construction is entirely different. Initially a thin walled tube is taken and formed, by hydraulic presses, into the corrugated shape shown in Fig. 9.10. Bellows can be produced in quite large diameters, up to about 300 mm. The larger sizes, however, are used mainly on control valves and not for pressure measuring instruments.

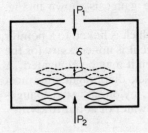

Fig. 9.9 Diaphragm stack
The stack is compressed an amount δ under the action of a differential pressure $P_1 > P_2$

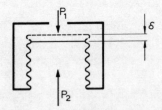

Fig. 9.10 Metallic bellows unit
The bellows unit is deflected an amount δ under the action of a differential pressure $P_1 > P_2$

A typical industrial gauge used for differential pressure measurement is shown in Fig. 9.11. The double bellows arrangement on the left hand side is connected via a linkage to a recording pen or pointer while the right hand bellows acts as a seal for the range adjusting spring.

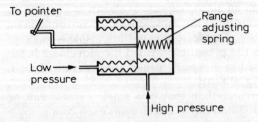

Fig. 9.11 Industrial bellows gauge used to measure differential pressure

The materials most commonly used for the manufacture of diaphragms are steel, phosphor bronze, nickel silver and beryllium copper. Bellows materials have largely consisted of 80–20 brass (80 per cent copper and 20 per cent zinc), phosphor bronze, stainless steel and beryllium copper.

Ring balance

This apparatus consists of a hollow or annular circular ring divided into two sections by a partition B and a seal fluid (Fig. 9.12). The sections on either side of the partition are connected to the two pressure sources. The ring is pivoted on a knife edge at its centre and when a pressure difference is

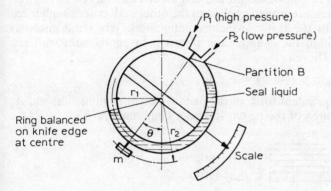

Fig. 9.12 Ring balance

applied across the partition a rotating moment is set up. The ring starts to rotate in a direction away from the higher pressure until the opposing moment, created by the mass at the foot of the ring, balances the rotating moment. Now

$$\text{rotating moment} = (P_1 - P_2)Ar_1$$

where $(P_1 - P_2)$ is the differential pressure, A is the cross-sectional area of the tube and r_1 is the mean radius of the ring.

Also

$$\text{restoring moment} = mgr_2 \sin \theta$$

where m is the mass, r_2 is the radius of its point of application, θ is the angle of rotation and g is the acceleration due to gravity.

Therefore

$$(P_1 - P_2)Ar_1 = mgr_2 \sin \theta$$

or

$$P_1 - P_2 = \frac{mgr_2}{Ar_1} \sin \theta$$

Therefore the differential pressure applied to the ring balance is proportional to the angle of rotation, i.e. the angle of rotation is a measure of differential pressure. Typical ranges for this instrument would be within the limit 0–300 mm water.

9.3 Gauge pressure measurement

The *dead weight free-piston gauge* has been used for the precise determination of steady pressures for nearly eighty years. The gauge (Fig. 9.13) consists of an accurately machined piston of known weight which is inserted into a close fitting cylinder, both of known cross-sectional area. A number of masses of known weight are first loaded on one end of the free piston and fluid pressure is then applied to the other end until enough force is developed to lift the piston–weight combination. When the piston is floating freely within the cylinder the piston is in equilibrium with the system pressure. Therefore

$$P(\text{dead weight pressure}) = F_e / A_e$$

where F_e is the equivalent force of the piston–weight combination and A_e is the equivalent area of the piston–cylinder combination.

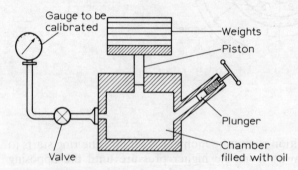

Fig. 9.13 Dead weight pressure tester

The film of fluid leaking from the system through the piston–cylinder clearance provides lubrication and the piston is also rotated to further reduce the friction.

Perhaps the most commonly used gauge for the measurement of gauge pressure is the *Bourdon tube gauge*. The gauge consists of a metal tube of approximately elliptical cross-section which is formed into a C-shape by special machines. The tube is fixed at one end, which is open to accept the applied pressure, but free at the other end, which is closed. When the pressure within the tube is increased the cross-section of the tube tends to become round and the entire tube tends to straighten out. Thus the free end of the tube will move, and this motion will be proportional to the pressure difference between the inside and the outside of the tube. The motion of the free end may be magnified and transmitted to an indication pointer by a lever and pinion and quadrant arrangement (see Fig. 9.14). The reference pressure in the case containing the Bourdon tube is usually atmospheric, and therefore the pointer indicates gauge pressure.

Two alternative forms of the Bourdon tube are the helical tube and the flat spiral. The principle of operation for both these gauges is the same as for the C-type, i.e. one end of the tube is closed and sealed, but left free to move, the other end being fixed. If a pressure is now applied to the inside of the tube greater than that outside then the free end will deflect and this movement can be transferred to an indicating pointer as before.

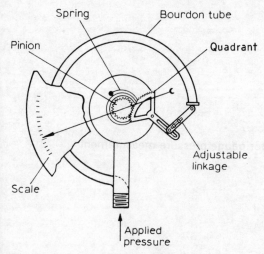

Fig. 9.14 Bourdon tube pressure gauge

Bourdon tubes are normally used for measuring pressures up to $500 \, MN/m^2$. The materials most commonly used in this country are phosphor bronze or similar bronze alloys, steel and beryllium copper. The measurement of very high pressures depends on a Bourdon tube constructed from a metal with a high elastic limit. Therefore phosphor bronze which has a fairly low value is ruled out for high pressure applications and a tough steel or beryllium copper is used.

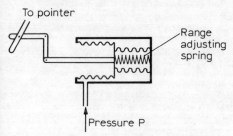

Fig. 9.15 Bellows gauge for gauge pressure measurement
Deflection $\propto P - P_a \propto P_g$
where P_a is the atmospheric pressure and P_g is the gauge pressure.

Single diaphragms, diaphragm stacks and bellows may also be used for gauge pressure measurement. The basic arrangements are the same as for the measurement of differential pressure but in this case one of the pressures is arranged to be atmospheric. Fig. 9.15 illustrates an industrial bellows-type gauge pressure instrument.

The U-tube manometer may conveniently be used for gauge pressure measurement if one limb of the manometer is open to atmospheric pressure as shown in Fig. 9.16.

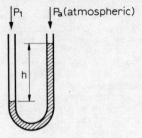

Fig. 9.16 U-tube manometer for gauge pressure measurement

Now

$$P_1 - P_a = \rho g h$$

and

$$P_1 = P_g + P_a$$

where P_g is the gauge pressure. Therefore

$$P_g = \rho g h \quad \text{or} \quad h = P_g / \rho g$$

Thus h is a measure of the gauge pressure P_g.

9.4 Absolute pressure measurement

The *cistern manometer* discussed in Section 9.2 may be modified by closing the end of the tube as shown in Fig. 9.17.

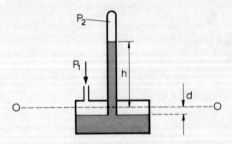

Fig. 9.17 Cistern manometer for gauge pressure measurement

It may be shown that

$$P_1 + P_2 = \rho g h (1 + A_2 / A_1).$$

If P_2 is now made zero, i.e. a perfect vacuum is produced in the space above the liquid, then

$$P_1 = \rho g h (1 + A_2 / A_1)$$

and therefore the height of the liquid column is proportional to the absolute pressure P_1. A particular case is the barometer where P_1 is equal to the atmospheric pressure P_a. The most common cistern barometer in general use is the Fortin type, in which the height of the mercury surface in the cistern can be adjusted (Fig. 9.18).

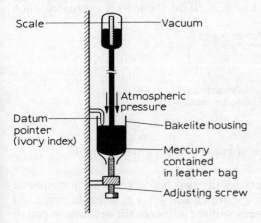

Fig. 9.18 Fortin barometer

The cistern in this case is a leather bag supported in a bakelite housing. The datum adjusting screw is turned until the mercury in the cistern just makes contact with the ivory index, when the mercury surface is aligned with zero on the instrument scale. The indicated height of the mercury column in the glass tube is then determined by lining up the lower edge of the sighting ring with the top of the meniscus in the tube. The vernier scale is then read to give the indicated mercury height at the barometer temperature t.

A barometer using a bellows capsule or diaphragm measuring element is called an *aneroid barometer*. The capsule is evacuated until it contains a

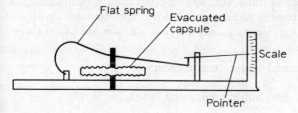

Fig. 9.19 Aneroid barometer

high vacuum and then sealed. The force on the bellows due to atmospheric changes is opposed by a strong spring and the motion of the bellows as the atmospheric pressure changes is transmitted through a mechanical magnification system to a pointer, which indicates the atmospheric pressure in millimetres of mercury on a scale. A typical aneroid barometer is shown in

Fig. 9.19. The aneroid barometer is calibrated using the Fortin mercury barometer as a standard. Multiplication is so high that movement friction is important and therefore the gauge should be tapped to reduce friction for a true reading.

Diaphragm stacks or *bellows* instruments can be used to measure absolute pressure as shown in Fig. 9.20. If one bellows is evacuated, then

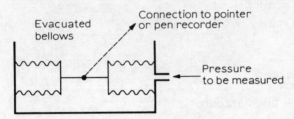

Fig. 9.20 Bellows instrument for absolute pressure measurement

by suitable matching the effects on the two bellows due to atmospheric pressure and ambient temperature are equal over a reasonable range. As these effects are in opposition they will not influence the instrument pen or pointer. With the external atmospheric effects balanced out and negligible pressure in one bellows, the deflection of the pen or pointer must be proportional to the total pressure in the other, i.e. the absolute pressure applied to this bellows. These gauges may be used for measuring absolute pressures up to about $500 \, kN/m^2$.

9.5 High vacuum measurement

Some of the instruments previously described can be used for the measurement of vacuum conditions. For example, Bourdon tube instruments may be obtained which measure pressures down to 20 mm mercury and diaphragm instruments may be obtained which measure pressures as low as 1 mm mercury. This section, however, will be concerned with instruments available for the measurement of pressures below 1 mm mercury absolute.

The region below 1 mm mercury may be conveniently split into three sections as follows:

(*a*) Medium high vacuum: 1 to 10^{-3} mm mercury
(*b*) High vacuum: 10^{-3} to 10^{-7} mm mercury
(*c*) Ultra high vacuum: 10^{-7} mm mercury and lower.

Macleod gauge

The basic elements of the Macleod gauge are shown in Fig. 9.21. The capillary A is sealed at the top and the limbs B and C are connected to the vacuum system. A and B are the same diameter and are capillary tubes while C is of wider bore and helps to reduce errors due to capillary.

Initially the movable reservoir is lowered until the mercury column drops below the level of the opening W. At this stage all three limbs are connected to the pressure to be measured. The reservoir is then raised until the mercury fills the bulb and rises in the capillary A such that the gas in A is compressed. In practice the mercury in B is always raised to the same level as the top of the capillary A, which is the zero on the scale. The gas in limb A is compressed according to Boyle's Law.

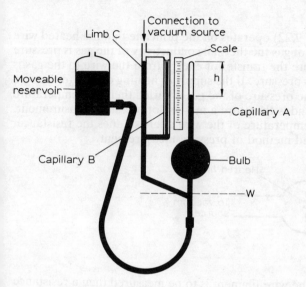

Fig. 9.21 Macleod gauge

If V is the volume of the bulb and limb A above the level W, p the pressure of the gas in the system connected to B and C, v the volume of the gas in the sealed limb after compression and p_1 the pressure of the gas in this limb after compression, then

$$pV = p_1 v$$

where p and p_1 are measured in millimetres of mercury. Also

$$v = ah \quad \text{and} \quad h = p_1 - p$$

where a is the cross-sectional area of the limb A and h is the difference in levels between A and B.

Substituting,

$$p = \frac{ah^2}{V - ah}$$

For the measurement of low pressures the value of V should be large compared with a. The ratio V/a is termed the compression ratio and in practice its upper limit is restricted due to the fact that if a is made too small the mercury tends to stick in the capillary tube and if V is made too large an excessive weight of mercury may be involved.

The range of the Macleod gauge is from 10 to 10^{-4} mm mercury and it is frequently used as a calibration device for other high vacuum measuring equipment. A serious disadvantage of the Macleod gauge is that if the gas whose pressure is being measured contains any condensable vapours then Boyle's Law is not obeyed and errors may occur.

Pirani gauge

The Pirani gauge (Fig. 9.22) operates on the principle that if a heated wire is placed in a chamber of gas the thermal conductivity of the gas is pressure dependent and therefore the transfer of energy from the wire to the gas is proportional to the gas pressure. If the supply of heating energy to the wire is kept constant and the pressure of the gas is varied then the temperature of the wire will alter and is therefore a method of pressure measurement. Alternatively, if the temperature of the wire alters so does the resistance, thus providing a second method of pressure measurement.

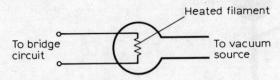

Fig. 9.22 Pirani gauge

If the resistance of the wire filament is to be measured then a resistance bridge is used. The usual method is to balance the bridge at some datum pressure and use the out-of-balance currents at all other pressures as a measure of the relative pressures.

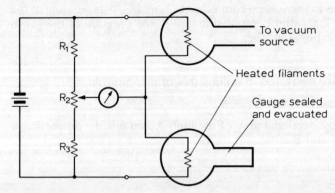

Fig. 9.23 Arrangement to compensate for ambient temperature changes

The heat loss from the filament is also a function of the ambient temperature and compensation for this effect may be achieved in practice by connecting two gauges in series as shown in Fig. 9.23. The measurement gauge is first evacuated and both it and the sealed gauge are exposed to the same environment conditions. The bridge circuit is then adjusted through the resistor R_2 to give a null condition. When the measurement gauge is exposed to the test pressure conditions the deflection of the bridge from the null reading will be independent of changes in ambient temperature.

The range of the Pirani gauge is from 10^{-4} mm to 5 mm of mercury approximately.

Thermionic or hot cathode ionization gauge

The gauge consists of a thermionic triode assembly contained in a glass envelope which may be connected to the system whose pressure is to be measured. A typical assembly is shown in Fig. 9.24. The anode is at a negative potential and the grid is at a positive potential with respect to the filament. The electrons emitted from the filament collide with gas molecules and ionize them; the positive ions then travel to the negatively charged anode. An ionization current will now travel round the anode circuit, this current being a measure of the absolute gas pressure in the gauge. Ultimately electrons will reach the positively charged grid and form an electron current round the grid circuit. The following approximate relation holds:

$$p = kc\, I_1/I_2$$

where p is the absolute pressure, c is a probability factor, k is a constant depending on the potentials used in the gauge and the geometry of the electrodes, I_1 is the ionization current (anode circuit current) and I_2 is the electronic current (grid circuit current).

Provided therefore that the potentials and the electronic current are not altered the absolute gas pressure is proportional to the ionization current.

In the triode arrangement shown in Fig. 9.24 the filament is either pure

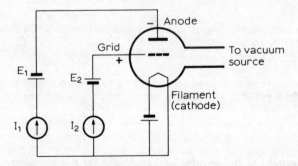

Fig. 9.24 Thermionic or hot cathode ionization gauge

tungsten, thoriated tungsten or platinum alloy coated with barium and strontium oxides. The grid is normally in the form of a cylindrical molybdenum wire helix surrounding the filament. The anode is usually an open-ended nickel cylinder surrounding the grid but in one design it consists of flat nickel plates parallel to the flattened sides of the helix.

A disadvantage of the hot ionization gauge is the tendency to produce X-rays when ionizing electrons strike the grid. The X-rays cause a secondary emission at the anode resulting in a current in the anode circuit in the same direction as that due to the ions. Because of this disadvantage the lower limit of the gauge is usually restricted to 10^{-8} mm mercury.

Cold cathode ionization gauge

In its most simple form this gauge consists of a discharge tube comprising a glass tube, with two sealed-in electrodes connected to the vacuum system (Fig. 9.25). When a high voltage is applied to the electrodes a discharge occurs at a low pressure and as the pressure is reduced the colour and shape of the discharge can give a rough indication of the state of the vacuum and the gases present. At a pressure of about 10^{-2} mm mercury the discharge blacks out and this condition may be used to give an approximate indication of the vacuum present.

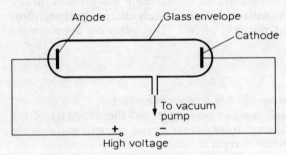

Fig. 9.25 Simple cold cathode ionization gauge (discharge tube)

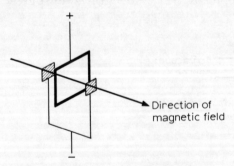

Fig. 9.26 Typical arrangement of the anodes and cathodes for the Penning gauge

A more sophisticated development is the *Penning gauge* in which two electrodes, an anode and a cathode, are contained in a glass envelope (Fig. 9.26). In the simplest design the cathode consists of two parallel flat plates whereas the anode consists of a parallel loop of wire between them. The gauge is placed between the poles of an electromagnet so that the magnetic field is at right angles to the plates. Electrons emitted from the cathode move towards the loop anode in helical paths. The path length is increased by a large amount and the probability of collisions between electrons and molecules of gas to form ions is far greater than for the triode type of ionization gauge. As a result a relatively large discharge current is obtained for a moderately high voltage.

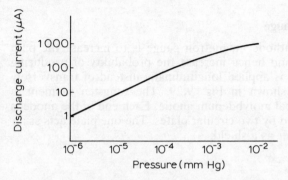

Fig. 9.27 Typical calibration curve for the Penning gauge

A typical calibration curve of pressure versus meter reading is shown in Fig. 9.27. It can be seen that the graph is linear for the lower pressures but above about 10^{-4} mm mercury non-linearities occur.

Cold cathode magnetron gauge

A diagram of a typical gauge of this type is shown in Fig. 9.28. The cathode consists of two circular metal discs, the centres of which are joined together by a thin cylinder. The cylinder acts as an electron source. The anode is a

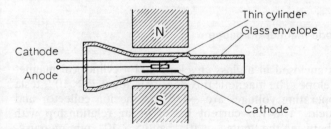

Fig. 9.28 Cold cathode magnetron gauge
The cathode consists of two discs with their centres connected by a thin cylinder.

metal cylinder placed co-axially to the thin cylinder joining the discs. The anode–cathode assembly is enclosed in a glass envelope and placed between the poles of a magnet N–S as shown. Electrons emitted from the cathode follow a cycloidal path owing to the magnetic and electrical fields. They collide many times with gas molecules thus producing ions which travel straight to the anode. A current is thus set up and follows a linear relationship with pressure in the range 10^{-4}–5×10^{-1} mm mercury:

$$I = Kp^{1.7}$$

where I is the ionization current, K is a constant and p is the absolute pressure.

Hot cathode magnetron gauge

The object of the hot cathode magnetron gauge is to increase the path length of the electrons and hence increase the probability of producing ions. The magnetic field is applied longitudinally instead of transversely and a typical gauge is shown in Fig. 9.29. The tungsten filament is surrounded by a cylindrical molybdenum anode. Each end of the anode is nearly but not quite closed by two circular plates. The one plate acts as an ion collector and the other as a shield.

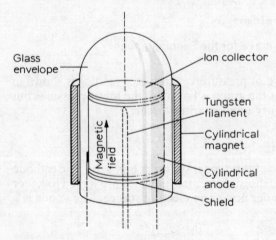

Fig. 9.29 Hot cathode magnetron gauge

The assembly is enclosed in a glass envelope and a cylindrical magnet slides over the envelope. The magnetic flux density is about 25×10^{-3} tesla and the normal operating voltages are -45 V on the ion collector and -10 V on the shield. The ion current has a linear relationship with absolute pressure between the limits 4×10^{-14} and 5×10^{-8} mm mercury.

Alpha particle ionization gauge (alphatron)

Alpha particles emitted by a weak radioactive source collide with gas molecules to produce ions. The gauge contains a collector plate and grid assembly and positive ions are attracted towards the grid. An ionization current is created which is proportional to the gas pressure within the gauge. A schematic diagram is shown in Fig. 9.30. The ionic current is of the order of 2×10^{-10} A/mm mercury absolute pressure. At the lower pressures therefore the ionic current will be very small resulting in the need for complex d.c. amplification. A limit is placed on the lower end of the range therefore and the gauge is normally used within the range 10 mm to 10^{-3} mm mercury.

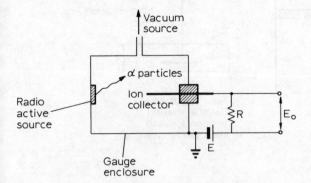

Fig. 9.30 Alpha particle ionization gauge (alphatron)

9.6 Measurement of fluctuating pressure

When a pressure is changing slowly it is usually possible to follow this variation by taking periodic readings. As the rate of pressure variation increases, however, the difficulty of making these measurements will increase and the usefulness of the normal static pressure gauge diminishes. As the rate of pressure variation approaches the lowest natural frequency of vibration of a static pressure gauge, readings become impossible and some form of high speed recording instrument must be used.

Engine indicator

One of the most common measurement problems in engineering is the measurement of the cylinder pressure in a reciprocating machine, such as an air compressor or an internal combustion engine. Normally a graphical record of cylinder pressure against time (a p–t diagram) or against cylinder volume (a p–v diagram) is required. A typical engine indicator together with a p–v diagram or indicator card is shown in Fig. 9.31.

A mechanism causes a stylus to rise in a straight line such that the height of the rise is proportional to the pressure in a small cylinder at the base of the indicator which is connected to the engine cylinder. The rotating drum is designed to provide a lateral motion proportional to the cylinder volume. A card is mounted on the drum and the stylus will record the simultaneous variation of pressure and cylinder volume. The stylus is normally metallic and the card is suitably treated such that the stylus will leave an impression. A p–t record may be obtained using the engine indicator by rotating the drum at constant speed (Fig. 9.32).

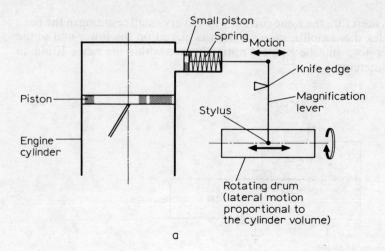

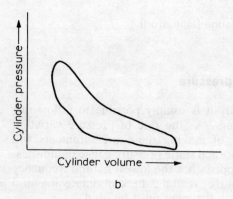

b

Fig. 9.31 Mechanical engine indicator

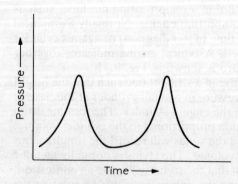

Fig. 9.32 Typical pressure/time relationship for engine indicator

The engine indicator described above has two major disadvantages:

(1) The serious problem of mechanical inertia.
(2) The effective volume of an engine cylinder will be changed when the engine indicator is connected. With small engines this increase in cylinder volume may be so great that $p-t$ diagrams using a mechanical indicator are almost worthless.

Generally speaking electrical pressure transducers are used for recording $p-t$ relationships at high speed. Electrical transducers may be divided into active and passive transducers. An active transducer is one which generates its own electrical output as a function of the mechanical displacement, whereas a passive transducer requires an auxillary electrical input which it modifies as a function of the mechanical displacement, the modified electrical signal being the output from the passive transducer.

Active electrical pressure transducers

The only active electrical pressure transducer in common use is the piezoelectric transducer. This transducer operates on the principle discussed in Chapter 7. Piezoelectric pressure pick-ups have the crystal geometry arranged to give maximum piezoelectric response in a desired direction with little or no response in other directions. Fig. 9.33 shows a piezoelectric

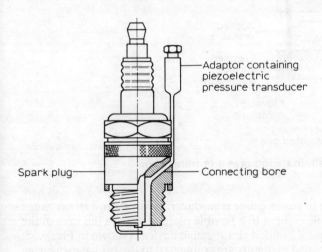

Fig. 9.33 Piezoelectric pressure transducer

pressure transducer of the Kistler type where the piezoelectric crystal is contained in a spark plug adaptor. The adaptor may be fitted to a standard type of spark plug and thus the combustion pressures of petrol engines may be easily measured.

Passive electrical pressure transducers

Passive electrical pressure transducers may be conveniently subdivided under the following headings:

(1) Variable resistance types
(2) Capacitance types
(3) Variable inductance types.

Variable resistance transducers operate on the principle that the electrical resistance of a wire varies as the length of the wire is varied. In the unbonded strain gauge transducer four wires are connected between a fixed frame and a movable armature as shown in Fig. 9.34. The wires are located to the frame and movable armature by electrically insulated pins. The wires are installed under an initial tension and form the active legs of a conventional bridge circuit. When pressure is applied to the elastic element the movable armature is displaced causing two of the wires to elongate while the tension in the other two wires is reduced. The change in resistance due to length changes causes a bridge unbalance proportional to the applied pressure. The use of four wires considerably increases the bridge sensitivity.

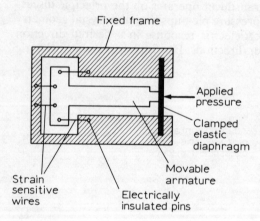

Fixed frame

Applied pressure

Clamped elastic diaphragm

Movable armature

Strain sensitive wires

Electrically insulated pins

Fig. 9.34 Unbonded strain gauge pressure transducer

In the bonded type of strain gauge transducer, a wire or foil strain gauge is fastened by a suitable cement to a flexible plate that takes the load of the elastic element. A typical bonded strain gauge device is shown in Fig. 9.35. Normally two strain gauge elements are connected to the bridge measuring circuit so as to achieve temperature compensation (see Chapter 6).

Other variable resistance type pressure transducers operate on the principle of movable contacts such as those found in potentiometers or slide-wire rheostats. In a typical arrangement the elastic element, say a helical Bourdon tube, is connected to a wire wound potentiometer. As pressure is applied to the open end of the Bourdon tube the tube unwinds and causes the wiper, which is connected to the closed end of the tube, to move over the potentiometer, thus varying the resistance of the measuring circuit (Fig. 9.36).

The *variable capacitance* type pressure transducer usually uses a metal diaphragm as the elastic element which serves as one plate of a capacitor. If the pressure is varied the diaphragm moves with respect to a fixed plate and the resulting change in capacitance can be measured by means of a suitable bridge circuit.

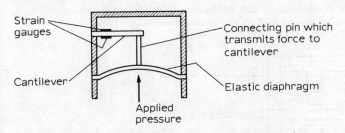

Fig. 9.35 Bonded strain gauge pressure transducer

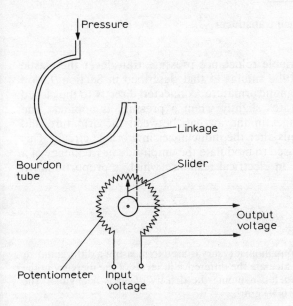

Fig. 9.36 Potentiometric pressure transducer

An important *variable inductance* type pressure transducer is the linear variable differential transformer type (see Section 4.16). The armature of the transducer is displaced by means of an elastic element which is subject to the pressure being measured. When the armature is centred the output voltage is zero, this situation being taken to represent zero pressure. When the armature is displaced from the central position the final output voltage varies approximately linearly with pressure for small armature displacements and this voltage is therefore a measure of the applied pressure.

Another class of pressure transducers whose electrical output signals are derived from variable inductances in the measuring circuits are the *variable reluctance* types. The elastic element in one type is a flat magnetic diaphragm located between two magnetic output coils. A change in the applied pressure produces a displacement of the diaphragm. This displacement changes the inductance ratio between the output coils and results in an output voltage proportional to the applied pressure (Fig. 9.37).

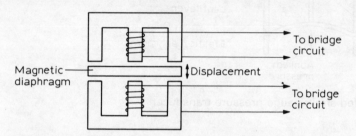

Fig. 9.37 Variable reluctance transducer

In a second type of variable reluctance pressure transducer the elastic element is a flat twisted tube similar to that described in Section 9.3 on Bourdon tubes. A flat magnetic armature, connected directly to the closed end of the Bourdon, rotates slightly when a pressure is applied. The accompanying small changes in the air gap between the armature and electromagnetic output coils alter the inductances in a bridge circuit. This variation in inductance is used to modulate the amplitude or frequency of a carrier voltage producing an electrical response which is proportional to the applied pressure.

Study problems

9.1   A U-tube manometer containing mercury is used to measure a differential air pressure of $50\,kN/m^2$. Calculate the difference in levels of the mercury in the two sides of the manometer assuming the density of air is negligible. The density of mercury is $13\,600\,kg/m^3$.

Answer: $375\,mm$

9.2   A mercury U-tube manometer is used to measure a differential air pressure. If the manometer is then used to measure the same pressure differential in an oil pipeline calculate the percentage difference in manometer readings. The connecting lines to the manometer are completely filled with oil. The density of oil is $800\,kg/m^3$ and that of mercury is $13\,600\,kg/m^3$. The density of air may be neglected.

Answer: h_{oil} is $6\cdot25\%$ higher than h_{air}

9.3 An inclined tube manometer is constructed from an upright metal cylinder which is connected at the base to a tube inclined at 30° to the horizontal. The apparatus is filled with water and the upper end of the cylinder is connected to a gas supply at a pressure of $500 \, N/m^2$. If the inclined tube is open to atmosphere and the ratio of cylinder to tube cross-sectional area is 50 to 1, calculate the distance moved by the liquid level in the inclined tube. The density of water is $1000 \, kg/m^3$.

Answer: 98 mm

9.4 For the manometer of the previous example calculate the percentage error involved if the fall in level of the water in the metal cylinder is ignored.

Answer: 4%

9.5 (*a*) Describe with the aid of a sketch the principle of operation and construction of the Bourdon tube pressure gauge.

(*b*) Sketch a typical pinion gear movement used in a Bourdon tube gauge and calculate the angle through which the segment would have to rotate about the pivot in order that the pointer shaft will revolve through 270°. The gear ratio between the pinion and segment is 15 to 1.

Answer: 18°

9.6 A cistern manometer containing mercury of density $13\,600 \, kg/m^3$ has a cistern of area $0.02 \, m^2$ and a tube of area $4 \times 10^{-5} \, m^2$. Calculate the height of the measurement column if the applied differential pressure is $70 \, kN/m^2$.

Answer: 524 mm

9.7 A simple water manometer is used to measure a differential air pressure and registers a differential head of 200 mm water. If the manometer is then used to measure the same pressure differential in a water pipeline, using mercury in place of water as the manometer fluid, estimate the differential head of mercury registered by the manometer. The density of air may be taken as $1.3 \, kg/m^3$ and water as $1000 \, kg/m^3$. The specific gravity of mercury is 13.6.

Answer: 15.9 mm

9.8 (*a*) Describe the principle and operation of a simple Macleod gauge.

(*b*) The closed limb of a Macleod gauge has a diameter of 1 mm and a volume V above the level of the opening W (Fig. 9.21) of $250 \, cm^3$. When the gauge is connected to a vacuum source the difference h in mercury levels is observed to be 4 mm. Calculate the pressure of the system under test.

Answer: $5.12 \times 10^{-5} \, mm \, Hg$

10 Measurement of solid and liquid level

10.1 Liquid level measurement

Liquid level measurement and control is essential in modern industrial plants which use large quantities of water, solvents, chemicals and other liquids which are required for processing materials and products. The instruments used for liquid level measurement in storage tanks may be broadly classified under the following headings:

   (i) Direct and indirect mechanical methods
  (ii) Pneumatic methods
 (iii) Electrical methods
 (iv) Ultrasonic systems
  (v) Nucleonic gauges.

The choice of instrument to be used in a particular application will depend on several factors such as the liquid level range, the nature of the liquid, the cost involved and the operating pressures.

10.2 Direct and indirect mechanical methods

Dip-sticks

The ordinary dip-stick marked in units of length is the simplest of all level measuring devices. Common applications are the measurement of oil level in the car engine or the height of fuel oil in a uniformly shaped storage tank. Accurate level measurement using dip-sticks is achieved by the Customs and Excise Department in both the brewing and the petroleum industry. A refinement of the simple rod-type dip-stick is the bob and tape where the bob weight is lowered to the bottom of the tank containing the liquid and the level is found by measuring the point on the tape reached by the liquid surface. It is obviously important to keep the tape vertical and taut when a reading is taken.

Hook gauges

Hook gauges are generally used for measurement of small changes in level in very large diameter storage tanks. A typical schematic arrangement of such a gauge is shown in Fig. 10.1. In practice the gauge is fixed at a datum or reference level. Small changes in level with respect to the datum may then be measured by adjusting the position of the hook until the tip just breaks the liquid surface.

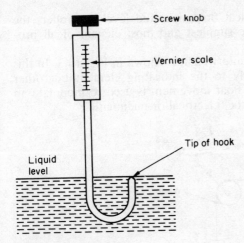

Fig. 10.1 Hook gauge

Sight glasses

The sight glass is normally a graduated glass tube mounted on the side of the tank as shown in Fig. 10.2. This method is very simple and gives a direct reading of level at the sight tube. Corrections may have to be made owing to variations in density if the temperature in the storage tank is much higher than the temperature surrounding the glass sight tube.

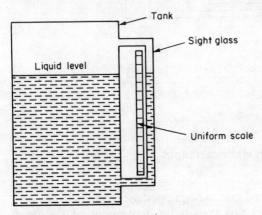

Fig. 10.2 Sight glass level gauge

Buoyant floats

Many kinds of float-operated devices are available for continuous level measurement. The primary element is the float which, because of its buoyancy, will follow the changing liquid level. The movement of the float is then relayed to a pointer or recorder by using some form of transducer or converting device. The mechanical float operated level controller, the ordinary ball-cock, is one of the simplest and most elegant of all proportional control systems.

A float level gauge using a counterweight is shown in Fig. 10.3. In this case the float is coupled directly to the indicating element but other systems are available where the float movement is used to modulate an external source of power, hydraulic, electrical or pneumatic.

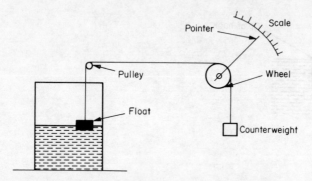

Fig. 10.3 Float level gauge with counterweight

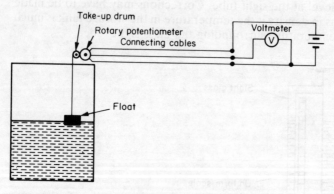

Fig. 10.4 Float level gauge with electrical output

An example of a float operated method equipped for electrical transmission is shown in Fig. 10.4. In this system the movement of the float produces an angular rotation of the take-up drum which is connected via suitable gearing to a rotary potentiometer type displacement transducer. The output voltage from the potentiometer is proportional to the angular movement of the drum and hence the linear float movement.

Indirect mechanical methods

Consider a tank of uniform cross-sectional area A which contains a liquid of density ρ, the level of the liquid to be measured being indicated by the height h above the bottom of the tank:

absolute pressure at the bottom of the tank = $\rho g h$ + atmospheric pressure

Now

gauge pressure = absolute pressure − atmospheric pressure

or

gauge pressure = $\rho g h$

As the gauge pressure is proportional to the height h, a meter is required which will measure gauge pressure. A typical Bourdon-type pressure gauge

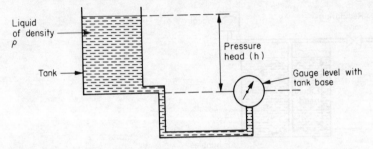

Fig. 10.5 Level measurement using a pressure gauge

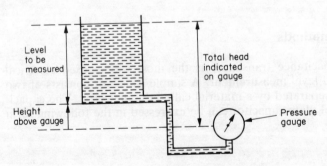

Fig. 10.6 Pressure gauge subject to zero error

as described in Chapter 9 can therefore be used to measure gauge pressure at the base of the tank. A suitable system is shown in Fig. 10.5 where the scale of the instrument is calibrated directly in level measurement units.

Strictly speaking the indicating gauge should be mounted at exactly the same height as the bottom of the tank in order to indicate the level correctly. Figure 10.6 shows the gauge with the connecting pipe full of liquid. The total head of liquid acting on the gauge is the height of liquid above the gauge and it can be seen that the readings will be subject to a 'zero error'. If the zero error is not too large, however, this could possibly be calibrated out on the gauge scale.

10.3 Pneumatic methods

The principle of a bubbler level gauge is illustrated in Fig. 10.7. The air pressure in the bubbler tube is adjusted until bubbles can be seen slowly leaving the bottom of the tube. The pressure gauge then measures the air pressure required to overcome the pressure of the liquid head above the bottom of the tube. Normally the gauge is calibrated directly in head units but, provided the cross-sectional area of the tank is constant, volume units may be used.

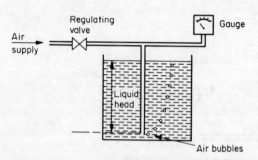

Fig. 10.7 Principle of the bubbler level gauge

10.4 Electrical methods

The variable capacitance transducer is the most widely used electrical method for liquid level measurement. A simple capacitor consists of two electrode plates separated by a material called the dielectric. The capacitance of a parallel plate capacitor can be expressed in the following form

$$C = \frac{KA\varepsilon}{d}$$

where C is the capacitance, K is a constant, A is the overlapping area of the plates, ε is the dielectric constant and d is the distance between the plates.

A capacitance transducer can be used to measure the level of liquid in a tank and Fig. 10.8 shows a schematic arrangement of a suitable system. A metal electrode is placed inside the tank and insulated from it. The tank itself is earthed and forms one of the plates. The transducer therefore consists of two concentric metal cylinders and a change in liquid level alters the dielectric constant and hence the capacitance. The capacitance transducer is connected to one arm of a Wheatstone bridge circuit and changes in capacitance will alter the output voltage from the bridge. The bridge output voltage can therefore be calibrated directly in terms of liquid level.

Capacitance transducers can be used to measure levels from a few millimetres to hundreds of metres. The method may be used for corrosive liquids provided a suitable metal electrode is used, e.g. stainless steel.

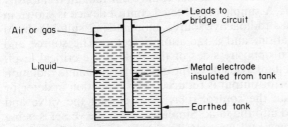

Fig. 10.8 Principle of the capacitance level gauge

10.5 Ultrasonic systems

Ultrasonic systems use an ultrasonic signal source and a matched receiver. Figure 10.9 illustrates the principle of ultrasonic level indication where the ultrasonic transmitter and receiver are placed above the 'full' level of the tank. In this case two echoes are received, one from the surface of the liquid and one from the bottom of the tank. The time separation between receiving the two echoes is a measure of the liquid level in the tank and the echoes may be displayed on a suitable analogue device such as a cathode ray oscilloscope.

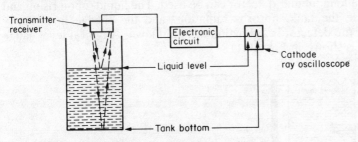

Fig. 10.9 Ultrasonic level measurement

This method of level measurement is very expensive but can be used for 'difficult' liquids, i.e. corrosive or radioactive, as none of the equipment is in contact with the liquid to be measured.

10.6 Nucleonic gauges

Owing to the ready availability of radioactive materials nuclear techniques can now be employed for the extension of some of the more conventional methods of level measurement. Nuclear gauges have the advantage that they can operate entirely from outside the containing vessel. These systems may be designed to provide on/off control at a fixed level in the vessel, or to provide continuous indication of level over a given range.

Nucleonic-type measuring units consist of a radioactive source, a radioactive detector and a rate meter to detect changes in radiation intensity received by the detector. A simple on/off level control device is shown in Fig. 10.10 and consists of a radioactive source, mounted in a suitable shield to provide good collimation, and a radiation detector. The source and detector are mounted on opposite sides of the tank at the critical level. When the contents of the tank rise above the critical level gamma radiation is absorbed and the detector output is reduced. This reduction in detector output is used to operate the control relay, thus closing the valve and stopping the flow of fluid into the tank. Similarly, when the vessel is being emptied, the increase in signal strength as the contents fall below the critical level may be used to operate the control valve.

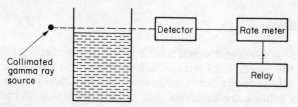

Fig. 10.10 On/off nucleonic level gauge

When continuous level measurement is required a strip gamma-ray source and a long tubular detector can be used. The liquid, upon rising and falling inside the tank, absorbs radiation, and the change in intensity received by the detector is a function of liquid level. A typical level gauge installation is shown in Fig. 10.11.

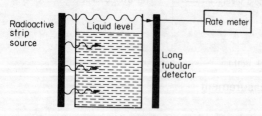

Fig. 10.11 Continuous level nucleonic gauge

Long tubular detectors are not a commercial item and if they have to be specially manufactured, then such installations can prove expensive.

Perhaps the most popular continuous level gauge is the moving source and detector system. This system is essentially the on/off system discussed previously in which the collimated source and detector are arranged to traverse vertically together. The traversing gear is normally driven by an electric motor which is controlled by the relay current. The source and detector can therefore follow any change in level and are always positioned in line with the liquid surface.

10.7 Solid level measurement

Many industrial processes require continuous level indication of the levels of solid substances in storage tanks, typical examples being the measurement of the level of flour and grain. Of the methods already described for liquid level measurement the capacitor probe, the nucleonic gauge and the ultrasonic method can also be applied to the measurement of solid levels.

The most popular method used for solids is the indirect method of weighing the material in a tank or storage bin. Provided the cross-sectional area of the storage vessel is constant then the level will be linearly related to the weight.

The storage tanks may be weighed on mechanical scales or electrically using strain gauge load cells (Fig. 10.12). This technique of level measurement will only be accurate provided the density and the particle size of the material are uniform. The moisture content should also remain fairly uniform or errors can occur.

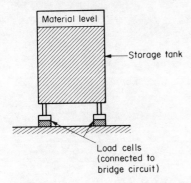

Fig. 10.12 Electrical weighing using load cells

Study problems

10.1 A storage tank contains oil of specific gravity 0·8 to a level of 3 m above the bottom of the tank. Calculate the pressure at the tank base resulting from this head of oil.

Answer: 23·54 kN/m^2

10.2 The air supply to the bubbler gauge illustrated in Fig. 10.7 is adjusted until bubbles just begin to form when the tube is immersed 300 mm below the surface. If the air pressure is to be measured using a mercury U-tube manometer, calculate the head in millimetres of mercury and in Newtons per square metre.

Answers: 22 mm; 2·94 kN/m^2

10.3 Explain why it is necessary to position a Bourdon tube pressure gauge level with the base of the tank when such a gauge is to be used for liquid level measurement. What factors are likely to affect the accuracy of the gauge readings?

10.4 Describe the principle of operation of an ultrasonic system for level measurement. State the main advantages and disadvantages of this system.

10.5 It is proposed to measure the volume of liquid contained in a storage vessel by means of a pressure gauge positioned level with the tank base. If the cross-sectional area of the tank is uniform, is it possible to calibrate the gauge directly in volume units?

Derive an expression for the volume in terms of pressure at the tank base, density of liquid, acceleration due to gravity and cross-sectional area of the tank. Hence suggest possible sources of error in the system.

11 Measurement of fluid flow

In practice the most widely used flowmeter is the constriction type of meter which depends on the measurement of differential pressure when fluid flows through a constriction. Before discussing this type of meter it is necessary to revise fluid flow theory.

11.1 Streamline or laminar flow

If flow along a straight, smooth walled pipe of uniform cross-section is considered and the paths of all the particles of fluid are parallel to the walls of the pipe, then the flow is described as streamlined or laminar flow. All particles must have the same streamwise direction, but not necessarily the same magnitude of velocity. This type of flow occurs generally in smooth pipes when the velocity of flow is low and also in liquids having a high viscosity (see Fig. 11.1).

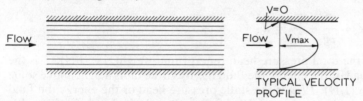

Fig. 11.1 Streamline or laminar flow in pipes

11.2 Turbulent flow

If the flow velocity is now increased, some particles of fluid will have both streamwise and transverse velocity components and the flow pattern will change. This velocity across the stream may produce violent swirls and eddies if the velocity of flow is high enough and such flow is called turbulent flow (see Fig. 11.2).

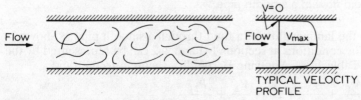

Fig. 11.2 Turbulent flow in pipes

11.3 Reynolds number

The flow through a certain device may be estimated by comparing it with the flow through a geometrically similar device provided the flow patterns are similar in both. In these circumstances the systems are said to be dynamically similar and this will occur provided the Reynolds number is the same in both devices. The Reynolds number Re is a dimensionless index and is defined by the equation:

$$Re = dV\rho/\eta$$

where d is the diameter at the plane of minimum cross-sectional area or 'throat' of the device, V is the mean velocity at the throat, ρ is the density of the fluid flowing and η is the absolute viscosity of the fluid.

A critical value of the Reynolds number will occur for a certain device above which the flow will change from laminar to turbulent flow. The transition from laminar to turbulent flow in circular pipes occurs above a value of $Re = 2000$.

11.4 Energy of a fluid in motion: Bernoulli's equation

Bernoulli's theorem states that the total energy of each particle of a fluid in motion remains constant provided no energy enters or leaves the system at any point, i.e.

$$H = Z + \frac{P}{\rho g} + \frac{V^2}{2g} = k$$

where H is the total pressure head (energy/unit weight, i.e. J/N), Z is the potential head or the energy the fluid has by virtue of its height above some fixed datum (J/N), $P/\rho g$ is the static pressure head or the energy the fluid has by virtue of its pressure (J/N), $V^2/2g$ is the velocity head or energy due to the kinetic energy of the fluid in motion (J/N) and k is a constant.

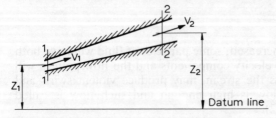

Fig. 11.3 Fluid flow in a smooth pipe

Consider the laminar flow of a fluid through a smooth pipe as shown in Fig. 11.3. The conditions at sections 1–1 and 2–2 can be represented by the symbols in Table 11.1. Applying Bernoulli's theorem to the fluid,

$$Z_1 + \frac{V_1^2}{2g} + \frac{P_1}{\rho_1 g} = Z_2 + \frac{V_2^2}{2g} + \frac{P_2}{\rho_2 g}$$

Table 11.1 Conditions in Fig. 11.3

	At section 1–1	At section 2–2	Units
Area	A_1	A_2	m²
Mean velocity	V_1	V_2	m/s
Pressure	P_1	P_2	N/m²
Density	ρ_1	ρ_2	kg/m³
Height of section centroid above datum	Z_1	Z_2	m

The equation may be applied to the steady flow of incompressible fluids in pipes. It is also sometimes referred to as the 'steady flow energy equation' provided there is no interchange of heat and work energy. In the case of incompressible flow (i.e. most liquids) the density remains constant. Therefore, in the above equation, $\rho_1 = \rho_2$.

11.5 Constriction flowmeters

The velocity of the flowing stream increases as it passes into the constriction and reaches a maximum in the plane of minimum cross-section of the flowing stream.

Because of the increase of velocity of the flowing stream at the plane of minimum cross-section, the kinetic energy will increase. Therefore if the total energy is to remain constant there must be a corresponding decrease in potential energy and a decrease in the pressure of the fluid.

Downstream of the plane of minimum cross-section the pressure on the pipe wall will increase as the area of the flowing stream increases and the velocity of the fluid falls to its original value. The pressure, however, does not quite regain its original value and the difference is known as the net pressure loss. The net pressure loss is due to the dissipation of energy as heat in the damping of turbulent eddies by internal friction.

Consider the streamline flow of an incompressible fluid through a constriction device as shown in Fig. 11.4. If V_1, the velocity upstream of the constriction, is small compared with the velocity at the constriction V_2, then V_1 may be ignored. Applying Bernoulli's equation it may be shown that

$$Q = C_d A_2 \sqrt{(2gh)}$$

where Q is the volume flow rate (m³/s), C_d is the discharge coefficient (actual volume flow rate/theoretical volume flow rate), A_2 is the area of minimum cross-section of the device and h is the equivalent differential pressure head (in metres of fluid being monitored).

When the 'velocity of approach' V_1 cannot be ignored compared with V_2 the volume rate may be calculated using the formula

$$Q = C_d E A_2 \sqrt{(2gh)}$$

where E is known as the velocity of approach factor and is given by

$$E = \sqrt{\frac{1}{[1 - (A_2/A_1)^2]}}$$

When the values of the Reynolds number are low and when small rough pipes are used the discharge coefficient C_d may be modified by multiplying by a correction factor z. The value of z depends on the area ratio, the

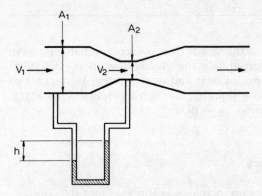

Fig. 11.4 Flow of fluid through a constriction device
A_1: cross-sectional area upstream of the constriction
A_2: cross-sectional area of the constriction

Reynolds number, and the size and roughness of the pipe. Values of C_d and z for various constriction devices are tabulated in BS 1042: Part I: 1964.

The above equation for volume flow can only be applied to incompressible fluids. When, however, the flow is compressible, as in the case of a gas, the equation is further modified by introducing an expansion factor ε.

11.6 Critical flow for compressible fluids

A simple convergent tube, i.e. a nozzle, may be used as a flow limiting device because when the flow rate is sufficiently high the pressure differential between the throat and the upstream pressure becomes quite large, and eventually sonic flow conditions may be achieved at the minimum flow area (throat). The flow is said to be 'choked' under these conditions and the flow rate takes on its maximum value for the given inlet conditions. If the flow of an ideal gas is considered and isentropic flow is assumed the critical pressure ratio for this choked condition is

$$(P_2/P_1)_{\text{crit}} = \left(\frac{2}{\gamma + 1}\right)^{\gamma/\gamma + 1}$$

where (P_2/P_1) is the ratio of the critical pressure at the throat to the upstream nozzle pressure and $\gamma = c_p/c_v$, where c_p is the specific heat of the gas at constant pressure and c_v is specific heat of the gas at constant volume.

11.7 Types of constriction device

Orifice plate

An orifice plate consists of a plate having an axial hole with a square edge on the upstream side and a bevel on the downstream side. The orifice plate is usually inserted between pipe flanges as shown in Fig. 11.5 and the pressure tappings may be in one of the following positions (Fig. 11.6):

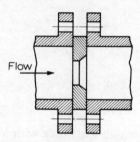

Fig. 11.5 Orifice plate

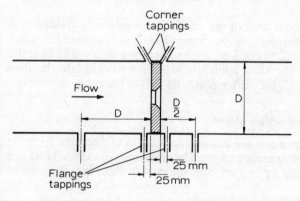

Fig. 11.6 Position of pressure tappings for an orifice plate

(a) *Corner tappings* The pressure tappings are located immediately adjacent to the upstream and downstream faces of the plate in the corners between the pipe and the plate.

(b) *D and D/2 tappings* The tappings are located at a distance of one pipe diameter upstream and one half of one pipe diameter downstream of the plate.

(c) *Flange tappings*   The tappings are located in the pipe flanges at a distance of 25 mm from the upstream and downstream faces of the orifice plate.

Two further orifice plates used to meter viscous liquids are the conical entrance orifice plate and the quarter circle plate. The former consists of a plate having an axial hole with a bevelled edge on the upstream side and a square edge on the downstream side. The pressure tappings are the same as for an orifice plate with corner tappings [Fig. 11.7(a)].

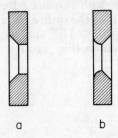

a   b

Fig. 11.7 (a) Conical entrance orifice plate
                (b) Quarter circle orifice plate

The quarter circle plate consists of a plate having an axial hole with a rounded edge on the upstream side and a bevelled edge on the downstream side [Fig. 11.7(b)]. The pressure tappings are the same for an orifice plate with corner tappings or, provided the pipe diameter is not less than 40 mm, with flange tappings.

Since the cross-sectional area of the orifice is considerably greater than that at the plane of minimum cross-section of the flowing stream (the vena contracta) the values of C_d for orifices are smaller than they would be if the cross-sectional area of the vena contracta was used to calculate the flow rate. Typical values of C_d for orifice plates lie within the range 0·62–0·65.

Eccentric and segmented orifice plates

When a fluid with suspended solid is encountered it is desirable to use a segment-type or eccentric orifice plate. The segment type (Fig. 11.8) has the circumference of the open part coincident with the pipe. Passage of

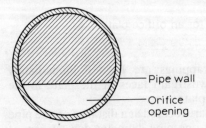

Pipe wall

Orifice opening

Fig. 11.8 Segmental orifice plate

solid material is not interfered with and there is no build-up of solid matter against the upstream face of the orifice plate as would occur with the normal concentric orifice.

The eccentric orifice plate is similar to the segmental type in that the lower part of the orifice opening is flush with the lower part of the pipe (Fig. 11.9).

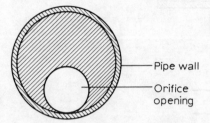

Fig. 11.9 Eccentric orifice plate

Nozzle and Venturi nozzle

The standard flow nozzle (Fig. 11.10) consists of a bell-mouthed convergent entry leading to a short cylindrical throat which projects into the downstream pipe. The pressure tappings are located immediately adjacent to the device in the corners and between the device and the pipe.

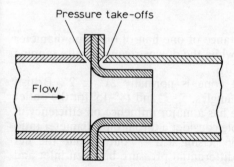

Fig. 11.10 Flow nozzle

A refinement of the flow nozzle is the Venturi nozzle which consists of a nozzle followed by a Venturi outlet (Fig. 11.11). The upstream tapping is located as for a nozzle but the downstream tapping is located in the throat. The exit diameter of the Venturi nozzle may be the same size as the downstream pipe or rather less (truncated).

Venturi tube

The Venturi tube consists of a conical convergent entry leading to a cylindrical throat followed by a conical divergent outlet. The upstream

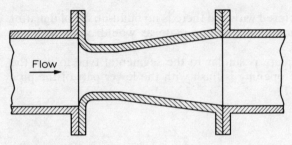

Fig. 11.11 Venturi nozzle

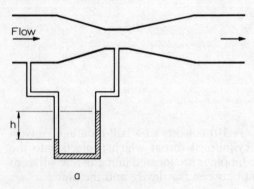

Fig. 11.12(a) Venturi tube

pressure tapping is located at a distance of one half of one pipe diameter upstream of the convergent entry, while the downstream pressure tapping is located in the throat [Fig. 11.12(a)].

The conical angle for the inlet cone is normally 21° ± 2°. British Standard 1042 specifies two conical angles, 5°–7° and 14°–15° for the outlet cone. The design of the outlet cone has a major influence on efficiency in terms of pressure loss. As an example consider a throat/pipe diameter ratio of 0·6 giving an area ratio of 0·36. Using a 5°–7° outlet cone the net pressure loss is about 11% of the differential pressure between inlet and throat. With the 14°–15° cone this loss is about 18%. These figures can be compared with about 65% for an orifice plate having the same area ratio.

The value of C_d for a Venturi will approach unity, a typical value being 0·97.

Dall tube

The Dall tube is similar in principle to the Venturi tube. It consists of two truncated cones separated by a narrow throat slot of length between 0·03d and 0·1d where d is the throat diameter [Fig. 11.12(b)].

The inlet cone has an included angle between 40° and 50° and the outlet cone an angle between 12° and 17°. The diameter of the inlet cone is less than that of the pipe, producing a sudden step. This step produces an impact pressure in addition to the static pressure at the step. The upstream pressure connection is made just before the step whereas the other connection is made at the throat. The Dall tube has the advantage of being much shorter than the normal Venturi and the pressure loss may be as low as 5% of the differential pressure, whereas the pressure loss with a normal Venturi would be between two and three times this value.

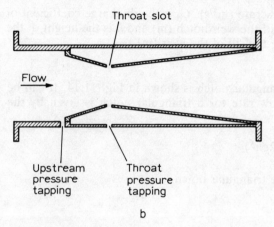

Fig. 11.12(b) Dall tube

Weirs

Discharges over weirs are extensively used to determine the mean flow velocity for open channel flows of liquids, when the channel dimensions and the depth of the liquid are known. The mean velocity and hence the volume flow may be found by taking only one measurement, i.e. the height of liquid h over the sill of the weir [Fig. 11.13(a)].

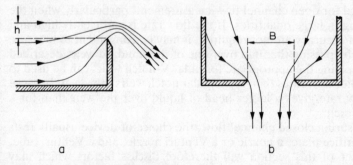

Fig. 11.13 Rectangular notch
(a) View showing height of liquid surface above the sill of the weir
(b) View showing side contraction

Weirs are normally classified by their shape and the two most common are the rectangular notch weir and the triangular notch weir.

Rectangular notch weir

A diagram of a typical rectangular notch is shown in Fig. 11.13. It can be shown that for a rectangular notch

$$Q = \tfrac{2}{3}C_d B\sqrt{(2gh^3)}$$

where Q is the volume flow rate (m³/s), C_d is the discharge coefficient of the weir, B is the breadth of the weir notch (m) and h is the height of the surface of the liquid above the sill of the weir (m).

Triangular or V-notch weir

A diagram of a typical triangular notch is shown in Fig. 11.14. It can be shown that the volume flow rate for a triangular notch is given by the following equation:

$$Q = \frac{8}{15}C_d \tan \tfrac{1}{2}\theta \sqrt{(2gh^5)}$$

where θ is the angle of the triangular notch.

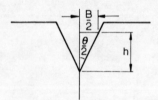

Fig. 11.14 Triangular notch

11.8 Selection of constriction devices

Weirs are used for open channel flow measurement, particularly when the fluid is flowing in large quantities. If the flow rate is sufficiently high and high orders of accuracy are not required, it may be convenient to measure the flow rate by passing the fluid over one of the standard weirs described above and applying the appropriate formula. V-notch weirs can be used to measure smaller flow rates than rectangular notch weirs, however, because the same flow rate gives a larger head of liquid over the weir than for a rectangular notch.

When measuring closed channel flow, the choice of device usually rests between an orifice plate, a nozzle or a Venturi nozzle, and a Venturi tube. The remainder of this section will therefore discuss factors which may influence the choice of one of these devices for a particular application.

A factor of prime importance is the initial cost of the device and in practice orifice plates are the most widely used owing largely to their low initial cost and simplicity of construction. Orifice plates may also be easily installed by insertion in an existing flanged joint in the pipeline. Nozzles are very short and require only a small installation space whereas Venturi tubes and Venturi nozzles require an installation length of between two and six pipe diameters.

When initial cost is considered it is very important also to consider running costs on large installations due to 'permanent head loss' or net pressure loss. The net pressure loss will be appreciable for orifices and nozzles where the fluid issues from the orifice or throat in the form of a jet, but very much smaller for Venturi nozzles and Venturi tubes where the fluid fills the whole cross-sectional area of the tube throughout its length. The loss depends on the angle of the divergent outlet and is greater for the shorter forms of Venturi nozzle and Venturi tube.

All the devices may be used for metering liquids, gases and vapours, but only the conical entrance and quarter circle orifice plates are suitable for metering viscous fluids flowing in small pipes (as small as 25 mm) at low Reynolds numbers (as low as 250 for conical entrance and 1000 for quarter circle). Venturi tubes may be used for viscous liquids at Reynolds numbers down to 5000 but only in pipes greater than 50 mm internal diameter.

Except in the case of viscous fluids the lower limit of flow rate that can be measured is smallest for orifice plates with corner or D and $\frac{1}{2}D$ tappings. It is several times larger for nozzles and Venturi tubes and several times larger still for Venturi nozzles and orifice plates with flange tappings. There is no upper limit to the rate of flow which can be measured except in the case of devices designed for metering viscous fluids, the upper limit of Reynolds number for these devices being 200 000 for conical entrance and 100 000 for quarter circle orifice plates.

The devices so far described are not capable of metering pulsating flow. However, pulsations in the system may be damped by providing a sufficient combination of volumetric capacity and throttling between the measuring device and the source of pulsations, which may be either upstream or downstream of the device. The volumetric capacity is provided by the volume of the pipeline and any receivers used, while throttling is provided by the frictional resistance of the pipeline, the pressure loss in bends and fittings and the pressure loss in the metering device itself.

All the devices require a certain minimum length of straight pipeline upstream of the devices, this minimum length being longer the larger the area ratio of the device. The minimum length is therefore shorter for nozzles, Venturi nozzles and Venturi tubes than for orifice plates, assuming the same rate of flow in the same size of pipe at the same pressure difference. The minimum length may also be shorter if multiple pressure tappings are used instead of single tappings. The minimum length will normally be within the range 10 to 100 pipe diameters depending on the area ratio and the layout of the upstream pipeline.

The lower limit of pipe size through which fluid flow may be measured varies with the surface finish of the upstream pipe and the measuring device used. Provided, however, the internal finish of the upstream pipe is sufficiently smooth, orifice plates may be used in pipes as small as 25 mm internal diameter, except where flange tappings are used when the lower limit is 50 mm. Nozzles, Venturi nozzles and Venturi tubes may be used in pipes down to 50 mm internal diameter. When the surface is less smooth the lower limit of pipe diameter is greater and tables of permissible lower limit of pipe size for varying stages of upstream pipe roughness are included in BS 1042:Part 1:1964.

If flow having a pressure difference greater than the critical is to be measured, all the devices are unsuitable except for the flow nozzle.

11.9 Fluid velocity meters

Fluid velocity meters may be classified as follows:

(1) Instruments which measure the local velocity at a point in the channel or duct through which the fluid is flowing.
(2) Instruments which measure the mean velocity.

11.10 Measurement of local velocity

The two most important instruments used for measuring local fluid velocity are:

(a) The Pitot static tube
(b) The hot wire anemometer.

Both of these instruments are used mainly for the measurement of gas velocities, usually air.

Pitot static tube

The Pitot static tube combines total and static pressure tappings in one probe in order to find the local flow velocity. However, by traversing the stream and finding the velocity at several points it is possible to obtain the

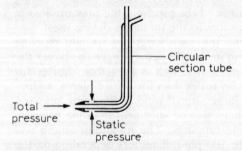

Fig. 11.15 Pitot static tube for local velocity measurement

average stream velocity and hence, by multiplying by the cross-sectional area, the quantity of fluid flowing.

The instrument (Fig. 11.15) consists of two concentric tubes, the outer tube having a series of holes drilled at right angles to the direction of flow. The inner tube when placed in the fluid stream transmits the sum of static and dynamic pressures while the annular space between the tubes transmits the static.pressure only. If the two pressures are connected across a U-tube manometer the difference between the total pressure head and the static pressure head can be measured. This pressure difference will be equal to the velocity head or pressure head produced by the loss of kinetic energy.

Now if the velocity of the fluid stream is V_1 the pressure head produced by the loss of kinetic energy of the fluid is $V_1^2/2g$. Therefore

$$h = V_1^2/2g$$

where h is the head, in metres, of the fluid flowing, measured by the manometer. Therefore

$$V_1 = \sqrt{(2gh)}$$

The whole of the stream flowing on to the end of the Pitot tube may not be brought to rest, as some may be deflected around the edge. The value of V_1 may therefore differ slightly from the true velocity and in order to compensate for this variation a coefficient C is introduced. The value of this coefficient will depend on the design of the tube and for a correctly designed tube this coefficient is unity.

Hot wire anemometer

A very fine electrical resistance wire will be cooled when placed in an airstream. The rate of cooling will be a function of the temperature difference between the air and the object and will also be affected by the velocity of the air.

The wire, usually less than 0·025 mm diameter and approximately 25 mm long, is heated electrically as part of a Wheatstone bridge circuit. It is cooled by the fluid flowing over it and the rate of cooling is proportional to the fluid velocity.

The hot wire anemometer is used in two ways:

(a) The wire is kept at a constant temperature by adjusting the current flowing through it.
(b) The voltage change in the Wheatstone bridge is recorded as the resistance of the wire varies.

The former is a null reading method and requires constant adjustment whereas the latter requires no resetting after an initial calibration curve of voltage against velocity has been plotted.

A typical hot wire anemometer and bridge circuit is shown in Fig. 11.16 together with a calibration curve.

The wire used is usually made of platinum or platinum alloy but tungsten may be used when additional strength is required.

11.11 Selection of a local velocity measuring instrument

Using a Pitot tube it is possible to measure velocities as small as 1 m/s to an accuracy of about 0·5%. Above speeds of about 60 m/s in air, corrections must be made to the Pitot tube reading to allow for compressibility effects, but even with supersonic flow fairly accurate results can be obtained by correcting the reading for pressure changes caused by a normal shock wave positioned at the entry to the total pressure tube.

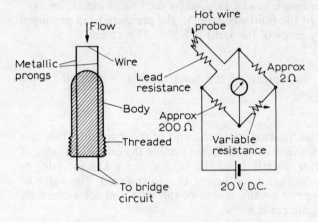

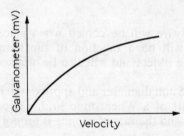

Fig. 11.16 Hot wire anemometer with typical bridge circuit and calibration curve

The most common application of a Pitot static tube is its use in aircraft when it is usually coupled to a Bourdon tube gauge calibrated in air speed units (m/s) instead of pressure units.

The hot wire anemometer is widely used for measuring low flows as small as 0·03 m/s in turbulent regions. It can, however, also be used for measuring supersonic flows.

Generally the hot wire anemometer is a more expensive instrument than the Pitot static tube. It is possible, however, where high accuracy and response is not essential to construct a hot wire probe for operation in air velocities as great as 60 m/s. The probe is constructed using a relatively thin piece of copper wire soldered to two darning needles which are mounted on a plastic stem. The ratio of the prong diameter to the wire diameter should be at least 10:1 in order to minimize the changes of resistance of the prongs as they are heated and cooled. This instrument is relatively inexpensive and can compete in accuracy and response with a Pitot static tube.

11.12 Mean velocity meters

The most common devices for measuring mean flow velocity are:

(*a*) The cup anemometer
(*b*) The vane anemometer
(*c*) The current meter
(*d*) The turbine meter
(*e*) The reed anemometer.

The *cup anemometer* (Fig. 11.17) consists of three or four hemispherical hollow cups mounted in a horizontal plane with their lips vertical. As the

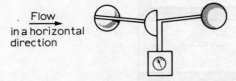

Flow
in a horizontal
direction

Fig. 11.17 Cup anemometer for mean velocity measurement

flow passes over the cups more drag force is experienced by the cup with its open end facing into the stream than the cups with their rounded faces towards the stream. The cup assembly is then caused to spin around its spindle which drives a geared dial and registers a reading approximately proportional to the flow velocity. The dial is calibrated in metres and a stop watch is used to calculate the velocity.

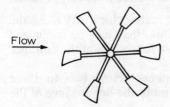

Flow

Fig. 11.18 Vane anemometer for mean velocity measurement

The *vane anemometer* (Fig. 11.18) consists of a small windmill which spins at different rates when subjected to varying velocities of flow. It is important that this instrument is correctly aligned to the flow direction if accurate readings are to be obtained.

The *current meter* (Fig. 11.19) consists of a rotating vane and aligns itself to the direction of flow by means of a pivoting joint. The speed of rotation of the blades can be recorded electrically by means of a tachogenerator.

The *turbine meter* (Fig. 11.20) consists of a rotating vane with its axis along the direction of flow. Fluid flowing through the meter causes the rotor to spin at an angular velocity which ideally is proportional to the velocity of the fluid. The angular velocity of the rotor is normally monitored by a magnetic pick-up and ferromagnetic turbine blades which

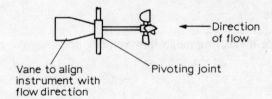

Direction of flow

Vane to align
instrument with
flow direction

Pivoting joint

Fig. 11.19 Current meter for mean velocity measurement

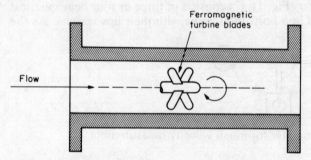

Ferromagnetic
turbine blades

Flow

Fig. 11.20 Turbine meter

form part of a variable reluctance magnetic circuit. The generated output voltage is roughly sinusoidal.

In practice the angular velocity of the rotor may not be exactly proportional to the velocity of flow of the fluid for the following reasons:

(i) The fluid may be swirling as it enters the meter which may cause the rotor to either speed up or slow down. This effect may be minimized by fitting a flow straightener in the form of four vanes at the entrance to the meter.

(ii) Energy losses occur at Reynolds numbers below two to three thousand. This effectively sets a lower limit to the linear range of the meter.

(iii) Mechanical friction at the bearings.

(iv) Magnetic drag between static and rotating parts.

The *reed anemometer* (Fig. 11.21) consists of a thin metal reed, the deflection of which is measured when a fluid stream passes over it. The deflection of the reed tip can be read directly on a scale or the change in resistance of a strain gauge fixed to a thin cantilever beam at the base of the reed can be calibrated against flow velocity.

11.13 Selection of mean velocity meters

The cup anemometer and vane anemometer are normally used for measuring the velocity of flow of gases. They may be selected to measure velocities in the range 0–15 m/s. The major application of the cup anemometer is the measurement of wind velocities in meteorology.

The current meter and turbine meter are normally used for measuring the flow velocity of liquids while the reed anemometer may be used for either liquids or gases.

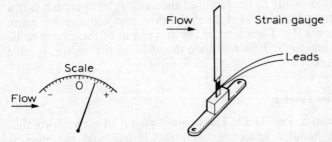

Fig. 11.21 Reed anemometer for mean velocity measurement

11.14 Variable area flowmeters

If the pressure differential across a particular installation is constant and the flow pattern is unchanged, then the rate of flow through the orifice will depend on the orifice area and the 'velocity of approach factor'. That is

$$Q = C_d A_2 E \sqrt{(2gh)}$$

where A_2 is the cross-sectional area of the orifice.

If the pressure differential is held constant by adjusting the orifice area then the area of the orifice at any particular instant is effectively a measure of the rate of flow through the orifice. This is the principle of operation of variable area flowmeters of which the following are typical:

(a) The gate meter
(b) The orifice and plug meter
(c) The rotameter.

Gate area meter

A typical gate flowmeter is shown in Fig. 11.22. The gate may be adjusted manually or by an automatically controlled electric motor to maintain a

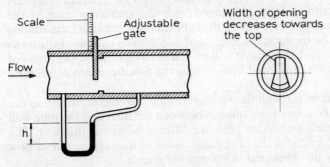

Fig. 11.22 Variable area gate meter

constant pressure drop across the orifice. The position of the gate is indicated by a scale which may be calibrated in terms of flow rate. It should be noted that the relationship between the flow rate and the area A_2 will not be strictly linear owing to the fact that the velocity of approach factor will increase with an increase in A_2, i.e. the flow rate will increase more rapidly than the area A_2. Therefore, if the movement of the gate is to be directly proportional to the flow rate then the width of the orifice A_2 must decrease at the top.

Orifice and plug area meter

This meter is shown in Fig. 11.23. The tapered plug is of such a form that the area of the annular space between the orifice and the plug is proportional to the lift of the plug. Therefore the height by which the plug rises when a fluid flows past it is a measure of the rate of flow.

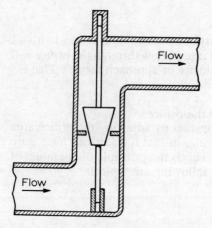

Fig. 11.23 Orifice and plug meter (variable area)

Rotameter

The rotameter, shown in Fig. 11.24, consists of a long graduated vertical tube having a uniform taper, arranged with the smaller section at the bottom. A float moves freely within the tube and is prevented from fouling the sides of the tube by means of a series of angled slots cut into the float so that as fluid flows past the float it will be caused to spin. In some forms of rotameter the float is prevented from fouling the tube by means of a central guide.

As the rate of flow through the rotameter increases the float rises in the tube, increasing the area of the annulus between the float and the tube wall and thus maintaining a constant pressure differential across the float. The displacement of the float in the tube is a measure of the volume rate of flow and the tube may be calibrated in volume flow units.

The rotameter is by far the most widely used of the variable area meters, but the orifice and plug meter is used quite extensively to measure the flow of water into district water main pipes.

Rotameters may be used to measure the flow of both liquids and gases. It is important, however, that the temperature remains constant otherwise the viscosity and the density of the fluid being metered may change and temperature fluctuations can produce considerable errors, particularly when gases are being metered. A further source of error is the tendency of the float to oscillate which makes accurate scale reading difficult.

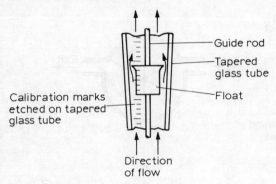

Fig. 11.24 Variable area rotameter

Glass tube rotameters may be selected to measure the flow rate of liquids ranging from very low flows of 30–300 ml/s up to flow rates as high as 0·5–5 litres/s. If air is the metered fluid, however, the equivalent range of flow is from about 0·2–2·0 ml/s to about 4–40 litres/s. When liquids are metered the smaller size glass tubes can be used up to a pressure of about 3·4 kN/m² whereas the larger tubes can only be used up to about 0·8 kN/m². When gases are metered the upper pressure limits are much lower.

Metal tube rotameters are used for measuring very high flow rates and may be used up to a pressure of about 200 kN/m², a temperature of about 300 °C and a flow rate as large as 120 litres/s.

11.15 Quantity flowmeters

Quantity meters measure the total quantity of fluid which has flowed in a certain time. If the quantity of fluid measured in a certain time is divided by that time, then the average rate of flow of the fluid can be determined. Quantity meters may be divided into two classes.

(1) Those which indicate the weight of fluid that has flowed;
(2) Those which indicate the volume that has flowed.

Weighing meters

When liquid flows in sufficiently small quantities a weighing tank may be used to obtain the weight of liquid discharged in a certain time. Provided the density of the liquid is known, the volume flow rate may then be calculated.

Volumetric meters

A large number of positive displacement meters are available for metering the flow of liquids where the highest degree of accuracy is required. The principle of operation is that as liquid flows through the meter it moves a

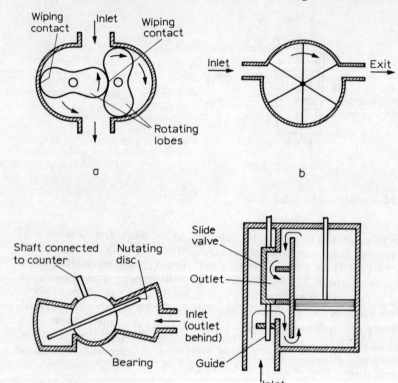

Fig. 11.25 Volumetric meters for liquids
    (*a*) Rotating lobe meter   (*b*) Rotating vane meter
    (*c*) Nutating disc meter   (*d*) Reciprocating piston meter

measuring element which seals off the measuring chamber into a number of compartments of definite volume. As the measuring element moves these compartments are successively filled and emptied. Thus, for one cycle of the measuring element a known quantity of liquid passes from the inlet to the outlet of the meter. The number of cycles of the measuring element may then be indicated by means of a pointer moving over a dial. Some typical liquid positive displacement flow meters are:

(*a*) The rotating lobe meter

(b) The rotating vane meter
(c) The nutating disc meter
(d) The reciprocating piston meter.

These meters are shown diagrammatically in Fig. 11.25.

Positive displacement meters are extremely useful for measuring pulsating flow as their accuracy is not affected by pulsations. Also, more accurate measurements may be made with liquids of higher viscosity than with many other types of flowmeter. Owing to their high accuracy these meters are frequently used for metering oil and water for accounting purposes. If the temperature, density and viscosity of the metered liquid vary from the

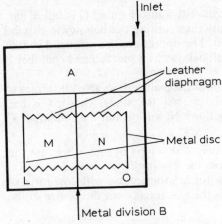

Fig. 11.26 Diagram showing the arrangement of the measuring compartments in the bellows-type gas meter

values at the calibration conditions, sources of error will occur. It is therefore usual to calibrate these meters *in situ* when they are to be used for metering expensive liquids for accounting purposes.

A number of volumetric meters are used for the metering of gases and the most common are:

(a) The bellows dry gas meter
(b) The water displacement gas meter
(c) The rotating lobe gas meter.

The *bellows meter* is used for low rate metering of low pressure gas, i.e. household gas supply.

The meter consists of an upper and a lower section, the upper section comprising a gas chamber A, which has a constant supply of gas from the inlet. A simple valve arrangement allows the gas supply to pass at predetermined intervals into the four measuring chambers below. The lower section is divided vertically by means of a metal division B to each side of which is attached a bellows comprising a leather diaphragm and a metal disc. The lower part of the case is therefore split into four separate measuring compartments as shown in Fig. 11.26.

The movement of the bellows is used to operate the valves which regulate the gas supply into the four measuring chambers and the quantity of gas delivered is measured by the number of times the measuring chambers are filled and emptied. This is achieved by counting the number of horizontal movements of the two diaphragms.

The method of operation of the instrument is as follows:

(a) Gas enters the chamber O and compresses the bellows N (which is full of gas), thus causing gas in N to exhaust through an exit port.

(b) When N is half exhausted a valve opens permitting gas to enter bellows M. Hence the bellows M expands and exhausts gas in chamber L to the outlet.

(c) When bellows N is completely exhausted and chamber O is full of gas, a valve opens N to the gas supply thus causing the bellows to expand and the gas in O to be exhausted. The operations are arranged so that when N is exhausted and O is full, bellows M is half full and chamber L half exhausted.

(d) When bellows M is full and chamber L exhausted, a valve allows gas to enter L thus causing M to exhaust. At the stage when M is half exhausted and L is half full, bellows N will be full and chamber O exhausted.

There will be a large pressure drop across this type of meter because the metering energy is taken directly from the gas itself.

A simple *water displacement meter* for laboratory use with low rates of flow of gas is shown in Fig. 11.27. As the gas enters near the centre of the

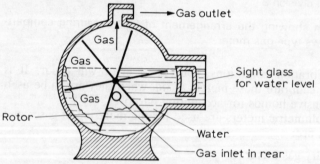

Fig. 11.27 Water displacement gas meter

instrument it flows into a segment of the rotor causing the rotor to 'float' on the water surface. The rotor will be caused to rotate by the gas flow and gas is discharged at the top outlet. Metering consists of counting the revolutions as each rotor segment will discharge a known quantity of gas. At small flow rates the pressure drop across the meter will be low, but will increase rapidly with increased flow rates. These meters are normally designed for gas flow rates of 6–90 litres/hour.

The *rotating lobe meter* is similar to that used for liquids. These meters are normally used up to a pressure of about $70 \, N/m^2$ but models are available up to $340 \, N/m^2$.

11.16 Electromagnetic flowmeters

If a conducting fluid is allowed to flow with velocity U along a pipe of internal diameter d and an electromagnetic system directs a magnetic field B across a section of the pipe so that it acts at right angles to the direction of motion of the fluid, an induced voltage V is produced (Fig. 11.28).

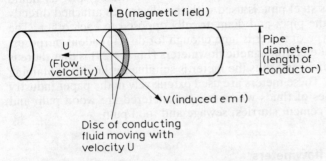

Fig. 11.28 Principle of the electromagnetic flowmeter

By Faraday's Law of Induction, when an electrical conductor moves through a magnetic field in a direction at right angles both to the magnetic field and its length, an e.m.f. is generated of value

$V = BlU$ volts

where B is the magnetic flux density (tesla, i.e. W/m^2), l is the length of the conductor (m) and U is the velocity of the conductor (m/s).

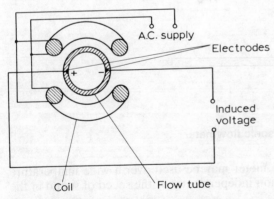

Fig. 11.29 Electromagnetic flowmeter

The length of the conductor is proportional to the diameter of the flow tube and the velocity is proportional to the mean flow velocity. If the magnetic flux density is constant the induced voltage will therefore be proportional to the mean flow velocity and the value of the induced voltage will thus represent a direct indication of mean flow velocity.

In practice two types of meter are commonly used. The first has a non-conducting pipe liner to prevent short-circuiting the e.m.f. and is used for fluids with low conductivities such as water. The electrodes are mounted flush with the non-conducting liner such that they make contact with the fluid. The output voltage from this type of meter is low and will normally require amplification.

The second type is used with high conductivity fluids such as liquid metals. A stainless steel pipe is used with the electrodes attached directly to the outside of the pipe, and diametrically opposed to each other. The output from this type of meter is high enough for direct readout purposes.

An advantage of electromagnetic flowmeters (Fig. 11.29) is that there is no obstruction to flow and thus the meter is suitable for liquids containing suspended matter. These meters are used extensively in the paper industry and a few examples of fluids which may be metered are wood pulp and paper mill stocks, cement slurries, sewage and food pulp.

11.17 Ultrasonic flowmeters

Ultrasonic flowmeters do not obstruct the flow of fluid; consequently there is no head loss and the meter requires less maintenance than most other

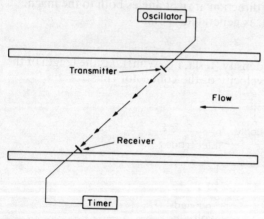

Fig. 11.30 Single path ultrasonic flowmeter

flowmeters. In practice the meter may be used over a wide temperature range provided it can function independently of the speed of sound in the fluid.

The majority of devices are based on the fact that a linear relationship exists between the apparent velocity of sound in a flowing fluid and the velocity of the fluid. Provided the direction of the ultrasonic wave is not perpendicular to the flow of fluid, the component of flow velocity in the direction of the ultrasonic wave will alter its velocity.

The basic principle of a single path ultrasonic flowmeter is shown in Fig. 11.30. The method employs a transmitter and receiver to measure the apparent sound velocity along a diametral path on an inclined cross-section. A meter of this type can only measure the mean flow velocity along the acoustic path and therefore to obtain the volume flow rate the effect of the velocity profile of the fluid has to be considered. As the single path ultrasonic flowmeter does not inherently allow for the velocity profile, calibration is therefore required.

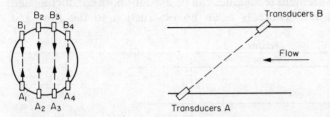

Fig. 11.31 Multiple path ultrasonic flowmeter: (*a*) transverse section of pipe (*b*) longitudinal section of pipe

This problem is overcome in the multiple path ultrasonic meter. In this meter (Fig. 11.31) the ultrasonic velocity is measured in both directions along several chordal paths on an inclined cross-section, and the mean velocity across this cross-section is then derived using an automatic integration technique. The Westinghouse system uses four chordal paths with the spacing of the paths chosen according to the Gaussian integration formulae so that the sum of the measured mean velocities multiplied by a constant weighting factor equals the volume flowrate.

Ultrasonic flowmeters of this type are very expensive but possess many of the advantages of the electromagnetic flowmeter without some of its disadvantages. Repeatability is quite good and can be maintained for long periods, and good accuracy can be obtained without frequent recalibration. Zero drift is not a serious problem. The ultrasonic flowmeter can be used with any fluid, non-conducting as well as conducting. It presents no obstruction to the flow and consequently has negligible lead loss and can be used to meter slurries as there is no tendency for the pipe to become blocked.

The chief disadvantage of the meter is the very high cost of associated instrumentation. This becomes less important, however, in the larger pipe sizes or where several meters installed on the same site can share the same instrumentation. Ultrasonic flowmeters are relatively new developments but where high accuracy and stability are required they are likely to find considerable use.

11.18 Nuclear techniques

Nuclear techniques are used for flow measurement in process control applications. The time taken for the passage of an injected radioactive tracer between two points in a pipeline is recorded using two radiation detectors and a suitable recorder. A schematic diagram of a suitable system is shown in Fig. 11.32. Provided the volume of fluid between the observation points is known the volume flow rate can be calculated:

$$\text{volume flow rate} = \frac{\text{volume between observation points}}{\text{time taken}}$$

Nuclear flow measurement techniques can be used for both conducting and non-conducting fluids. There is again no obstruction to the flow and

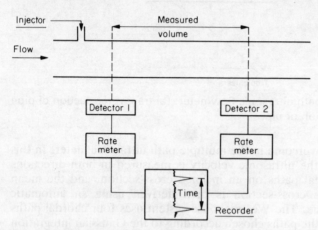

Fig. 11.32 Nuclear flowmeter

therefore negligible lead loss. These techniques are therefore applicable to the measurement of the flow rate of slurries.

The major constraint on the use of radioactivity for any purpose is the health hazard attending all ionizing radiation, and the resulting legal restrictions placed on its use. Generally the most sensible criterion is to avoid using radioactivity unless it shows clear advantages in economics, safety of operation or in cost or quality of product over rival techniques. In any event the lowest practicable radiation source strength should be employed. Having made this point it must be stated that the hazard, though real, is so well controlled by legislation and codes of practice, supported by industrial training and discipline, that no industrial injury or death in the UK has yet been reported as being directly attributable to this cause.

Study problems

11.1 Water flows from a tank over two adjacent notches, one a V-notch, the other a rectangular notch. The head over each notch is equal and is $2\frac{1}{2}$ times the breadth of the rectangular notch. If the discharge from each notch is equal, determine the angle of the V-notch. The coefficient of discharge for the V-notch is 0·6 and that for the rectangular notch is 0·63.

Answer: 55° 24′

11.2 In a test on a Venturi meter the flow of water is measured by means of a weighing tank. The meter has a main diameter of 75 mm and a throat diameter of 37·5 mm and the pressure difference is measured on a mercury U-tube, the mercury being in contact with the water. If 1160 kg of water is collected in 2 minutes while the manometer reading remains steady at 320 mm of mercury, calculate the coefficient of the meter.

Comment on the result obtained, mentioning the factors which can influence the value of this coefficient. The density of water is 1000 kg/m³.

Answer: $C_d = 0.95$

11.3 A sharp edged orifice of 12 mm diameter is situated in the base of an otherwise closed tank. At a given instant the head of water above the orifice is 1·8 m. If the discharge of water is to be 1·5 kg/s find the pressure of air which must be pumped in above the water. $C_d = 0.6$. Density of water is 1000 kg/m³.

Answer: 226·7 kN/m²

11.4 A Pitot tube used to measure air velocity along a wind tunnel is coupled to a manometer which shows a difference in head of 3·8 mm mercury at a particular point in the tunnel. Find the air velocity at this point assuming that the coefficient of the tube is 0·98. Take the density of air as 1·293 kg/m³ and the specific gravity of mercury as 13·6.

Answer: 27·44 m/s

11.5 Water flows through a Venturi meter which has entry and throat diameters of 120 mm and 60 mm. The pressure drop between inlet and throat is 80 kN/m² and the coefficient of the meter is 0·98. Calculate the rate of flow through the meter assuming that the density of water is 1000 kg/m³.

Answer: 0·04 m³/s

11.6 When water is discharged through a 50 mm diameter sharp edged orifice under a head of 4·6 m the measured rate of flow is found to be 2 m³ in 3 minutes. Determine the discharge coefficient of the orifice and the discharge when the head is 6 m above the orifice.

Answers: $C_d = 0.596$; 1.27×10^{-3} m³/s

11.7 A Venturi meter has its axis mounted vertically, the inlet and throat diameters being 150 mm and 75 mm respectively. The throat is 225 mm above the inlet and the discharge coefficient is 0·96. Petrol of density 780 kg/m³ flows through the meter at the rate of $5·55 \times 10^{-2}$ m³/s. Calculate:

(*a*) The pressure difference between inlet and throat.
(*b*) The difference in level which would be registered by a vertical mercury manometer, the tubes above the mercury being full of petrol.

The density of mercury is 13 600 kg/m³.

Answers
(*a*) 64·31 kN/m²
(*b*) 0·498 m

11.8   (a) Show that $Q = C_d A \sqrt{2gh}$ for a sharp edged orifice plate in a horizontal pipe through which is flowing an incompressible fluid, where Q is the volume rate of flow (m³/s), C_d is the coefficient of discharge of the orifice, h is the pressure drop across the orifice as measured by a U-tube manometer in metres of the particular fluid flowing, and A is the cross-sectional area of the orifice (m²).

(b) Draw suitable diagrams showing the pressure tapping positions for flow measurement using a sharp edged orifice plate with:

   (i) Flange tappings
  (ii) Corner tapping
 (iii) D and D/2 tappings.

12 Viscometry

Viscosity is the 'stickiness' of a fluid and arises from the cohesion and interaction between the fluid molecules. It is a measure of the fluid resistance to shear when the fluid is in motion, either by a body moving through a fluid or by a fluid moving around a body.

Pressure and temperature changes affect viscosity but while a change in pressure affects viscosity to a negligible extent only, temperature changes cause considerable variations. It should be noted that the viscosity of liquids decreases with increasing temperature whereas the viscosity of gases increases.

The presence of viscosity represents the reluctance of a fluid to motion and objects moving in viscous fluids will soon come to rest unless power is applied to maintain the motion. In practice, when a body is required to move through a viscous fluid a large proportion of the available power is required to overcome viscous effects. It is therefore most important to know the magnitude of the drag forces acting on a body and, as these forces are proportional to the fluid viscosity, instruments have been designed to measure this property.

12.1 Newton's Law of Viscosity

It has been shown experimentally that the flow velocity is not uniform across the section of a conduit and varies, from point to point. The velocity distribution may be represented by profiles as shown in Fig. 12.1.

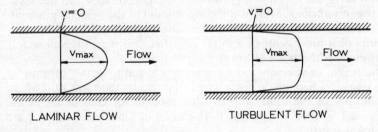

Fig. 12.1 Typical velocity profile

It is convenient to assume that fluid layers slide relative to adjacent layers in the direction of flow and that the relative velocity between adjacent layers varies across the flow. Consider two layers at an infinitesimal distance δy apart as shown in Fig. 12.2.

Over a distance δy the velocity changes by δv and thus the velocity gradient dv/dy given by

$$dv/dy = \lim_{\delta y \to 0} \delta v/\delta y$$

at a point P on the velocity profile is the tangent of the angle θ, as shown in Fig. 12.2. A Newtonian fluid is one in which the shear stress between adjacent layers is proportional to the velocity gradient, i.e.

$$\tau \propto dv/dy$$

or

$$\tau = \eta \frac{dv}{dy} \qquad (12.1)$$

where τ is the shear stress between layers, dv/dy is the velocity gradient and η is a constant known as the *coefficient of viscosity*.

From Eq. 12.1 it can be seen that

$$\eta = \tau \frac{dy}{dv} \qquad (12.2)$$

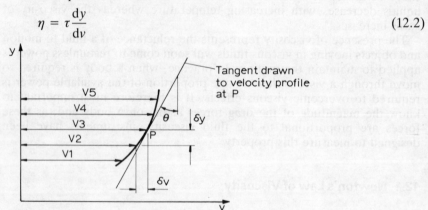

Fig. 12.2 Adjacent layers for viscosity calculation

It should be noted that a non-Newtonian fluid is one in which the shear stress between adjacent layers is not proportional to the velocity gradient. Newton's Law of Viscosity does not therefore apply to such a fluid.

The units of η are $N\,s/m^2$ or $kg/m\,s$. Another unit which is still widely used, however, is the poise (g/cm s).

The coefficient of viscosity η is frequently referred to as the absolute or dynamic viscosity. Kinematic viscosity v is defined by the ratio η/ρ (where ρ is the density of the fluid) and is often used in the calculation of the Reynolds number (see Chapter 11). The units of kinematic viscosity are m^2/s or stokes (cm^2/s).

12.2 Efflux viscometers

Certain instruments have been developed in the oil industry for the measurement of viscosity and a number of these are now in general use.

These instruments are known as short tube or orifice viscometers and the principal types are: Saybolt Universal and Saybolt Furol (USA); Redwood No. 1 and No. 2 (Great Britain); and Engler (Germany and other continental countries).

Saybolt viscometer

The time taken in seconds to discharge 60 ml through the outlet tube is measured and used as a scale of viscosity for comparison. The results are usually expressed in terms of Saybolt Universal seconds but may be readily converted to the absolute or dynamic viscosity if required. As the coefficient of viscosity depends on the temperature of the fluid under test, care must be taken to ensure that the fluid remains at a constant temperature throughout the test. A water jacket is used for this purpose (Fig. 12.3).

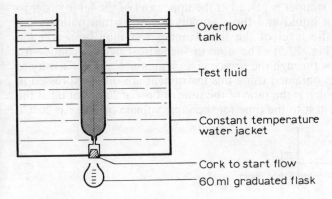

Fig. 12.3 Saybolt viscometer

The US Bureau of Standards recommends the use of the Saybolt Furol viscometer for oils in which the time of flow in a Saybolt Universal viscometer is inconveniently large. This viscometer is identical to the Universal apparatus with the exception of the outlet tube which is the same length but has a larger diameter.

Redwood viscometer

The Redwood viscometer is similar in construction to the Saybolt instrument and is shown in Fig. 12.4. The time is measured to collect 50 ml of fluid in the flask and the viscosity may be expressed in Redwood seconds which are proportional to viscosity. Two jet sizes are available and are denoted by the numbers 1 and 2. The number 2 jet has a larger diameter than the number 1 and is normally used for the more viscous liquids. The results of the Redwood test are usually expressed as Redwood Number 1 seconds or Redwood Number 2 seconds but may easily be converted to the coefficient of viscosity if required.

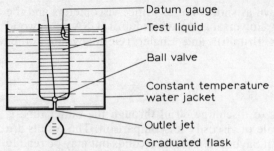

Fig. 12.4 Redwood viscometer

Labels: Datum gauge; Test liquid; Ball valve; Constant temperature water jacket; Outlet jet; Graduated flask

Engler viscometer

The oil is held in a shallow cup and discharges through an orifice in the base of the cup. A stopper is placed in the upper end of the jet in order to control the flow of liquid and three equally spaced datum pointers are provided so that the level of the liquid under test may be set in the horizontal plane (Fig. 12.5). The time in seconds—Engler seconds—for 200 ml of oil to flow through the orifice gives a measure of the viscosity of the oil. The results obtained using this instrument are often expressed in 'Engler degrees' which is the ratio of the time of flow of 200 ml of oil at the temperature of the test to the time for the same volume of water at 20 °C.

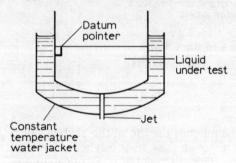

Labels: Datum pointer; Liquid under test; Jet; Constant temperature water jacket

Fig. 12.5 Engler viscometer

Table 12.1 shows viscosity conversions between kinematic viscosity in m^2/s, Redwood seconds, Saybolt seconds, and Engler degrees.

12.3 Torque or rotational viscometers

A thin film of the liquid to be tested is enclosed between two vertical concentric cylinders. With low viscosity liquids the inner cylinder is usually suspended by a torsion wire or spring and the outer cylinder is rotated at constant speed, usually by means of an electric motor. The torque produced can be readily measured by the deflection of the inner cylinder as shown in Fig. 12.6.

Table 12.1 Viscosity conversions

m²/s × 10⁴	Redwood seconds		Saybolt seconds		Engler degrees
	No. 1	No. 2	Universal	Furol	
0·05	38	—	42	—	1·3
0·1	52	—	59	—	1·84
0·2	86	—	98	—	2·88
0·3	125	—	141	—	4·07
0·4	165	—	187	23	5·34
0·5	205	23	233	25	6·63
1·0	400	41	459	49	13·3
1·5	600	61	707	72	19·8
2·0	809	82	946	95	26·4

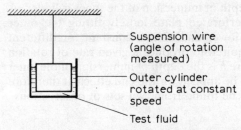

Fig. 12.6 Torque or rotational viscometer

For measurements on liquids of high viscosity which give a larger retarding couple the method usually adopted is to apply a known torque to the inner cylinder by a system of weights and pulleys. The rate of rotation of the cylinder when the motion has become uniform is then observed. Searle's viscometer operates on this principle, i.e. the inner cylinder rotates and the outer cylinder is fixed. The inner cylinder (Fig. 12.7) is carried on a spindle pivoted at top and bottom, the lower pivot acting as a support for the outer cylinder.

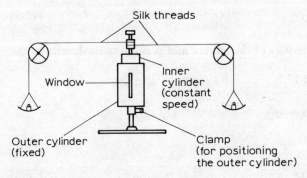

Fig. 12.7 Searle's viscometer

Two equal masses carried by silk threads passing over ball-bearing pulleys and wound round a drum fixed to the spindle provide the known couple. If the couple G maintains a constant speed equal to one revolution in t seconds the viscosity can be found from the equation:

$$\eta = \frac{Gt}{8\pi^2 h} \times \frac{(b^2 - a^2)}{a^2 b^2} \qquad (12.3)$$

where a is the radius of the inner cylinder, b is the radius of the outer cylinder and h is the immersed length of the inner cylinder.

Equation 12.3 assumes the length of the cylinders to be infinite. However, in practice both cylinders are of finite length and a correction must be applied to compensate for the viscosity effect at the cylinder ends. It should be pointed out, however, that a correction for end effects is not necessary when the viscometer is used for relative measurements only.

The outer cylinder, which has a narrow window through which the level of the liquid can be read on a scale engraved on the inner cylinder, can be moved up or down to vary the depth of immersion of the inner cylinder. A false bottom, consisting of a perforated plate loosely fitting the outer vessel, keeps conditions at the lower end almost constant for different heights of liquid. The couple required to produce a given rate of rotation will be proportional to $h + l$, where h is the depth of immersion of the inner cylinder and l is the correction to be applied for the end effect. It therefore follows that the correction l may be found from two sets of observations.

12.4 Falling sphere viscometer

When a sphere of diameter d is allowed to fall with uniform velocity in a viscous liquid the resistance to motion is given by Stokes's Law:

$$F = 3\pi \eta u d \qquad (12.4)$$

where u is the velocity of the sphere and F is the resistance to motion.

If a sphere is allowed to fall freely under the action of gravity in a viscous medium then the force exerted on it is equal to the apparent weight of the sphere:

$$F = \frac{1}{6} \pi d^3 (\rho_s - \rho_l) g \qquad (12.5)$$

where ρ_s is the mass density of the sphere and ρ_l is the mass density of the liquid.

From Eqs 12.4 and 12.5,

$$3\pi \eta u d = \frac{1}{6}\pi d^3 (\rho_s - \rho_l) g$$

or

$$\eta = \frac{d^2}{18u} (\rho_s - \rho_l) g \qquad (12.6)$$

The essence of the method is to allow a steel ball-bearing of known size to fall freely in a viscous liquid. The time taken for the sphere to pass with uniform velocity between two fixed points on the cylinder containing the test liquid is noted and the velocity calculated. The apparatus used is shown in Fig. 12.8. For normal use a stop watch may be used to record the time, and velocities up to 10^{-2} m/s can usually be recorded to within 1%.

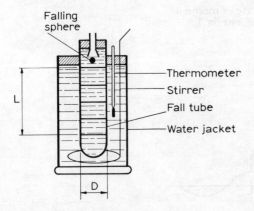

Fig. 12.8 Falling sphere viscometer

The observed velocity of fall in the cylinder of diameter D will differ slightly from the velocity of free fall u, because of the interference of the cylinder boundaries on the sphere. If v is the observed velocity in the cylinder of diameter D the value of u can be obtained from the following relationship:

$$\frac{u}{v} = 1 + \frac{9d}{4D} + \left(\frac{9d}{4D}\right)^2 \tag{12.7}$$

The fall of the sphere is often timed over the middle half of the tube but additional markings should be provided separating the timing distance into two or three equal parts so that the uniformity of the motion may be checked. Also, as the sphere must be falling at constant speed between the marks an initial length is required so that the acceleration from rest has reached zero by the time the sphere reaches the first timing mark.

12.5 Oscillational viscometers

Consider a torsional pendulum consisting of a bob having moment of inertia I about an axis of symmetry coincident with the suspension wire and oscillating in a viscous medium (Fig. 12.9). The dynamic viscosity can be determined from measurements of the periodic time and the logarithmic decrement of the amplitude.

A typical curve showing the angular displacement of the bob from its equilibrium position as the time increases is shown in Fig. 12.10. The

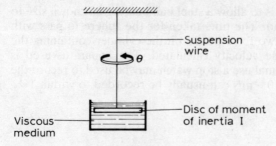

Fig. 12.9 Torsional pendulum

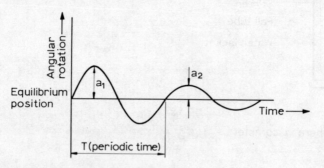

Fig. 12.10 Oscillations of torsional pendulum in viscous medium

logarithmic decrement δ can be determined from the ratios of the amplitudes of successive oscillations:

$$\delta = \log_e a_1/a_2$$

where a_1 and a_2 are the amplitudes of successive oscillations.

Oscillational viscometers have been developed using a number of simple geometrical shapes, the most popular being the sphere, disc and cylinder.

12.6 Capillary tube viscometers

Consider the tube cross-section shown in Fig. 12.11. If the Reynolds number (see Chapter 11) is below 1000, laminar flow will exist in the tube

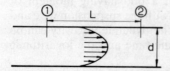

Fig. 12.11 Laminar flow through a capillary tube

and the familiar parabolic velocity profile will be experienced as shown. If the fluid is incompressible and the flow is steady, the volume rate of flow can be determined by the Poiseuille equation:

$$Q = \frac{\Delta p \pi d^4}{128 \eta L} \qquad (12.8)$$

where Q is the volume rate of flow and Δp is the pressure drop between positions 1 and 2.

A viscosity determination may be made by measuring the volume rate of flow and pressure drop for flow in such a tube. A small diameter capillary tube is used to reduce the size of the Reynolds number and ensure laminar flow.

Capillary viscometers can be divided into two classes:

(1) Instruments for measuring absolute viscosity directly from the dimensions of the apparatus and experimental data obtained.
(2) Viscometers used for determining relative viscosities by reference to certain standard liquids.

Greater accuracy is usually obtained with viscometers designed for relative measurements than with absolute instruments. This greater accuracy is due partly to simplification in design and partly to the elimination of errors made in the measurement of dimensions. The precise measurement of absolute values is therefore a subject chiefly of historical interest. The apparatus illustrated in Fig. 12.12 was that used by Poiseuille.

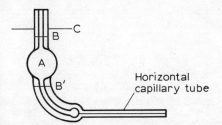

Fig. 12.12 Poiseuille's viscometer

The bulb A and the horizontal capillary attached are filled with and immersed in the liquid under test. The upper tube is joined to a compressed air reservoir connected to some form of manometer. The liquid in bulb A is forced out through the capillary and the time for the level to fall from B to B' noted. The effective pressure is that indicated by the manometer less a small head of liquid which varies during the experiment from BC to B'C. Provided the pressure in the compressed air reservoir is reasonably large the head to be subtracted may be taken as $\frac{1}{2}$(BC + B'C).

Poiseuille's viscometer had many disadvantages some of which are listed as follows:

(a) The exact length of the capillary could not easily be measured.

(*b*) Owing to the shape of bulb A differences in the rate of drainage down the walls led to errors in the volume delivered for different rates of flow or with different liquids.

(*c*) Solid impurities in the fluid were almost certain to enter the capillary.

Many capillary viscometers have been designed to overcome these difficulties. The basic principle of all of these instruments, however, is the same as the Poiseuille viscometer already discussed.

Viscometers for relative measurements

Relative viscometers can be divided into two classes:

(1) Those using an externally applied pressure;
(2) Those relying solely on the hydrostatic head of liquid in the viscometer to produce flow.

Instruments using an externally applied pressure
Absolute viscometers can readily be used for relative measurements, and because of this, construction is simplified. A typical device used by Ubbelohde is shown in Fig. 12.13. The viscometer is filled by suction until

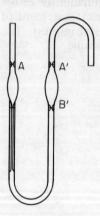

Fig. 12.13 Ubbelohde's viscometer

the liquid stands at A and B'. The liquid is then forced through the capillary by air pressure, the time taken for the liquid to move between the marks B' and A' being noted. If the kinetic energy term is neglected the viscosity of the test liquid can be calculated from the relationship

$$\eta = \eta' Pt/P't' \qquad (12.9)$$

where P is the air pressure when the liquid under test is forced through the capillary, t is the time taken for the liquid under test to pass between the marks B' and A' and P' and t' are the pressure and time for a standard liquid of known viscosity η'.

Gravity viscometers

If the jet of a simple pipette is replaced by a capillary tube and the liquid under test allowed to flow out under its own hydrostatic head a measure of the kinematic viscosity can be obtained by timing the meniscus between two marks. A typical pipette viscometer used by Barr is shown in Fig. 12.14.

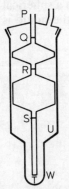

Fig. 12.14 Barr's pipette viscometer

The pipette PT is enclosed in an outer vessel UW. The test liquid is sucked up into the pipette as far as the mark Q; the pipette is then placed in the outer vessel as shown and allowed to drain. When a reading is required the liquid is sucked up to a level above R and the fall from R to S timed.

Many relative measurements made in viscometry have been carried out with instruments based on the Ostwald Viscometer shown in Fig. 12.15.

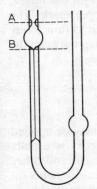

Fig. 12.15 Ostwald viscometer

The apparatus is charged with a constant volume from a pipette and the liquid is then drawn into the left hand limb above the mark A. The liquid is then allowed to flow back and the time taken to fall from A to B measured. The absolute viscosity η of a test liquid can be calculated using the relationship

$$\eta = \eta' \rho t / \rho' t' \tag{12.10}$$

where ϱ is the density of the test liquid, t is the time taken for the test liquid to fall between A and B, and ρ' and t' are the density and time for a standard liquid of known viscosity η'.

Suspended level viscometers

Ubbelohde introduced a modification of his viscometer to include a suspended level. The lower end of the capillary is widened into a spherical shoulder as shown in Fig. 12.16. By introducing an air vent the liquid is

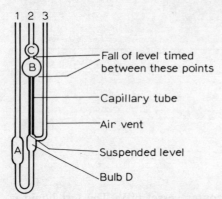

Fig. 12.16 Suspended level viscometer

induced to flow only down the walls of the bulb D thus automatically fixing the lower liquid level at the lower end of the capillary. A small sample of the test fluid is introduced into tube 1, tube 3 is blocked with the finger, and the liquid drawn into tube 2 to a point above the upper mark. The finger is then removed from tube 3 and the liquid is allowed to flow freely through the capillary. The fall of the upper level is then timed between the marks on the bulb B.

12.7 Viscosity of gases

Many methods used for measuring the viscosity of liquids may be applied to gases and possibly vapours. A modification to the theory is usually required, however, to allow for the compressibility of the gas and other factors. Capillary viscometers are used extensively for measurements on gases but as gases are much less viscous than liquids the capillary must have an extremely fine bore. Because of the fineness of the bore, accurate measurement of the tube radius is made more difficult but this difficulty is removed if viscosity comparisons only are to be made.

Because a gas is compressible the density will decrease along the tube and therefore it is not simply the volume but the mass traversing any cross-section which is constant. If ρ is the density and Q the volume passing any cross-section per second then the product ρQ is constant. Since the density is proportional to the pressure the product pQ will also be constant, where p is the pressure of the gas at a particular cross-section. The absolute viscosity can then be calculated from the formula

$$p_0 Q_0 = p_1 Q_1 = \frac{(p_0^2 - p_1^2)\pi d^2}{256\eta L} \qquad (12.11)$$

where p_0 and p_1 are the pressures at the tube entrance and outlet respectively, Q_0 is the volume of liquid entering the tube per second, Q_1 is the volume of liquid flowing out per second and L is the length of the tube.

A typical capillary viscometer used for measuring the viscosity of gases is the apparatus used by Schultze (Fig. 12.17). In this apparatus the pressure difference $(p_0 - p_1)$ is maintained at a constant value by regulating the supply or withdrawal of liquid. Gas contained in the bulbs A and B is forced through the capillary at constant pressure by raising the mercury C up the scale D. The volume of gas is recorded electrically as the mercury meniscus passes the contacts F and G.

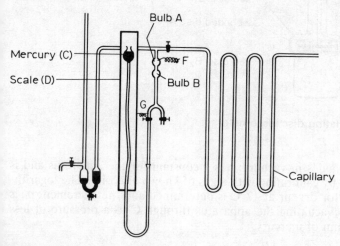

Fig. 12.17 Schultze's viscometer

Viscometers of the concentric cylinder type have frequently been used for measuring the viscosity of gases. The apparatus is usually of the form in which the inner of two concentric cylinders is suspended while the outer one rotates at a steady speed. Viscometers of this type have already been discussed in connection with liquids (Section 12.3).

The oscillating disc viscometer has been used extensively for gases and vapours. In this instrument, which has already been discussed in connection with liquids, observations are made of the damping imposed on an oscillating disc attached to a suspension wire. Figure 12.18 shows the suspended disc A oscillating midway between two fixed discs of slightly larger diameter, B_1 and B_2.

The fixed discs are held apart by three pegs and are supported by a rod D, which passes up the tube and is sealed at the top. The suspension wire is fused to a small projection from the top of this rod. The dynamic viscosity may be calculated from the formula:

$$\eta = c\left(\frac{\delta}{T} - \frac{\delta_0}{T_0}\right) \tag{12.12}$$

where δ and T are the logarithmic decrement and periodic time respectively at the temperature and pressure of the test, and δ_0 and T_0 the

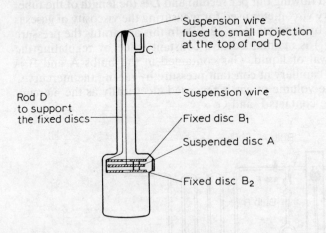

Suspension wire
fused to small projection
at the top of rod D

C

Rod D
to support
the fixed discs

Suspension wire

Fixed disc B_1

Suspended disc A

Fixed disc B_2

Fig. 12.18 Oscillating disc viscometer

corresponding values in vacuum; c is a constant for the apparatus and is normally found by calibrating with a gas of known viscosity. The logarithmic decrement for dry air at 17 °C is determined and the decrement δ_0 is obtained after evacuating the apparatus through C to a pressure of less than 1×10^{-4} mm of mercury.

12.8 Miscellaneous methods

Oscillation of a liquid in a U-tube

The liquid contained in a U-tube of uniform bore is displaced by applying a pressure to one side and then suddenly releasing it (Fig. 12.19). If a_1 and a_3 represent successive amplitudes on the same side of the equilibrium level, when $a_1/a_3 > 5$ the damping is large and the logarithmic decrement δ is constant and independent of the initial amplitude. The dynamic viscosity can now be calculated from the following formulae:

$$\eta = \tfrac{1}{16}\delta d^2 \rho / T \tag{12.13}$$

and

$$T^2 = \frac{2\pi^2 l}{g}\left(1 + \frac{\delta^2}{4\pi^2}\right) \tag{12.14}$$

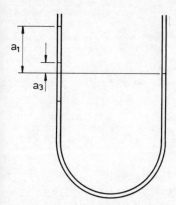

Fig. 12.19 Oscillation of liquid in a U-tube

where l is the total length of the liquid when measured along the axis of the U-tube of diameter d, ρ is the density of the liquid and T is the periodic time of oscillation.

Consistent results can only be obtained using a viscometer of this type when $a_1/a_3 > 5$, using initial amplitudes of up to 160 mm.

Rolling sphere viscometer

A simple method for determining the viscosity of a liquid is to measure the speed with which a sphere will roll down an inclined cylindrical tube filled with liquid. As the ball is always in contact with the tube at one point visual observation is possible in a glass cylinder even with opaque liquids. The range of the instrument may be easily extended by using a ball of different diameter.

Falling cylinder system

In the falling sphere viscometer discussed in the previous section the clearance between the sphere and the container is large. The apparatus here, however, operates on the principle of a cylindrical metal bulb falling in a vertical metal tube of only slightly greater diameter. The apparatus used by Bridgman is shown in Fig. 12.20.

The steel bulb A is made in two parts so that masses may be placed inside to accelerate the fall if necessary. The falling bulb forces liquid from the bottom to the top of the tube through the annulus and a coaxial fall is ensured by having three small projections at each end of the tube. These guides (G in the figure) at each end make electrical contact with the walls of the tube and the circuit is completed when the bulb touches the electrode E, insulated from the outer tube by C. The measured time of fall is proportional to the viscosity of the liquid and the coefficient of viscosity can be calculated from the formula:

$$\eta = (\sigma - \rho) \frac{(a - b)^3}{3b} \frac{t}{s} \qquad (12.15)$$

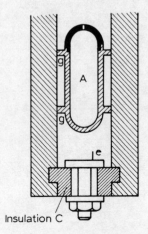

Fig. 12.20 Falling cylinder viscometer

where σ is the density of the bulb, ρ is the density of the liquid, a and b are the radii of the tube and bulb respectively and t is the time taken for the bulb to fall a distance s.

This formula does not allow for the change in density of a liquid due to compression and it is usual to calibrate such an instrument with a liquid of known viscosity. Then for a fixed distance of fall the viscosity may be calculated from the formula:

$$\eta = kt(\sigma - \rho) \tag{12.16}$$

where k is the constant for the instrument.

Air bubble viscometer

Various industries have made viscosity comparisons by observing the rate of rise of an air bubble in a vertical tube containing the test liquid.

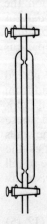

Fig. 12.21 Air bubble viscometer

Provided the bore of the tube is only slightly larger than the bubble diameter the bubble will rise slowly. In its most simple form this apparatus consists of a burette tube closed by taps at each end. The tap at the lower end is arranged so that a bubble of constant volume can be released into the vertical tube (Fig. 12.21).

A slower rate of rise may be obtained by inclining tubes at a small angle to the horizontal. A purely comparative system may be obtained using a series of inclined tubes filled to the same level with oils having viscosities increasing in constant steps. A similar tube is then filled to the same level with the sample and the time taken for an air bubble to rise in the sample is compared with the standards. The range within which the viscosity of the sample must be is then quickly determined.

Direct reading viscometer

The principle of operation of the apparatus described by Rhodin depends on the viscous drag exerted on the walls of a movable body placed in a channel through which the fluid under test flows at a constant velocity. The body is capable of movement in the direction of flow against the action of a spring or mass.

The instrument is shown in Fig. 12.22. Liquid is forced up the tube A via

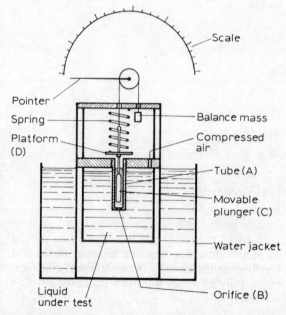

Fig. 12.22 Rhodin's direct reading viscometer

the aperture B by means of compressed air which is maintained at constant pressure by a relief valve. The viscous drag on the plunger C is balanced by compression of the spring; plunger movement is indicated on the scale by means of the pointer. The balance mass may be adjusted so that its weight equals the apparent weight of the plunger immersed in the liquid. To compensate for variations in specific gravity, masses may be placed on the platform D.

Michell cup and ball viscometer

The apparatus (Fig. 12.23) consists of a cup attached to a handle and a steel ball of the same curvature as the cup. Contact between the surfaces of the ball and cup is prevented by three small projections on the surface of the cup. The projections are accurately ground to project about 0·01 mm so that a space of this thickness remains between the ball and the cup. The interspace and a groove formed round the edge of the cup are filled with liquid which is held in the interspace and groove by surface tension. The weight of the ball provides the force tending to·draw the two surfaces apart. A thermometer may be inserted in the hollow insulated handle.

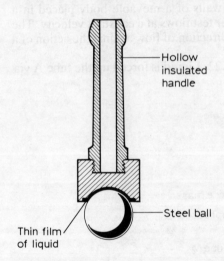

Fig. 12.23 Michell cup and ball viscometer

In practice the instrument is lifted vertically and the time taken for the ball to fall off is noted with a stop watch. The absolute viscosity of the test liquid may be determined by dividing the time by the instrument constant. The instrument constant $k = t/\eta$ may be easily found by calibrating with a liquid of known viscosity.

12.9 Viscosity index

The viscosity index of an oil is an indication of the relative rate of change of the viscosity with temperature change and is used extensively in the oil industry.

The viscosity index (VI) can be calculated using the following relationship:

$$VI = \frac{100(L - U)}{L - H} \qquad (12.17)$$

where U is the kinematic viscosity at 100 °F of the sample, L is the kinematic viscosity at 100 °F of an oil of zero viscosity index having the same viscosity at 210 °F as the sample and H is the kinematic viscosity at 100 °F of an oil of 100 viscosity index having the same viscosity at 210 °F as the sample.

The values of L and ($L - H$) are tabulated in the Institution of Petroleum Standards publication IP 73/53. Therefore if the kinematic viscosity of an oil is known at both 100 °F and 210 °F the viscosity index can be easily calculated.

As the temperature rises a fluid tends to become less viscous and the rate at which the fluid will thin out depends on the viscosity index. As an example consider two fluids which have the same viscosity at 100 °F but one fluid has a viscosity index of 80 whereas the other has a viscosity index of 70. An increase in temperature will cause the fluid of viscosity index 70 to thin out faster than the fluid of viscosity index 80.

Study problems

12.1 A flat plate having a cross-sectional area of 400 mm² slides along a horizontal surface at a velocity of 2 m/s. The plate is supported by a film of lubricating oil of 0·04 mm thickness and coefficient of dynamic viscosity 5 × 10⁻⁴ N s/m². Calculate the resistance to the motion.

Answer: 1 N

12.2 Define the following terms: (*a*) viscous flow; (*b*) coefficient of dynamic viscosity; (*c*) kinematic viscosity; (*d*) non-Newtonian fluids.

12.3 A medium lubricating oil at 20 °C has a specific gravity of 0·89 and a kinematic viscosity of 1·75 × 10⁻⁴ m²/s. Calculate the coefficient of dynamic viscosity in N s/m².

Answer: 0·156 N s/m²

12.4 Calculate the viscosity of glycerine if, during a test using a falling sphere viscometer, the uniform velocity of a steel ball falling through a tank of glycerine is found to be 0·07 m/s. The radius of the ball is 2 mm and the densities of steel and glycerine are 8000 kg/m³ and 1300 kg/m³ respectively.

Answer: 0·35 N s/m²

12.5 Describe, with the aid of a sketch, the principle of operation of the Saybolt viscometer. Explain the difference between seconds Saybolt Universal and seconds Saybolt Furol.

12.6 Describe, with the aid of a diagram, the following methods for determining the viscosity of a liquid:

(*a*) Concentric cylinders method
(*b*) Stokes's method
(*c*) Torque method.

13 Measurement of temperature

Measuring the temperature of a body depends upon the establishment of thermodynamic equilibrium between the body and the device used to sense the temperature, e.g. a thermometer bulb or thermocouple wires. In practice this condition is rarely attained since it is difficult to establish complete instantaneous equilibrium and great care must be exercised in choosing a method suited to the problem so that satisfactory conditions for temperature measurement are obtained. Temperature sensors possess thermal characteristics dependent largely upon their size and shape and the materials from which they are made, and these characteristics, for instance high heat capacity, affect their ability to conduct, radiate or reflect heat from their surroundings. The introduction of a temperature sensor into a body tends to modify the temperature conditions at that point, and the body will be modified by any holes drilled, or by insertion of protective pockets to accommodate temperature sensors.

In most cases the sensor is connected to a recording instrument by means of an intermediate system, such as a Bourdon tube or electrical conductors, along which the signal is carried. The intermediate system and the recorder may be subject to temperature or other changes and compensating devices are usually incorporated to reduce or eliminate errors.

Heat is transferred from place to place by conduction, convection and radiation, and it is necessary to take these into account when choosing a temperature measurement method.

13.1 Conduction

Heat flow along a conductor is analogous to flow of electricity. Heat flows along a conductor provided that the conductor is subject to a temperature gradient. Some substances are good conductors, e.g. metals; others are poor conductors, e.g. glass, plastics, oxides. The temperature gradient across a poor conductor is steep; thus poor conductors are good insulators. To a rough approximation the conductivities of metals are of the order of one thousand times those of other solids and liquids except mercury, which is a liquid metal, and ten thousand times as great as gases.

It is desirable that heat be conducted as rapidly as possible to the temperature sensor which should be directly immersed in the heated medium or, if this is not possible, a protective pocket should be provided and the sensor immersed in a good conductor such as mercury. This technique will reduce time lag.

13.2 Convection

Liquids are poor thermal conductors, and gases for most practical purposes can be regarded as non-conductors. When liquids and gases transfer heat by moving from one place to another, this is called convection. Convection may be either 'natural' or forced. The domestic hot water radiator is an example of natural convection; it transfers most of its heat by warming the surrounding air which expands, rises and is replaced by cooler air. On the other hand, the electric fan heater transfers most of its heat by mechanically directing a stream of air over a hot element; this is forced convection.

13.3 Radiation

Radiant heat (infra-red radiation), like light, is considered to take the form of an electromagnetic wave; it travels at the same speed as light (300 000 km/s) in vacuum and air; it can be focused in the same way and is reflected, transmitted, absorbed and radiated by materials. Its essential differences from light are

(a) it is not visible
(b) it has a longer wavelength, ranging from $0.75\,\mu m$ to about $100\,\mu m$
(c) when it falls on the skin it produces the sensation of warmth.

All substances radiate heat at all temperatures above absolute zero; thus if an attempt is made to measure the temperature of a hot gas surrounded by cooler walls using a thermocouple it is found that the temperature recorded is lower than that of the gas. The couple and the walls exchange radiation; thus the thermocouple grows cooler by emitting more radiation than it receives until it reaches radiation equilibrium with the cooler walls. They will then continue to transfer radiation equally to each other.

13.4 Temperature scales

Many substances change their state from solid to liquid and liquid to gas at a constant temperature. The effect of barometric pressure on the solid/liquid change of state is negligible, but the liquid/gas change is affected by barometric pressure, an increase in pressure raising the boiling point and a decrease reducing it.

The positions of the freezing and boiling point graduations on a mercury thermometer are established by placing the thermometer in melting ice and then in steam from boiling water. In both cases distilled water is used, and for the boiling point allowance must be made for any deviation from a barometric pressure of 760 mm of mercury. These fixed points, defined as 0 °C and 100 °C, are often called the ice point and the steam point.

Mercury in glass thermometers depend on change of volume of the mercury with change of temperature. Other types of thermometers, based on other properties such as change of electrical resistance or change of pressure, give their own temperature scales and these agree exactly with each other only at the fixed points where their readings are defined as 0 °C and 100 °C or some other accepted equilibrium temperature. The scale established by a platinum resistance thermometer differs from the mercury in glass scale except at the fixed points, because the platinum resistance response does not follow the same law as that of mercury in glass. A comparison of two such scales is shown in Table 13.1.

Table 13.1 Comparison of thermometers

Mercury in glass (°C)	0	50	100	200	300
Platinum resistance (°C)	0	50·25	100	197	291

13.5 Absolute thermodynamic temperature scale

The absolute thermodynamic temperature scale was originally established in 1854. The term 'thermodynamic' means that the temperature scale conforms to the laws of thermodynamics and is independent of any thermometric substance.

The combination of Boyle's and Charles's Laws applied to a 'perfect' gas states that:

pressure × volume = a constant × absolute temperature

The scale may be established by various methods but the constant volume gas thermometer is the most widely used. The unit degree on the scale was originally defined as one hundredth part of the temperature interval between the freezing point and boiling point of pure water. This temperature interval was called the fundamental interval. The present thermodynamic scale is called the kelvin scale and its sole defining point is the triple point of water 273·16 K (0·01 °C). The present kelvin degree does not differ from the degree originally established in 1854. The ice point corresponds to 273·15 on the kelvin scale and is thus zero on the Celsius scale.

No gases perfectly obey the gas laws but at a pressure of about one atmosphere their behaviour approaches the ideal and their temperature scales correspond. The departure of a gas from perfect behaviour can be observed and corrections made. The constant volume gas thermometer which consists essentially of a metal bulb filled with hydrogen or nitrogen is used to measure increase in pressure which, because temperature change is directly proportional to pressure change, provides a means whereby thermodynamic temperature may be established accurately.

The establishment of the thermodynamic scale by gas thermometry is a difficult technique requiring great skill, and in view of this the International Practical Temperature Scale was established which conforms closely to the absolute scale using instruments for fixed point determination which conveniently and accurately reproduce temperatures within the scale range.

13.6 International Practical Temperature Scale (IPTS) 1968

The primary fixed points on the IPTS are shown in Table 13.2. They are determined at specified equilibrium states between phases of pure substances and in most cases at one standard atmosphere ($101\,325\,\text{N}/\text{m}^2$).

The methods used to establish the scale are shown in Table 13.3, and intermediate values between the points are established by the use of a formula appropriate to the interval under consideration. A large number of secondary points are also defined in the IPTS which allow intermediate temperatures on the primary scale to be determined and also provide fixed points for instrument calibration beyond $1337 \cdot 58\,\text{K}$. Some of the secondary points are shown in Table 13.4.

Table 13.2 Defining fixed points of the IPTS (1968)

Equilibrium state	Kelvin scale $T(K)$	Celsius scale $t(°C)$
Equilibrium between the solid, liquid and vapour phases of equilibrium hydrogen (triple point of equilibrium hydrogen)	13·81	−259·34
Equilibrium between the liquid and vapour phases of equilibrium hydrogen at a pressure of $33\,330 \cdot 6\,\text{N}/\text{m}^2$ (25/76 standard atmosphere)	17·042	−256·108
Boiling point of equilibrium hydrogen	20·28	−252·87
Boiling point of neon	27·102	−246·048
Triple point of oxygen	54·361	−218·789
Boiling point of oxygen	90·188	−182·962
Triple point of water	273·16	0·01
Boiling point of water	373·15	100
Freezing point of zinc	692·73	419·58
Freezing point of silver	1235·08	961·93
Freezing point of gold	1337·58	1064·43

The English translation of the IPTS 1968 appeared in *Metrologia*, 1969, **5** (2).

Table 13.3 Methods used to establish the IPTS

Range	Method	Output measured
13·8 K to the antimony point 630·74 °C	Platinum resistance thermometer	Electrical resistance
630·74 °C to the gold point 1064·43 °C	Pt/Pt + 10% Rh thermocouple	Electromotive force
Above 1337·58 K (1064·43 °C) the IPTS is defined by Planck's Law of Radiation		

Table 13.4 IPTS secondary points

Substance[1] (solid/liquid equilibrium)	Temp. T(K)	Temp. t(°C)
Mercury	234·288	−38·862
Water (ice point)	273·15	0
Bismuth	544·592	271·442
Lead	600·652	327·502
Antimony	903·89	630·74
Nickel	1728	1455
Platinum	2045	1772
Rhodium	2236	1963
Iridium	2720	2447
Tungsten	3660	3387

[1] The triple points and boiling points of a number of gases are also specified for the range from 13·956 K.

There is no IPTS from absolute zero to 13·81 K, but temperatures in the range 0 K to 20 K are measured by magnetic, vapour pressure and ultrasonic (noise) thermometers.

13.7 Temperature measuring instruments

Temperature measuring instruments can be divided into two groups, electrical and non-electrical:

Non-electrical methods
(1) Liquid, vapour pressure and gas thermometers
(2) Bimetal strip thermometers
(3) Refractory cones, paints and crayons.

Electrical methods
(4) Electrical resistance pyrometers
(5) Thermocouple pyrometers
(6) (i) Total radiation pyrometers
     (ii) Photoelectric pyrometers
     (iii) Optical pyrometers.

Those listed under (6) measure emitted radiation in various ways. Non-electrical methods are dealt with in Sections 13.8–13.13 and electrical methods from Section 13.14 onwards.

13.8 Liquid in glass thermometers

Mercury is usually used in liquid in glass thermometers although other liquids, such as alcohol and pentane, which have lower freezing temperatures than mercury and do not cause contamination through breakage, are also used (see Table 13.5).

Table 13.5 Liquids used in liquid in glass thermometers

Liquid	Range (°C)	Range (K)
Mercury	− 35 to +510	238 to 783
Alcohol	− 80 to + 70	193 to 343
Toluene	− 80 to +100	193 to 373
Pentane	−200 to + 30	73 to 303
Creosote	− 5 to +200	268 to 573

Increase in temperature causes the liquid to expand and rise up the stem. When measuring temperatures above the boiling point of mercury (357 °C at atmospheric pressure) the space above the liquid is filled with nitrogen under pressure, thus raising the boiling point and allowing temperatures up to 510 °C to be measured (Fig. 13.1).

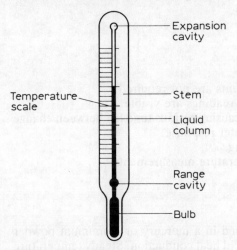

Fig. 13.1 Liquid in glass thermometer

Range variation is provided for by incorporating a small cavity above the bulb which the mercury has to fill before rising up the stem. Liquid in glass thermometers have considerable heat capacity and do not respond quickly to rapid changes of temperature; and glass which has been heated and then cooled does not immediately return to its original volume, thus tending to produce a low reading, although for many purposes this discrepancy is of little importance.

Thermometers may be classified as 'chemical' or 'industrial', the former being used as standards in laboratories or for checking industrial plant, and are carefully and regularly calibrated against standard instruments when in use. Such calibrations may be carried out by the National Physical Laboratories or other independent authority, or by the manufacturer or user. Industrial thermometers may be fitted into pipelines or other apparatus to give routine temperature indications. A protective sheath is often provided to reduce the risk of breakage; an extra long stem may be incorporated for dipping into hot liquids or the thermometer may be of the registering type to indicate maximum and minimum temperatures. Wherever possible thermometers are calibrated, standardized and used when totally immersed up to the readings but where necessary they may be standardized for partial immersion.

As with all measuring instruments, a tolerance must be applied to the accuracy of the readings. In the case of thermometers this is based on a percentage of the scale range but also depends upon how one degree division is divided. In general the smaller the scale length for one degree, and the greater the temperature range, the broader the accuracy tolerance. Special types having a small scale range, usually $5\,°C$ and a one degree interval 50 mm long, can give estimated values of the order of $0\cdot001$ to $0\cdot002\,°C$ when used in conjunction with a low power telescope.

The essential characteristics of liquid in glass thermometers are summarized as:

(1) Inexpensive.
(2) Simple.
(3) Easily portable.
(4) Fragile.
(5) Additional indication instruments are not required.
(6) Can be used only where stem readings are visible.
(7) Relatively high heat capacity causing serious time lag between change of temperature and thermometer response.
(8) Not suitable for distant reading.
(9) Not suitable for surface temperature measurements.

Application

Solids
The thermometer may be immersed in a mercury or aluminium powder filled hole in the solid to ensure rapid heat conduction. Steady temperature conditions in the area of measurement are necessary to ensure accurate readings and the hole volume should be small compared with the volume of the solid.

Liquids
Total immersion, i.e. immersion up to the column reading in the continually stirred liquid, is the most certain way to measure the mean liquid temperature, but where part of the column is exposed corrections should be applied.

Gases
Because gases are poor heat conductors, reading errors are caused by radiation exchange between the thermometer and the container walls

which may be at a different temperature from the gas. Bright metal shields round the thermometer, forced gas flow or fanning are used to improve measurement accuracy. Vapour condensation must be avoided as the latent heat of condensation can cause reading errors.

13.9 Liquid in metal thermometers

Within the range -40 to $+650\,°C$, and particularly where continuous indication is required at positions up to 65 m from the temperature point, liquid in steel thermometers offer many advantages. These instruments are of the bulb, capillary Bourdon tube type, filled with liquid under pressure, and measuring change of volume of the liquid. The bulb has a high heat capacity and is subject to considerable lag but it has the advantage of being more robust than a glass thermometer. The most widely used liquids, with their corresponding ranges of application, are shown in Table 13.6.

Table 13.6 Liquids used in liquid in metal thermometers

Liquid	Range (°C)	Range (K)
Mercury	−39 to +650	234 to 923
Xylene	−40 to +400	233 to 673
Alcohol	−46 to +150	227 to 423
Ether	+20 to + 90	293 to 363

The Bourdon tube may be spiral or helical and under the influence of increasing temperature the volume of liquid expands, tending to straighten or unwind the tube; the movement of the free end is transmitted through a linkage to a pointer which moves over a scale.

The main advantages of the instruments are as follows:

(1) An approximately linear scale.
(2) Wide temperature range.
(3) Ample power available to operate the Bourdon tube giving good pointer control.
(4) The liquid can be under high pressure thus reducing 'head' errors.
(5) There are no inaccuracies due to barometric pressure variations.
(6) Long capillaries allow large differences in bulb and indicator levels.
(7) Remote indication of temperature; errors in the system may arise from:
   (*a*) Bourdon tube zero errors, e.g. if the tube temperature changes then the indicator will give incorrect readings; this may be compensated by means of a bimetal helix attached to the indicator and acting in opposition to the error.
   (*b*) Capillary tube errors due to change of temperature. This error may be reduced in one of the following ways: a micro-bore capillary ensuring that any volume change is insignificant compared with the

temperature effect on the bulb, or a second capillary alongside the main capillary not attached to the bulb and operating a second Bourdon tube mechanically connected to the main Bourdon tube in opposition to the temperature error (Fig. 13.2).

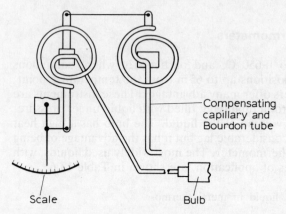

Compensating
capillary and
Bourdon tube

Scale

Bulb

Fig. 13.2 Compensated liquid in metal thermometer

(c) The cross-section of the capillary may be made into an annulus by inserting an invar wire along its whole length, which reduces the volume of liquid in the capillary so that its cubical volume change when subjected to temperature change is exactly equal to the change in volume in the space between the wire and the capillary walls. Another method based on the same principle is the introduction of compensating chambers at intervals along the capillary tube. These chambers compensate for both the liquid in them and also for the liquid in the intervening portions of capillary tube (Fig. 13.3).

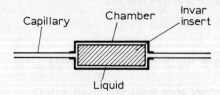

Capillary   Chamber   Invar insert

Liquid

Fig. 13.3 Capillary compensating chamber

Accuracy
This is of the order of $\pm\frac{1}{2}\%$ of the scale range up to 300 °C and $\pm1\%$ above this temperature.

Bulbs and pockets
The bulb size of these instruments usually ranges from about 25 mm up to 375 mm in length and 12 to 18 mm in diameter depending on requirements, and to reduce time lag to a minimum the surface area to liquid volume ratio

is made as large as possible. To register small temperature changes the volume of liquid in the bulb must be increased; thus small temperature ranges require longer bulb lengths. Increased bulb length may be achieved by using special bulb shapes to improve sensitivity (Fig. 13.4). The bulb may be directly immersed, in which case the instrument response is rather better than the mercury in glass thermometer which often requires a metal pocket for protection. When used in high pressure systems above $3.5 \, MN/m^2$ it is usual to use a pocket which enables the bulb to be removed without emptying the system. Brass, titanium, monel and specially coated pockets are among the metals and methods used to afford corrosion protection.

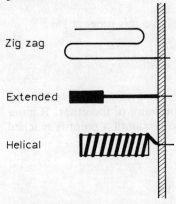

Zig zag

Extended

Helical

Fig. 13.4 Special bulb shapes

13.10 Constant volume gas expansion thermometers

In this bulb, capillary, Bourdon tube thermometer used mainly for measuring liquid temperatures, change of temperature is sensed through change of pressure of an inert gas which fills the instrument, and the instrument thus acts as a pressure gauge. Temperatures in the range -130 to $540\,°C$ may be measured, a given instrument range being usually not less than $50\,°C$.

The main advantage of this instrument is its rapid response to temperature change as gas has a much lower heat capacity than liquids or solids.

Gases have a much higher coefficient of cubical expansion than liquids or solids, e.g. $N_2 \, 3.6744 \times 10^{-3}$ and $Ne_2 \, 3.6617 \times 10^{-3}$ as compared with $Hg \, 0.181 \times 10^{-3}$ and carbon steel 0.033×10^{-3}, but the ratio of bulb size to capillary plus Bourdon tube must be very large if ambient temperature effects on the latter are to be small enough not to affect the accuracy of the instrument.

Capillary errors
(1) Capillary errors increase with bulb temperature.
(2) Capillary errors decrease as the differential range increases (maximum temperature minus minimum temperature).

Two methods are used to compensate for these errors:

(1) A large differential range
(2) A second or auxiliary capillary as described in Section 13.9.

By adequate compensation and careful design these thermometers offer the advantages of low temperature measurement, small bulb size compared, say, with mercury in steel, and long capillaries (up to 60 m).

Bourdon tube compensation is by means of a bimetal strip; there are no 'head' errors, but changes of barometric pressure or altitude make zero reading adjustment necessary.

Accuracy
This is $\pm\frac{1}{2}\%$ of the range up to 320 °C and above this range $\pm1\%$.

13.11 Vapour pressure thermometers

If a vapour, e.g. ether, is introduced into an evacuated chamber the pressure in the chamber rises owing to the pressure of the ether. If more ether is introduced the pressure continues to rise until a point is reached

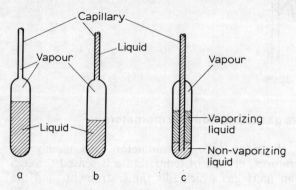

Fig. 13.5 Vapour pressure thermometers

when pressure change does not occur, a small quantity of liquid ether appears in the chamber and the vapour is said to be saturated. When liquid is not present the vapour is said to be unsaturated. Increase or decrease of chamber volume does not cause a change in the vapour pressure provided liquid is still present; thus saturated vapours to not obey Boyle's Law because their pressure is independent of their volume. Similarly, saturated vapours do not obey Charles's Law because their pressure changes roughly exponentially with change in temperature.

The vapour pressure thermometer has a Bourdon capillary and bulb partially filled with a volatile liquid such as methyl chloride or sulphur dioxide; the rest of the system is filled with vapour. An increase in temperature at the bulb causes further vaporization, the resulting pressure increase causing movement of the Bourdon tube.

The condition described occurs in the instrument when the ambient temperature of the capillary and Bourdon tube is higher than that of the bulb [Fig. 13.5(a)]. When the ambient temperature of the capillary and Bourdon is less than that of the bulb they are filled with condensed vapour, that is, liquid, and the pressure of the vapour in the bulb is transmitted through the liquid [Fig. 13.5(b)]. The rearrangement of the liquid/vapour system and certain other closely related factors involving lag in response and inaccuracy of reading make vapour pressure thermometers unsuitable for cross-ambient temperature measurement. Differences in level between the bulb and the Bourdon tube from that established at calibration introduce a 'head' error, for although the pressure at the bulb may remain constant the pressure due to a capillary full of vapour will be less than that due to a similar column of liquid.

A thermometer which overcomes the cross-ambient difficulties has the Bourdon, capillary and part of the bulb filled with a non-vaporizing liquid [Fig. 13.5(c)], which prevents the volatile fluid from entering the capillary and Bourdon tube, but these can be successfully used only when the bulb is in the upright position.

Table 13.7 Liquids used in vapour pressure thermometers

Liquid	Boiling point (°C)	Critical[1] temperature (°C)	Range (°C)
Methyl chloride	− 23·7	143·1	0–50
Diethyl ether	34·5	193·8	60–160
Ethyl alcohol	78·5	243·1	90–170
Water	100	374·0	120–220
Toluene	110·5	320·6	150–250
Argon	−185·7	−122	(2)

[1] The temperature at which both liquid and vapour have equal densities.
[2] Used for measuring the temperature of liquid gases down to −253 °C (20 K).

Vapour pressure thermometers have a lower initial cost than mercury in steel but because of their limitations they are unsuitable for universal application. Their main characteristics are as follows:

(1) A non-linear scale; this can be modified by a lever system or by choosing an instrument whose scale over the mid-section into which the temperature readings should fall is approximately linear.
(2) Scale range; this is of the order of 100 °C or less and is accurate to ±1% of the differential range, e.g. diethyl ether 60–160 °C.
(3) The time lag of these instruments is much less than for most other types.
(4) Non-ferrous metals can be used throughout.
(5) Distant reading 65 m.
(6) Temperatures between −50 and 310 °C are usually measured but the range for most commercial instruments lies within 0 and 250 °C.

(7) Normal ambient temperature change at the capillary and Bourdon does not appreciably affect the accuracy of the dial reading and is virtually independent of the capillary length.
(8) Barometric altitude and head errors are corrected by resetting the pointer.
(9) Smaller bulb sizes can be used than for a mercury in steel thermometer of the same range.
(10) Where the introduction of mercury or other contaminants into the measured substance through breakage might be harmful, e.g. food, a harmless filler liquid can be chosen.

A selection of liquids used in vapour pressure thermometers is given in Table 13.7.

13.12 Bimetal strip thermometers

A bimetal strip consists of two different metals or alloys having different coefficients of expansion (e.g. invar and brass) firmly bonded together by welding. When the strip is heated or cooled, differential expansion or contraction occurs causing the strip to bend (Fig. 13.6). The metal having the higher coefficient of expansion is shown hatched on the diagram.

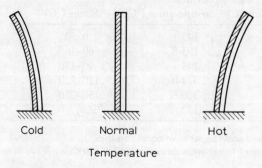

Cold   Normal   Hot

Temperature

Fig. 13.6 Bimetal strip

Many switching devices, such as those in oven thermostats, electric irons and car winker lamps, operate on this principle. They are also used as temperature sensors or as compensators for ambient temperature change in liquid in metal, vapour pressure and gas expansion thermometers, in aneroid barometers, and as balance wheel compensators in some watches.

The usual industrial form of bimetal thermometers [Fig. 13.7(a)] is a continuous strip wound into several compensating helices one inside the other; this has the advantage of compactness while providing the long length of strip required for adequate indicator movement, and also ensures that there is no lateral displacement of the free-floating transmission spindle which need not then be constrained by positive bearings.

Spiral bimetal strip thermometers [Fig. 13.7(b)] are widely used for measuring ambient and oven temperatures and clip-on types are available for checking the temperature of hot water pipes. Steam chambers, asphalt, tarmacadam, dough and paint are among the many applications for these thermometers.

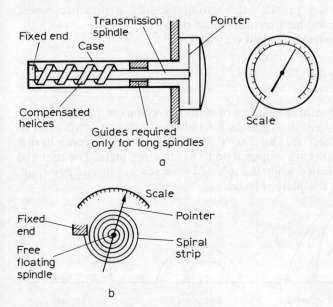

Fig. 13.7 Bimetal strip thermometer

The essential characteristics of these thermometers are:

(1) Inexpensive: often used instead of liquid in glass thermometers.
(2) Compact: the volume of metal used in the protective sheath is small and thus of low thermal capacity, reducing lag.
(3) Robust: good resistance to mechanical shock owing to freely floating spindle.
(4) Close linearity throughout the temperature range.
(5) Range of application: low temperature −30 to 200 °C; high temperature, 0 to 550 °C.
(6) Accuracy: (low temperature) 1% of scale range; (high temperature) 2% of scale range.
(7) Stem diameters as small as 4 mm are available. Stem lengths range from 75 mm for liquids of low specific heat and thermal conductivity, e.g. water. Longer stems are required for oil, and for air and gas 250 mm may be required.

In dry, clean non-corrosive gases stems may be perforated to improve response, and stainless iron (13% Cr) which has low conductivity may be used to reduce heat leakage.

13.13 Temperature indication by change of state of solids

Temperature indication by change of state of solids falls into two groups:

(1) Change of shape or size: this group includes pyrometric cones, thermoscope bars, heat recorders and rings.
(2) Change of colour: paints and crayons.

Change of shape or size

Pyrometric cones
These are made of various mixtures of materials, china clay, talc, feldspar, quartz, etc., which are arranged in a numbered series to correspond to temperatures between 600 and 2000 °C. A minimum of three cones having various melting points are mounted on to a refractory plate. The required temperature is indicated when the selected cone reaches its end point, i.e. its tip just touches the plate (Fig. 13.8).

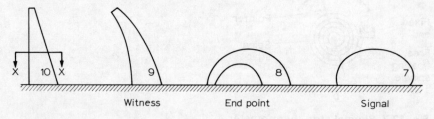

Witness   End point   Signal

Section X-X

Fig. 13.8 Pyrometric cones

Holdcroft thermoscope bars
Four small bars approximately 55 mm long by 6 mm square are supported horizontally at their ends and about 12 mm apart. The lowest numbered bar begins to bend with temperature increase and the required temperature is indicated when the chosen bar just begins to bend, the remaining bars being unaffected. Range 600–1550 °C.

Watkins heat recorders
These are similar in principle to indicating cones. Five cylindrical pellets approximately 9 mm long by 6 mm diameter are mounted in a holder. On heating some pellets will melt, one will just melt on its top surface and the others will be unaffected. The pellet which just melts on its surface indicates the temperature.

Bullers rings
This method assesses temperature by comparing the diameter of an unfired clay ring before and after heating. A number of rings, approximately

64 mm external diameter and 22 mm bore, are placed in a holder, several holders being distributed throughout the kiln. Rings are withdrawn during the heating cycle, cooled and measured. Firing is completed when a given contraction is obtained. Range 960–1400 °C.

Change of colour

Paints and crayons
These are useful for small scale heating of steel parts, weldments, for stress relief and pre-heating, etc. The paint or crayon changes colour or appearance at a fixed temperature.

Cones, bars, recorders and rings are used in heat treatment kilns for ceramic wear, grinding wheels, bricks, refractories, electrical porcelain, earthenware, sanitary ware, tiles and china, and temperatures are measured to about ±10 °C. They are often used in conjunction with a pyrometer which will give the actual temperature throughout a firing cycle at a particular point in the furnace or kiln, and act as a check against the rate of heating which must not be too rapid if correctly fired products are to be obtained.

13.14 Thermoelectricity

In certain circumstances heat may be converted into electrical energy or electrical energy converted into heat. This thermoelectric reversible process should not be confused with the irreversible conversion of electrical energy into heat (the Joule effect) that occurs when an electric current passes through a resistance causing an increase in temperature of the resistance.

(1) A potential difference always exists between two dissimilar metals in contact with each other.
(2) A potential gradient exists even in a single metal if there is a temperature gradient.

Thus if two dissimilar metals are joined together to form a closed circuit (a thermocouple) and one junction is maintained at a different temperature from the other, a current will flow spontaneously through the circuit; this is called the Seebeck effect. The magnitude of the current and its direction depends upon the thermoelectric characteristics of the two metals concerned and the temperature of their junctions.

The variation of thermocouple e.m.f. with temperature is illustrated by the curve for the tungsten/molybdenum thermocouple (Fig. 13.9).

In this case when the cold junction temperature is constant at 0 °C, an increase in temperature at the hot junction produces an e.m.f. increasing in the negative direction, and at about 800 °C the e.m.f. is a maximum; this is known as the neutral temperature. Further increasing the temperature to about 1200 °C reduces the e.m.f. to zero; this is known as the inversion temperature, beyond which the e.m.f. becomes positive. If a thermoelectric pyrometer is used to measure a range of temperature in which the neutral temperature for the couple falls, then two different temperatures will give the same e.m.f. value; thus a temperature range measured by a thermocouple should not include its neutral or inversion temperature.

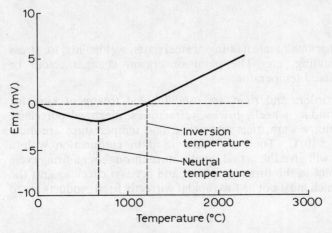

Fig. 13.9 Variation of e.m.f. with temperature (W–Mo thermocouple)

Law of Intermediate Metals

In practice the measurement of temperature using thermocouples involves at least the introduction of a millivoltmeter into the circuit which increases the number of junctions, but provided the temperature where the junctions are introduced is not changed the e.m.f. of the circuit is not affected.

Law of Intermediate Temperatures

The Law of Intermediate Temperatures is illustrated in Fig. 13.10.

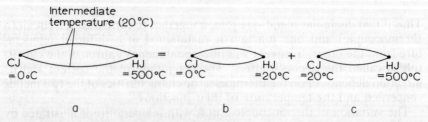

Fig. 13.10 Law of intermediate temperatures

Consider a given thermocouple [Fig. 13.10(a)] having an e.m.f. E_1, a cold junction temperature at 0 °C and a hot junction at 500 °C. The thermocouple is the sum of two other similar couples, one having a cold junction at 0 °C and a hot junction at 20 °C [Fig. 13.10(b)], the other having

tures than mercury and do not cause contamination through breakage, are
also used (see Table 13.5).

Table 13.5 Liquids used in liquid in glass thermometers

Liquid	Range (°C)	Range (K)
Mercury	− 35 to +510	238 to 783
Alcohol	− 80 to + 70	193 to 343
Toluene	− 80 to +100	193 to 373
Pentane	−200 to + 30	73 to 303
Creosote	− 5 to +200	268 to 573

Increase in temperature causes the liquid to expand and rise up the stem.
When measuring temperatures above the boiling point of mercury (357 °C
at atmospheric pressure) the space above the liquid is filled with nitrogen
under pressure, thus raising the boiling point and allowing temperatures up
to 510 °C to be measured (Fig. 13.1).

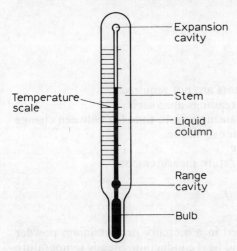

Expansion
cavity

Temperature
scale

Stem

Liquid
column

Range
cavity

Bulb

Fig. 13.1 Liquid in glass thermometer

Range variation is provided for by incorporating a small cavity above the
bulb which the mercury has to fill before rising up the stem. Liquid in glass
thermometers have considerable heat capacity and do not respond quickly
to rapid changes of temperature; and glass which has been heated and then
cooled does not immediately return to its original volume, thus tending to
produce a low reading, although for many purposes this discrepancy is of
little importance.

Thermometers may be classified as 'chemical' or 'industrial', the former
being used as standards in laboratories or for checking industrial plant, and
are carefully and regularly calibrated against standard instruments when in

a cold junction at 20 °C and a hot junction at 500 °C [Fig. 13.10(c)]. The e.m.f.s for these two couples are designated E_2 and E_3 respectively. Thus

$$E_1 = E_2 + E_3$$

This law is used when making corrections to thermocouple readings when the cold junction temperature is different from the temperature at which the couple was calibrated. Thus if a thermocouple calibrated at 0 °C is used at a cold junction temperature of 17 °C, the thermocouple will read correctly if the 'lost' e.m.f. is added to the reduced e.m.f.; the 'lost' e.m.f. values may be taken from tables of corrections for the couple concerned. In the case of base metal couples where the temperature/e.m.f. relationship is virtually linear the addition of the difference between the calibration and actual temperature to the scale reading is all that is required; for precious metal couples the correction is between 0·4 and 0·5 of this difference. Adjustment for ambient temperature variation can be made by disconnecting the cold junction and resetting the scale pointer to ambient temperature, the junction then being reconnected. Automatic compensation can also be incorporated by means of a bimetal strip which moves the scale pointer the required amount.

13.15 Thermoelectric pyrometers

The essential features of thermoelectric pyrometers are:

(1) Two dissimilar conductors in the form of rod or wire electrically insulated except at the hot junction. The hot junction wires may be welded or soldered together or may be completely separated depending upon their application.
(2) A refractory sheath to afford protection from injurious furnace gases. An outer metal sheath may also be used to prevent mechanical damage.

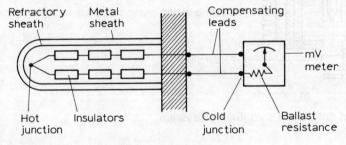

Fig. 13.11 Thermoelectric pyrometer

(3) Cold junction temperature control.
(4) An instrument for measuring the e.m.f., either a millivoltmeter or for more accurate measurement a potentiometer system.
(5) Compensating leads to allow the measuring instrument to be sited at a considerable distance from the couple without the necessity for using

expensive couple materials as extension leads. Compensating leads for precious metal thermocouples are usually pure copper and a suitable copper nickel alloy which have the same thermoelectric e.m.f. as the couple wires themselves, but within the temperature range of the cold junction. A ballast resistance is incorporated in the millivoltmeter to ensure that it has a large resistance compared with the couple circuit so that any temperature changes and thus any changes of resistance of the compensating leads will be too small to affect the accuracy of the system (Fig. 13.11).

Cold junction temperature control

This may be achieved by immersing the cold junction in a thermos flask filled with melting ice, but this is only suitable under laboratory conditions. A method for both laboratory and industrial cold junction control is the Zeref/Zerac method (Fig. 13.12).

The cold junction is immersed in a copper cylinder containing double distilled water; the cylinder is closed at one end and fitted with a bellows at the other end. Heat is extracted by a compact thermoelectric solid state heat pump. As ice is formed the resulting expansion inflates the bellows which at a certain stage operates a microswitch and stops the pump; the ice begins to turn to water and the bellows deflates, eventually switching on the heat pump; thus the cold junction is kept at the true ice point of water. The Zerac ice point reference system can maintain 100 cold junctions at the reference temperature.

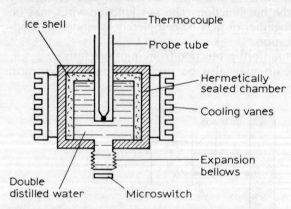

Fig. 13.12 Zeref solid state cold junction system

Thermocouples in common use are listed in Table 13.8.

The e.m.f.s generated in base metal couples are much greater than those generated in precious metal couples and they are thus more sensitive to small temperature changes. Because of their relative cheapness, thicker, stronger wires can be used (up to 3 mm) but they are unable to withstand high temperatures without melting and damage by gas attack. The tolerances for base metal thermocouples vary from ±2 °C at the lower part

Table 13.8 Common thermocouples and their characteristics

Type	Thermocouple	Approximate sensitivity (mV/°C)[1]	Normal temperature range (°C)	Maximum temperature (°C)[5]	Service characteristics
Base metal	Copper/constantan[2]	0.03	−200 + 400	+ 600	High resistance to condensed moisture corrosion.
Base metal	Iron/constantan	0.05	−200 + 800	+1000	A low-cost couple withstanding oxidation and reducing atmospheres.
Base metal	Chromel[3]/alumel[4]	0.04	−200 +1200	+1350	Withstands oxidizing atmospheres.
Precious metal	Platinum/platinum 90% /rhodium 10%	0.006	0 +1400	+1700	Withstands oxidation but e.m.f. is affected by the presence of metals, carbon or silicates in a reducing atmosphere.

[1] At lower temperatures, e.g. 20°C.
[2] 60% Cu 40% Ni (Eureka)
[3] 90% Ni 10% Cr
[4] 95% Ni 2% Al 3% Mn
[5] Short time immersion (seconds)

to $\pm\frac{3}{4}$°C at the upper part of their temperature ranges. Precious metal couples withstand high temperatures well and smaller wire diameters are used (0·5 mm or less) which helps to reduce cost and facilitates 'point' measurement of temperature. Their tolerances range from ± 1 °C at lower temperatures to ± 3 °C at high temperatures.

13.16 Applications of thermocouple pyrometers

Because of its reliability and sensitivity the Pt/Pt–10% Rh couple is used to define the International Practical Temperature Scale in the range 630·74 to 1064 °C, and in general because of their versatility thermocouples can be made to suit virtually any temperature measurement application, although it may not always be convenient or economical to do so. Apart from normal industrial applications, furnace temperature measurement, etc., thermocouples are manufactured small enough for such delicate applications as the temperature of nerves, tiny insects, transistors and so on. Thermal conduction along the couple wires can be reduced almost to vanishing point by the use of very fine wires which may be sited in the most difficult and inaccessible places. Thermocouples are used for measuring the temperature of solids, liquids and gases, and the hot junction must be applied in such a way as to suit the characteristics of the substance measured.

In Figs. 13.13(a) to (k) various methods of thermocouple application are indicated.

Figures 13.13(a) to (d) illustrate methods of surface measurement. The junction is welded to the surface (capacitance discharge welding offers an excellent method of attachment) or soldered. In (a) the wires run along the surface and in close contact with it for a short distance, which reduces or eliminates heat conduction away from the junction. In (b) an alternative method is shown where direct attachment is unsuitable. The junction is attached to a thin copper plate which is firmly held in position by clamping or strapping to ensure good heat transfer to the bead. In (c) the surface temperature may be estimated by extrapolation along X–X. Brick or concrete walls, etc., may be measured as shown in (d); alternatively a piece of asbestos sheet may be used to cover the groove which contains the couple.

Diagram (e) illustrates temperature gradient measurement across a wall and in (f) pairs of couples are shown enabling average temperatures across a liquid medium to be measured. Care must be taken when measuring still liquids to ensure that the liquid is fully mixed to prevent local temperature variations, and the couples should not be sited in 'dead' areas, e.g. corners. Heat transfer to the hot junction can be improved by immersing the couple in mercury or aluminium powder as illustrated in (g) and (h) but this method limits the application of the couple to the upright position. Liquid metals may be measured by direct insertion of the unjoined couple, but care must be taken to ensure that insertion is well below the surface slag (j). A disposable silicon protective sheath is used when measuring liquid steel, and the immersion time is only a few seconds.

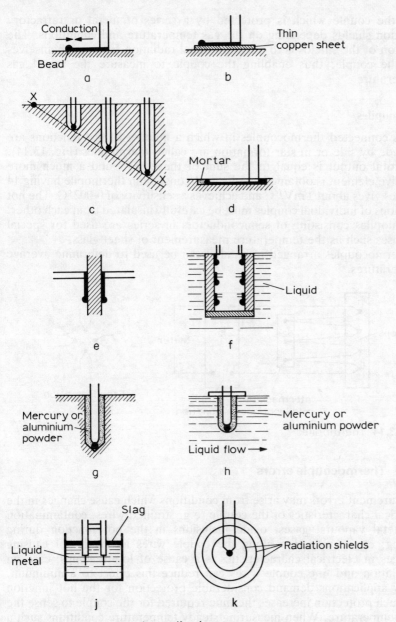

Fig. 13.13 Thermocouple applications

Gas temperature measurement poses particular difficulties because of radiation interchange between the couple and the cooler enclosure or furnace walls; this means that the couple indicates a lower temperature than that of the gas in which it is immersed. The suction pyrometer is used to overcome this difficulty (*k*). Gas is drawn from the furnace and flows over the couple which is protected by a series of metal or refractory radiation shields depending on the gas temperature and conditions. The function of the shields is to maintain equal radiation between themselves and the couple, thus enabling the couple to measure the actual gas temperature.

Thermopiles

Series connected thermocouples in which a number of hot junctions are laid side by side or in star formation are called thermopiles (Fig. 13.14). The total output is equal to the sum of the e.m.f.s and a much more sensitive element is obtained. A chromel/constantan thermopile having 14 couples gives about $1 \, mV/°C$ and achieves a sensitivity of $0·002 °C$. The hot junctions of individual couples must be carefully insulated from each other. Thermopiles consisting of semiconductors in series are used for special purposes such as the temperature measurement of sheet glass.

Thermocouples arranged in parallel can be used to determine average temperatures.

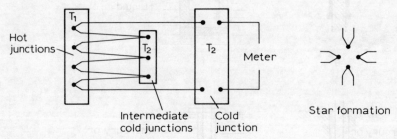

Fig. 13.14 Thermopiles

13.17 Thermocouple errors

Measurement errors may arise from conditions which cause changes in the electrical characteristics of the couple, e.g. strained wires, contamination by metal vapours, gases, oxide inclusions in the hot junction during joining, etc. Conduction along the couple wires although not causing changes in electrical characteristics is a cause of low readings; care on installation and fine couple wires can reduce this effect to a minimum. Many applications demand considerable protection for the hot junction and such protection increases the time required for the couple to sense the true temperature. When measuring steady temperature conditions such a time lag may not be serious, but it becomes an important factor when temperatures are fluctuating as the thermocouple may never with certainty register the true temperature at a given time (Fig. 13.15).

A simple check for non-metallic inclusions in the couple circuit is to apply a flame to one of the wires in the circuit. If the circuit is sound no change of reading should be seen on the meter as the e.m.f. gradients developed balance each other (see also Section 13.14).

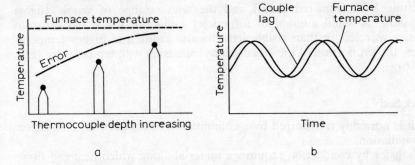

Fig. 13.15 Thermocouple errors
(*a*) Steady temperature　(*b*) Fluctuating temperature

13.18 Temperature measurement by detection of radiation

A body radiating heat at a given intensity emits a range or spectrum of radiation of varying wavelengths and as temperature falls the radiation intensity also falls. The fall in radiation intensity is accompanied by a

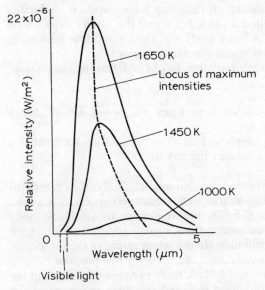

Fig. 13.16 Black body radiation intensities

corresponding increase in radiation wavelength. If the temperature of the body is increasing, then the intensity of radiation increases and the average radiation wavelength decreases. At about 500°C some of the radiation wavelengths are small enough to constitute visible light and the body begins to glow red; a further increase in temperature increases the proportion of light wavelengths emitted and when the body is white hot it is emitting both infra-red (heat) and the whole range of visible (light) radiation. A small amount of ultraviolet radiation, which has an even shorter wavelength than visible light, is also emitted at higher temperatures, the proportion of these radiations increasing with temperature (Fig. 13.16).

Black body

Heat is normally transferred by a combination of conduction, convection and radiation.

Transfer by conduction requires a material along which heat can flow, and transfer by convection requires the displacement of a heated material. Radiation requires no medium for heat transfer; thus if a radiating body were suspended in a vacuum all heat lost or gained by the body would be by radiation, as conduction and convection would be entirely prevented by the vacuum.

Likewise, if the surface of the body were a perfect reflector, then the quantity of heat in the body would not change and thus it would remain at constant temperature. It must be emphasized that such conditions do not arise in practice, although very highly reflective surfaces can be manufactured.

A body which is able to absorb all radiation falling upon it, reflecting and transmitting none, is called a black body and this ability depends on the condition of its surface. A black body will absorb and lose heat more rapidly than a non-black body under similar conditions.

Surfaces which readily absorb radiation have the following characteristics:

(1) Colour: the nearer the colour is to black the better will it absorb radiation.
(2) Surface finish: a matt or rough surface absorbs radiation better than a smooth, bright surface, whatever the colour.

The heat radiated by a black body is characteristic only of its temperature and in practical terms any almost totally enclosed space such as the interior of a muffled furnace fulfils the requirements of black body radiation. Thus if the radiation issuing from a small aperture in a furnace can be measured, the results will indicate the temperature of the interior of the furnace. Total radiation pyrometers are used for this purpose.

A body which is not radiating as a black body radiates less heat and the ratio of this to black body radiation is called the *total emissivity* of the surface. Thus a black body can be said to have an emissivity of one, whereas bodies which reflect or transmit some of the radiation falling upon them have an emissivity of less than one.

If E is the radiation falling upon the body (W/m^2), a is the fraction of radiation power absorbed by the body and e is the total emissivity, then

$$e = \frac{aE}{E} = \frac{\text{radiation emitted from the body}}{\text{radiation falling upon the body}}$$

A selection of total emissivity values for various materials is shown in Table 13.9.

Table 13.9 Total emissivity values for various metals

Material	Condition	Total emissivity
Steel plate	Rough	0·97
Steel	Polished	0·08
Cast iron	Strongly oxidized	0·95
Cast iron	Polished	0·21
Aluminium	Oxidized	0·11
Aluminium	Polished	0·028

N.B. Emissivity values vary with temperature and tend to increase with temperature.

Stefan–Boltzmann Law

The total energy radiated by a black body is characteristic only of its absolute temperature and is proportional to the fourth power of that temperature.

If E is the total energy radiated per unit area per unit time, then

$$E \propto K^4 \quad \text{or} \quad E = \sigma K^4$$

where Stefan's constant $\sigma \approx 5·7 \times 10^{-8}\,\text{W/K}^4\text{m}^2$ and K is the absolute temperature.

In practice, the pyrometer besides receiving heat from the radiating source also radiates heat to the source; thus the net radiation affecting the pyrometer will be:

$$E = \sigma(K_2^4 - K_1^4)$$

where K_1 is the pyrometer temperature and K_2 the temperature of the radiating source, but the fourth power of K_1 is small compared with that of K_2 and may be neglected.

If the emissivity of the body at the given temperature is e, then

$$E = e\sigma K^4 \tag{13.1}$$

The temperature of a body radiating in the open can be found if the emissivity of its surface is known.

If K is the true temperature and K_a is the apparent temperature taken with a radiation pyrometer positioned so that the body fills the whole field of view, then

$$E = \sigma K_a^4 \tag{13.2}$$

The energy received by the pyrometer equals the quantity of energy which it would receive from a perfect black body radiating at temperature K_a, that is, at a lower temperature than the temperature of the body being measured. Now the energy emitted by a non-black body is expressed by Eq. 13.1. From Eqs. 13.1 and 13.2 we have

$$e\sigma K^4 = \sigma K_a^4 \quad \text{i.e. } K^4 = K_a^4/e$$

Therefore

$$K = K_a/{}^4\sqrt{e} \tag{13.3}$$

13.19 Total radiation pyrometers

Total radiation pyrometers are used mainly in the range 700–2000°C. The advantage of most types is that they are not in contact with the hot body. They measure all the radiation emitted from the hot body and are

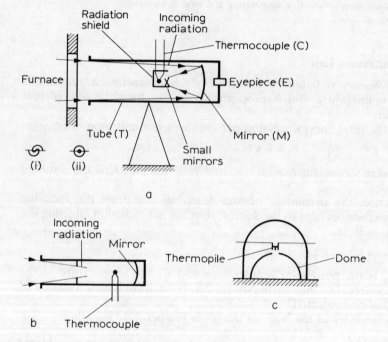

Fig. 13.17 Total radiation pyrometers
  (a) Féry focusing type
  (b) Foster fixed focus
  (c) Surface pyrometer

calibrated for black body conditions. The radiation emitted from the furnace is focused on to the hot junction of a thermocouple, a thermopile or a platinum resistance element which are blackened to improve their ability to absorb radiant energy. Three types of radiation pyrometers are shown in Fig. 13.17.

Féry total radiation pyrometer

The main features of a Féry pyrometer [Fig. 13.17(*a*)] are:

(*a*) A blackened tube T open at one end to receive radiation and carrying an adjustable eyepiece E at the other.
(*b*) A thermocouple C shielded from incoming radiation and carrying a blackened copper target disc.
(*c*) A concave mirror M to provide maximum reflection of radiation on to the couple and centrally pierced to allow light to reach the eyepiece. The position of the mirror may be adjusted by means of a rack and pinion.
(*d*) Two small flat mirrors having semicircles cut out of them are mounted between the couple and the mirror M and inclined at a slight angle from the vertical plane. The resulting hole which is smaller than the target allows radiation from M to reach the couple.

The pyrometer is carefully positioned in line with the hole in the furnace door and as close as possible to reduce radiation absorption by the atmosphere. The eyepiece is adjusted to focus on the target and the concave mirror is adjusted to focus the radiations from the furnace on to the target. The function of the small mirrors is to aid focusing. When the radiation is not focused on to the target, the mirrors appear as shown at (i); when focusing is achieved they appear as at (ii).

Foster pyrometer

This is a fixed focus thermocouple instrument [Fig. 13.17(*b*)] arranged in such a way that provided the cone of radiation fills the tube the distance of the pyrometer from the source is unimportant.

'Land' surface pyrometer

This pyrometer [Fig. 13.17(*c*)] is specially designed for measuring the temperature of surfaces in the open. It is also used for determining the total emissivity of a surface. The emissivity of a surface can be made to approach very closely black body conditions if a gold plated dome of high reflectivity is placed over the surface. In these circumstances virtually all the radiation both emitted and reflected is contained within the dome and the radiation passing through a small focusing lens on to a thermopile is virtually black body radiation. A black hemispherical insert can be fixed into the dome when required to determine the emissivity of a particular surface. Two readings are taken, one with the reflector exposed and the other when the reflector is covered by the black insert. Thus the true and apparent temperatures of the surface are obtained and the emissivity can be determined.

Sources of error

(1) The intervention of gas, flame, smoke or vapours between the radiating body and the pyrometer reduces the quantity of radiation received by the instrument.

(2) Radiation absorbed between the body and the instrument.
(3) Misalignment of the instrument with the radiating body.
(4) Failure of the radiating source to fill the whole field of view of the instrument. Radiation decreases as the square of the distance from the source but the area of the cone of radiation received by the instrument increases in the same proportion within the limits of size of the source (Fig. 13.18).
(5) Overheating of the pyrometer. Where the temperature is high because of operating conditions, e.g. when the pyrometer is permanently fixed to a furnace, then pyrometers are water cooled.

The accuracy of total radiation pyrometers is of the order of ±2% of the scale range.

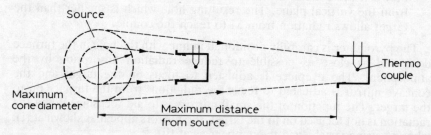

Fig. 13.18 Cone of radiation

13.20 Optical pyrometers

The curves shown in Fig. 13.16 indicate that a radiating body emits a spectrum of radiation wavelengths and that the wavelength at which maximum energy is emitted grows shorter as temperature increases. This is shown by the displacement of the peaks of the curves towards the left of the diagram. Further, the quantity of energy emitted at the maximum energy wavelength also increases as temperature increases.

If λ_m is the wavelength of maximum radiation and K is the absolute temperature, then

$$\lambda_m \propto 1/K$$

i.e. λ_m is inversely proportional to K. Therefore

$$\lambda_m K = \text{constant}$$

This is Wien's displacement law. Wien's second law states that

$$E_m \propto K^5 \qquad \text{i.e.} \qquad E_m = \text{constant} \times K^5$$

where E_m is the energy emitted at wavelength λ_m.

Formulae have also been evolved by Wien and by Planck which allow the energy emitted by a hot body at a given wavelength to be determined.

Optical pyrometers are based on comparison of the energy emitted by a hot body at a given wavelength with that of a black body calibrated lamp.

They are used in the range 600–3000 °C. The intensity of red light of approximate wavelength 0·65 µm is matched against a calibrated light source in the Féry disappearing filament pyrometer which is the instrument in most common use (Fig. 13.19). It should be remembered that light is simply the visible form of electromagnetic radiation and red light has the longest wavelength and is thus the first visible sign of radiation.

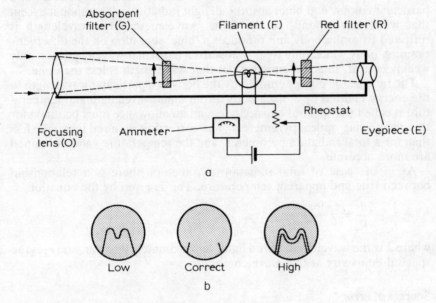

Fig. 13.19 Disappearing filament pyrometer

The pyrometer takes the form of a telescope. The lens O focuses radiation from the source at the plane of the filament F, the eyepiece E can also be focused at the same plane, and the removable red filter R prevents all radiation from the hot source except the red from reaching the eye. The battery, rheostat and ammeter carrying a temperature scale are all incorporated in the instrument. The current through the filament is adjusted by means of the rheostat. When the current passing through the filament is too low, the filament will emit radiation of lesser intensity than that of the source; it will thus appear dark against a bright background; when the current is too high it will appear brighter than the background; but when the correct current is passing through the filament, the filament 'disappears' into the background because it is radiating at the same intensity as the source [Fig. 13.19(*b*)].

For temperatures up to 800 °C the red filter may be removed. The ammeter has two overlapping scales, a lower temperature scale up to 1300 °C and a higher temperature scale 1000–1800 °C. When the higher scale is used an absorbent filter of known transmission factor is fitted between the lens O and the filament, thus enabling the same lamp to be used for higher temperatures without overloading the lamp filament.

Another type of optical pyrometer matches the 'red' wavelength from the hot body with the radiation of similar wavelength emitted by an electric lamp which has been previously calibrated.

Spectral emissivity

The colour of a body affects its ability to absorb radiation. A body of a particular colour, e.g. blue, absorbs all light radiation falling upon it except that which corresponds to the 'blue' wavelength. This wavelength is reflected from the body and produces a 'blue' sensation on the observer's brain. A body which only weakly absorbs a particular wavelength can only weakly emit it; thus the emissivity at that wavelength is less than one.

The ratio of the energy emitted by the body at a particular wavelength to the energy emitted by a black body at the same wavelength and temperature is called the spectral emissivity e_λ and an allowance must be made for this when using optical pyrometers. The correction required is usually less than for a total radiation pyrometer, and the temperature values obtained are more accurate.

As in the case of total radiation pyrometers, there is a relationship between true and apparent temperature. This is given by the equation

$$\frac{1}{K} - \frac{1}{K_a} = \lambda \frac{\log_{10} e_\lambda}{6245}$$

where λ is the wavelength of red light, approximately $0.65 \,\mu\text{m}$, and e_λ is the spectral emissivity at that wavelength.

Sources of error

These are similar to those affecting total radiation pyrometers.

The accuracy of optical pyrometers is of the order of $\pm 10\,°\text{C}$ in the upper range.

13.21 Photoelectric pyrometers

All the devices previously discussed depend on change of temperature of the temperature sensor to operate the measuring system, either as a response (bulb thermometers, thermocouples, etc.) or as a matching device (the filament pyrometer).

Photoelectric cells do not operate on this principle, but on the changes brought about by the effect of light falling on certain materials. Of the three types of photoelectric cells the photoemissive, the photoconductive and the photovoltaic, it is the last which is used for almost all temperature measurement. This is the silicon solar cell which is used to convert sunlight into electricity in space vehicles; it has also been proposed as a means of providing the energy to operate vehicles in hot sunny climates. It has the advantage of providing a current without a battery (Fig. 13.20).

The mechanism of the process is as follows: when light falls onto the cell, electrons are released in such a way as to set up an e.m.f. in a circuit connected to it; this e.m.f. is allowed to operate against a load resistance of about 500 Ω and the current is measured by means of a deflection galvanometer or a self-balancing potentiometer.

Photoelectric cells do not respond to light of all wavelengths, but only to those of less than a certain critical value, this value depending on the material being irradiated. Below the critical wavelength the response

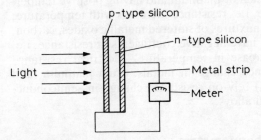

Fig. 13.20 Silicon solar cell

improves as the wavelength decreases and also increases with the intensity of radiation.

The layout of photoelectric pyrometers is similar to that of optical and total radiation pyrometers, thermistors being used to compensate for changes in ambient temperature between zero and 80 °C.

The advantages of this type of pyrometer include high accuracy (±0·2% of scale temperature), stability (i.e. little drift from calibration with time) and speed of response, which is of the order of one millisecond, making it very suitable for automatic control.

Spectral emissivity affects the accuracy of reading and allowance must be made for this. Photoelectric pyrometers are particularly suited to the measurement of small radiant sources and can be used effectively at a greater distance from the body than other pyrometers. They also have the advantage of good sensitivity in the red or near infra-red, responding best to wavelengths of between 0·5 and 1 μm.

Sources of error

The error sources are similar to those of other pyrometers but in addition errors may be introduced by light falling on the hot body from a window or other source. This is a particular danger when measurements are made in the open, especially if the surface of the material is highly reflective, and also when the temperature is low, as this increases the significance of any reflected light.

Temperatures upwards from 700 °C are usually measured with these instruments although with precautions against reflected light, etc. lower temperatures are possible. There is no known upper temperature limit, but calibration difficulties arise at temperatures above 2000 °C.

In addition to silicon, other materials are sometimes used which respond to different wavebands.

13.22 Temperature measurement by change of electrical resistance

The electrical resistance of conductors and semiconductors remains constant provided their physical and chemical conditions do not change. When the temperature of a conductor varies its resistance also varies.

Two kinds of electrical resistance thermometers are used: those using high purity metals, copper, nickel or platinum and having positive temperature coefficients of resistance, i.e. resistance increases with temperature; and those manufactured from mixtures of sintered metallic oxides, carbon, germanium alloys, etc., which have negative coefficients of resistance, i.e. resistance decreases with increase in temperature. Electrical resistance thermometers rely on resistance change in metals, often platinum, and thermistors (thermal resistors) rely on resistance change in semiconductors, usually germanium based alloys.

13.23 Electrical resistance thermometers

The most valuable feature of electrical resistance thermometers is their accuracy, sensitivity and stability, which by careful circuit design is of such

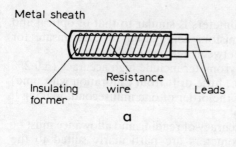

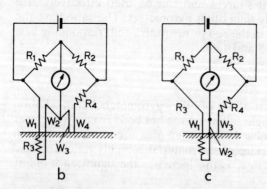

Fig. 13.21 Electrical resistance thermometer

a high order that they are suitable for IPTS determination. They are used for measurement in the range 10 to 1300 K but industrially from 73 to 873 K (-200 to $600\,°C$) although largely in the upper part of the range. A coil of wire is wound non-inductively on to an insulating former which is inserted into a refractory protective sheath [Fig. 13.21(a)]. Copper leads from the coil are connected into a Wheatstone bridge. When the leads from the thermometer are short they are made of large cross-section to reduce their resistance and thus remain largely unaffected by ambient temperature change, but when they are long, and to reduce cost, dummy leads are used and these take the form of three lead and four lead connections to the bridge [Figs. 13.21(b) and (c)].

Three lead connection

The thermometer resistance coil is connected by three lead wires, W_1, W_2 and W_3, to the bridge circuit. If leads W_1 and W_3 are of similar material, length, diameter and condition, then any change of ambient temperature will cause an equal resistance change in both. Thus the arms of the bridge to which they are connected sustain equal resistance changes and the bridge measures only the resistance change of the coil.

Four lead connection

In this case two leads W_3 and W_4 are short-circuited near the resistance coil and will just compensate for W_1 and W_2 connected to the coil; again the bridge remains in balance and measures only the change in the coil.

When very high accuracy and sensitivity are required one of the forms of balanced Wheatstone bridge is used.

Applications

Temperature readings from widely separated points can easily be brought together on to a central console well removed from the measured body; thus resistance thermometers can be employed where the capillary lengths of liquid expansion thermometers would be excessive.

Resistance thermometers are available in a very wide variety of forms which include bonded wafers, ribbons and tapes for surface temperature determination, and bare wire types giving improved response for air and non-corrosive fluid measurement; they are also used for measuring gas temperatures. Special probes are available in the form of needle or skewer probes for soft materials such as rubber or meat. A number of thermometers may be connected in series into a bridge to give the average temperature of liquids, slurries or granulated solids. Temperature differences can be found by connecting two exactly similar resistance elements to two arms of the bridge. The bulbs are held at the same temperature and the bridge balanced; the scale may then be calibrated for temperature difference between the bulbs.

Resistance thermometer bulbs may be designed for almost any desired resistance change corresponding to the fundamental interval (ice to steam point) but industrial instruments usually have an interval of 50 or $100\,\Omega$ as this gives a large resistance change in the bulb compared with the lead wires. The current used for resistance thermometer bridges may be either alternating or direct and will increase the temperature of the bridge circuit. However, this effect is small and for most purposes may be neglected.

Sources of error

(1) Impure resistance metal which can cause diffusion within the metal leading to segregation of phases and evaporation. The materials available are in fact of very high purity.
(2) A metal which has been strained will suffer a change in resistance characteristics; thus it must be annealed at a higher temperature than that at which it operates.
(3) Strains arising as a result of faulty installation, vibrations, etc., or strains developing from differential expansion between the measuring element and the solid to which the element is attached when measuring surface temperature.

Electrical resistance thermometers have an accuracy of ±0·75% of scale range at temperatures up to 600 °C.

13.24 Thermistors

Metal atoms mutually share their valency electrons. Thus their valency electrons are in a continuous state of motion through the metal as they move from atom to atom: the electrons are in a sense 'free'. As temperature rises the vibration of the atoms in the metal lattices increases, the volume of space occupied by the atoms increases and thus electron flow through the lattice becomes increasingly difficult.

The valency electrons in semiconductors (thermistors) are more firmly attached to their atoms and increase in temperature allows some of them to become detached so that they can flow; thus increase in temperature decreases electrical resistance by improving the conditions for flow. Thermistor elements used for temperature measurement have temperature coefficients of resistance many times greater than copper or platinum, e.g. at 25 °C platinum +0·0036, thermistors in general −0·045. Resistivity is also much higher than that of any pure metal; they are thus highly sensitive to small changes in temperature, and respond very rapidly to such changes. Typical resistance ratio curves are shown in Fig. 13.22. Semiconductors have an exponential temperature–resistance relationship of the form

$$R = ae^{b/K} \tag{13.4}$$

where R is the resistance (Ω), K is the absolute temperature and a and b are constants. b is known as the characteristic temperature.

If the value of R at temperature K_0 is R_0, then

$$R_0 = ae^{b/K_0} \tag{13.5}$$

Dividing Eq. 13.4 by Eq. 13.5,

$$R = R_0 \exp\left[b\left(\frac{1}{K} - \frac{1}{K_0} \right) \right] \tag{13.6}$$

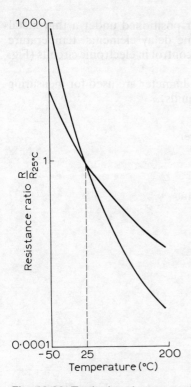

Fig. 13.22 Typical resistance ratio curves

The ordinary Wheatstone bridge circuit has an output when unbalanced which is hyperbolic with respect to resistance variation of a particular arm. It is possible by carefully matching the non-linear characteristics of the thermistor and bridge to achieve a linear output at the scale over a small temperature range.

Among a variety of semiconductor materials germanium containing exact proportions of arsenic, gallium or antimony is in most wide use, because unlike many other semiconductors it is very stable and its drift from calibration is slight; it also shows a very large decrease in resistance with increasing temperature.

The temperature range measured with thermistors is −250 to 650 °C although both lower and higher temperatures are possible. Under carefully controlled laboratory conditions, precise measurements are made within 0·001 K near 4 K.

Battery and mains operated instruments, both portable and fixed, are obtainable having scale ranges as small as 10 °C with 0·1 °C subdivisions or scales covering 130 °C with 1 °C subdivisions. Because of their high resistivity very small thermistor elements are possible allowing point temperatures to be measured. When required, continuous reading instruments may be used in the form of single or multi-channel units. Thermistors take the form of beads, probes, discs and rods, and are sometimes used bare but are usually glass coated or positioned under a thin metal cap; discs and rods are used more as time delay elements, temperature compensators, and for voltage and power control in electronic circuits (Fig. 13.23).

Glass and metal probes less than 2 mm diameter are used for measuring metal surface temperatures, gases and liquids.

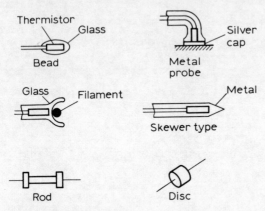

Fig. 13.23 Thermistors

Glass probes

These are made of specially toughened glass and are calibrated on metal surfaces or in liquids. They are particularly suited to materials or liquids which are poor heat conductors and have low heat capacity, e.g. insulating materials, powders, plastics, textiles, lacquered or painted surfaces. They are used for checking small components such as transistors, windings, brush gear and live cables up to 450 V providing proper precautions are taken.

Metal probes

These are calibrated directly on metal surfaces or in liquids or gases, and are used for checking surface temperatures, e.g. slip gauges and very small components. Because probe diameters are so small the quantity of heat drawn from the tested surface is insignificant and has virtually no effect on the temperature of the component. Metal probes are especially useful in the food industry where contamination by breakage of glass probes is undesirable. Special stainless steel needle types can be inserted into soft materials.

Germanium transistors are highly stable although there is a tendency for calibration to drift with time but stability of the order of 0·1 °C per annum can be obtained. To maintain calibration the instrument must not be used beyond the limits of its temperature range and vibration and stress avoided.

Special probes are used for lightly vibrating components.

13.25 Calibration

The need to establish fixed points on which temperature scales are based is discussed in Sections 13.4, 13.5 and 13.6. Instruments may be calibrated directly by reference to the equilibrium temperatures of substances (primary calibration) or by comparison with standard instruments which have been calibrated in this way (secondary calibration).

Primary calibration

The temperature sensor, e.g. a thermocouple or resistance thermometer, in the form in which it is to be used and connected in circuit is immersed in fully molten slowly cooling pure metal (see Table 13.4). At the onset of freezing, i.e. when solid begins to form, the fall in temperature of the

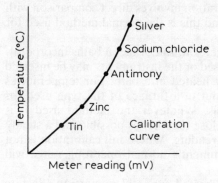

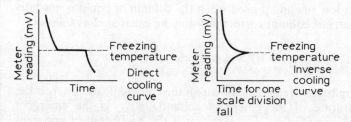

Fig. 13.24 Calibration curves

substance is arrested and remains stationary until it is completely solid. A direct or an inverse cooling curve indicates when the freezing temperature has been reached. A direct cooling curve is obtained by plotting meter readings at regular intervals against a time base during cooling and an inverse cooling curve by plotting the meter reading against the time required for it to fall through one scale division. The combined freezing points for a number of substances can then be plotted to form a full calibration curve for the instrument (Fig. 13.24). It is of course essential to ensure that all sources of error in the system be eliminated before any attempt at calibration is made.

Rare metal thermocouples can be calibrated at the gold point (1064·43 °C) by fixing a small piece of gold wire between the free ends of the thermocouple hot junction. This method makes use of the law of intermediate metals (see Section 13.14). The thermocouple is heated very slowly in the region of the melting point while meter readings are observed. When the temperature is sufficient to melt the wire the thermocouple circuit breaks and the meter reading at breakage is taken to be the gold point. This technique can also be used to determine the palladium point (1554 °C) and, with modifications, the platinum point (1772 °C), but it is not suitable for metals which oxidize rapidly unless special precautions are taken.

Secondary calibration

The simplest form of secondary calibration involves direct comparison with a previously calibrated instrument and this is the normal method used for temperatures up to the gold point.

For temperatures up to 550 °C water, oil, salt or metal baths incorporating a stirrer and heating system are used or the instruments may be inserted in a metal block which is uniformly heated in a bath. For temperatures above 550 °C calibration is carried out in a furnace of the type used for finding the freezing point of metals. Whatever the method used it is essential that the instruments be as close together as possible and a steady temperature obtained prior to each reading. Where full calibration is not required a point check in the instrument's normal operating range will indicate any serious fault.

Liquid in glass thermometers calibrated for total immersion (Section 13.8) will give a low reading if used when the column of liquid is not fully immersed. Emergent column corrections may be calculated as follows:

$$\text{correction} = N \times (t_2 - t_1) \times \text{a constant}$$

where N is the number of degrees shown on the emergent column, t_1 is the average temperature of the emergent column and t_2 is the emergent column temperature reading. The constant is the coefficient of apparent expansion of the liquid in glass, e.g. mercury 0·000 155, alcohol 0·001 04. An emergent column should be kept as short as possible.

Optical pyrometers

Standard optical pyrometers are calibrated by sighting on a black body immersed in freezing gold and the lamp current adjusted until matching is obtained.

For temperatures below the gold point sector discs are rotated between the pyrometer and the source. The angle of the sector removed from the disc is known and thus a known proportion of the total radiation previously received passes the disc to the instrument (Fig. 13.25). Different discs may be used to determine other temperatures. The temperature indicated on the instrument by this technique is calculated from the formula

$$\log \frac{J_2}{J_1} = \frac{C_2}{\lambda} \left(\frac{1}{1336} - \frac{1}{K} \right)$$

where C_2 is 14·32 mm degrees, λ is the wavelength (mm), K is the absolute temperature, and λK is less than 3 mm degrees, J_2 is the intensity of monochromatic light of wavelength λ radiated at the temperature K and J_1 is the intensity of monochromatic light of the same wavelength radiated by a black body at the gold point.

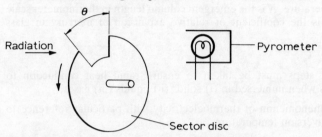

Fig. 13.25 Pyrometer calibration by sector disc

Temperatures above the gold point are determined by rotating sector discs between the pyrometer and a tungsten filament lamp. The brightness of the filament lamp is adjusted until the pyrometer is receiving the equivalent of gold point radiation; the radiation proportion is then known and the temperature of the filament lamp is calculated as before. The disc is removed and the pyrometer filament matched to the lamp filament.

Study problems

13.1 (a) Plot a graph of the defining fixed points of the International Practical Temperature Scale (1968) and comment on its shape.

(b) Why is it that thermometers and pyrometers of different types agree exactly with each other only at the fixed points?

(c) The platinum resistance thermometer is used to establish more than 70% of the primary values of the IPTS. Explain why this is so.

(d) A platinum resistance thermometer is calibrated at standard atmospheric pressure. At the boiling point of water its resistance is found to be 140 Ω and at the freezing point of zinc it is 256 Ω. Estimate the absolute temperature indicated when its resistance is 300 Ω. State any assumptions made.

Answer: 813·95 K

13.2 (a) Explain what is meant by the following terms when applied to the measurement of temperature: (i) conduction (ii) convection (iii) radiation (iv) black body radiator (v) emissivity.

(b) If the apparent temperature of a body having an emissivity equal to 0·95 is found to be 1400 °C, find its absolute temperature.

Answer: 1695 K

13.3 Explain the differences between vapour pressure thermometers and liquid in metal thermometers with particular reference to the pressure at which they are filled.

13.4 A mercury in glass thermometer has been calibrated at a given immersion depth. When in use the thermometer is insufficiently immersed by an amount equal to 20 °C on its scale. Using the following correction formula calculate the true temperature when the indicated temperature is 300°C and the ambient temperature 20°C:

$$t_1 = t_2 \pm KN\,(t_2 - t_3)$$

where t_1 is the true temperature, t_2 is the indicated temperature, t_3 is the ambient temperature, N is the emergent column length in thermometer scale units and K is the coefficient of relative expansion of mercury in glass (0·000 155).

Answer: 300·9 °C

13.5 Outline what steps must be taken to ensure rapid heat conduction to thermometers when immersed in (i) solids (ii) liquids (iii) gases.

13.6 Discuss the phenomenon of thermoelectricity with particular reference to neutral and inversion temperatures.

13.7 (*a*) Show that when the barometric pressure in a constant volume gas thermometer is changed, the change in absolute temperature may be calculated from

$$K_2 = K_1 \times \frac{P_2}{P_1}$$

where K_1 is the initial absolute temperature, P_1 is the initial barometric pressure and P_2 is the final barometric pressure.

(*b*) The indicated pressure in a constant volume gas thermometer when it is at a temperature equal to the triple point of water is 720 mm of mercury. Find the temperatures on the thermodynamic temperature scale which correspond to the pressures 765 mm Hg and 45 mm Hg.

(*c*) What would be the expected temperature if the pressure were reduced to zero?

Answers
(*b*) 290·2 K
(*c*) 17·1 K; 0 K

13.8 (*a*) Describe how an optical pyrometer may be used to measure furnace temperatures.

(*b*) A steel making furnace is heated to a temperature of 1600 °C. Calculate the rate of radiant heat loss to surroundings at 20 °C when a charging door 1·5 m wide × 1·2 m high is opened. Assume the furnace behaves as a black body.

Answer: 1262·7 kW

13.9 A thermistor has a characteristic temperature b of 3000 K. If its resistance is 100 kΩ at 300 K, what will its resistance be at 600 K?

Answer: 674 Ω

Bibliography

Ambrosius, E. E., Fellows, R. D. and Brickman, A. D. (1966) *Mechanical Measurement and Instrumentation*, Ronald Press.
Barna, P. S. (1969) *Fluid Mechanics for Engineers*, Butterworth.
Bass, H. G. (1971) *Introduction to Engineering Measurements*, McGraw-Hill.
Beckwith, T. G. and Lewis Buck, N. (1961) *Mechanical Measurements*, Addison–Wesley.
Benedict, R. P. (1969) *Fundamentals of Temperature, Pressure and Flow Measurement*, Wiley.
Bolton, W. (1980) *Engineering Instrumentation and Control*, Butterworth.
Bradshaw, T. (1952) *Experimental Fluid Mechanics*, Pergamon.
Brophy, J. J. (1966) *Semi-conductor Devices*, Allen & Unwin.
BSSM Strain Measurement Reference Book (1979).
Dinsdale, A. and Moore, F. (1962) *Viscosity and its Measurement*, Chapman & Hall.
Doebelin, E. O. (1966) *Measurement Systems: Application and Design*, McGraw-Hill.
Hayward, A. T. J. (1977) *Accuracy and Repeatability*, Mechanical Engineering Publications.
Hendry, A. W. (1977) *Elements of Experimental Stress Analysis*, SI edn, Pergamon.
Higgins, R. A. (1968) *Engineering Metallurgy*, Vol. 1, 3rd edn, English Universities Press.
Holister, G. S. (1967) *Experimental Stress Analysis*, Cambridge University Press.
Holman, J. P. (1971) *Experimental Methods for Engineers*, McGraw-Hill.
Hume, K. J. (1965) *Metrology with Autocollimators*, Hilger & Watts.
Hume, K. J. (1966) *Engineering Metrology*, Macdonald.
Institute of Petroleum (1953) *Standard IP 73/53*.
Jones, E. B. (1965) *Instrument Technology*, 2nd edn, Butterworth.
Kingslake, R. (1965) *Applied Optics and Optical Engineering*, Vol. 1, Academic Press.
Linford, A. (1961) *Flow Measurement and Meters*, Spon.
Low, B. B. (1954) *Strength of Materials*, Longman.
Merrington, A. C. (1949) *Viscometry*, Arnold.
Metrologia (1969) **5**(2), Springer.
Miller, J. T. (1964) *Revised Course in Instrument Technology*, United Trade Press.
Moore, M. B. (1960) *Theory and Application of Mechanical Engineering Measurement*, Van Nostrand.
Moore, W. R. (1970) *Foundations of Mechanical Accuracy*, Moore Special Tool Co.
National Physical Laboratory (1964) *Calibration of Temperature Measurement Instruments*, Notes on Applied Science No. 12, 3rd edn, HMSO.
National Physical Laboratory (1975) *The International Practical Temperature Scale of 1968*, 2nd edn, HMSO.
Nelkon, M. and Parker, P. (1962) *Advanced Level Physics*, Heinemann.
Neubert, H. K. P. (1968) *Strain Gauges: Kinds and Uses*, Macmillan.
Nichols, L. W. and Oakley, T. R. J. (1961) The influence of measuring force, stylus radius and surface finish on the accuracy of measurement of workpieces by a comparator, *Proc. Instn Mech. Engrs*, **195**, 207.
O'Higgins, P. J. (1966) *Basic Instrumentation, Industrial Measurement*, McGraw-Hill.
Open University (1974) *Instrumentation Units Course T291*.
Pearson, E. B. (1957) *Technology of Measurement*, English Universities Press.
Perry, C. C. and Lissner, H. R. (1962) *The Strain Gauge Primer*, McGraw-Hill.
Prandtl, L. (1960) *Essentials of Fluid Mechanics*, Blackie.
Preston, J. S. (1963) A radiometric method of perpetuating the unit of light, *Proc. R. Soc. London 'A'*, **272**, 133.
Rolt, F. H. (1964) *Use of Light Waves for Controlling the Accuracy of Block Gauges*, Hilger & Watts.

Ryder, G. H. (1968) *Strength of Materials*, SI edn, Macmillan.
Sharp, K. W. B. (1970) *Practical Engineering Metrology*, Pitman.
Spragg, R. C. and Whitehouse, D. J. (1971) *Proc. Instn Mech. Engrs*, **185**, 47.
Technograph (1967) Engineering Measurement Series.
Timoshenko, S. and Goodier, J. N. (1970) *Theory of Elasticity*, McGraw-Hill.
Tyson, F. C. (1961) *Industrial Instrumentation*, Prentice–Hall.

British Standard specifications

BS	DD6:1972	Methods for calibration of bonded electrical resistance strain gauges.
	817:1972	Surface plates and tables.
	818:1963	Cast iron straight edges (bow section and I section).
	852:1939	Toolmaker straightedges.
	869:1978	Toolmakers flats and high precision surface plates.
	888:1950	Slip (or block) gauges and their accessories.
	958:1968	Specification for spirit levels for use in precision engineering.
	1041:1943	Temperature measurement.
	1042:1964	Part I Flow measurement in pipes.
	1973	Part IIa Pitot tubes—Class A accuracy.
	1965	Part III Guide to the effects of temperature for the methods in Part I.
	1134:1972	Method for the assessment of surface texture.
	1780:1960	Bourdon tube pressure and vacuum gauges.
	1971	Part II Metric units.
	1790:1961	Length bars and their accessories.
	2634:1974	Roughness comparison specimens.
	2643:1955	Glossary of terms relating to measuring instruments.
	3064:1969	Sine bars and sine tables (excluding compound tables).
	4311:1968	Metric gauge blocks.
	5204:1975	Straight edges.
	1977	Part 2 Steel and granite straight edges of rectangular section.
	5233:1975	Terms used in metrology.
PD	6461:1980	Legal metrology.

Index